THE FRESHWATER SNAILS

(MOLLUSCA: GASTROPODA)

OF NEW YORK STATE

BY EILEEN H. JOKINEN
Institute of Water Resources
College of Agriculture and Natural Resources
The University of Connecticut
Storrs, CT 06269-4018

1992

New York State Museum Bulletin 482

ISSN: 0278-3355

ISBN: 1-55557-197-2

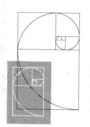

The University of the State of New York
THE STATE EDUCATION DEPARTMENT
The New York State Museum
Biological Survey
Albany, New York 12230

ACKNOWLEDGMENTS

I would like to thank the following individuals for their valuable assistance during this project: Jeffrey K. Barnes, Edward Blakemore, Richard Colson, Kirk Ducharme, Eric Kiviat, Barbara Kolb, Norton G. Miller, Richard Monheimer, Aarne Oja, Peter Rich, Douglas Smith, David Strayer, and two anonymous reviewers. Aarne Oja, Patricia Kernan, and the author drew the illustrations. The following museums granted access to their collections: University of Florida, University of Massachusetts, Bard College, Museum of Comparative Zoology (MCZ), American Museum of Natural History (AMNH), and the Academy of Natural Sciences of Philadelphia (ANSP): I thank their directors and staffs for assistance. Specimens of *Pyrgulopsis letsoni* were lent for purposes of illustration by the Museum of Zoology, University of Michigan.

This project was supported by a research contract with the Biological Survey, New York State Museum. The managing editor at the Biological Survey for this publication was Jeffrey K. Barnes.

CONTENTS

INTRODUCTION

The objectives of this research on the freshwater snail fauna of New York State include surveying the State to compile an up-to-date list of species; documenting snail locations relative to geology, the canal system, and watersheds; providing keys for identification; depositing collected specimens in the New York State Museum; providing ecological and habitat information, especially water chemistry parameters, for each species; and reviewing the history of freshwater malacology in the State.

Reviews of the internal anatomy, ecology, physiology, and biology of freshwater gastropods are not presented in this manual because a number of excellent publications are already available on these subjects, e.g., Baker (1928a); Burch (1982, 1989); Russell-Hunter (1983); Fretter & Peake (1975); and Brown (1991). However, summaries of the distributions, historical literature, habitats, and ecology are provided for each species. Also, common names are listed, and most of these are as listed in Turgeon et al. (1988), although alternate common names exist (see Clarke 1981).

The keys are artificial and designed to facilitate rapid identification wherever possible. The couplets are illustrated with drawings of pertinent characters, and full illustrations are provided separately. The key to the families precedes the discussions of the individual species, and each key to species within a family heads the section on that family.

Field sampling of 346 aquatic habitats in New York State and parts of Lake Champlain in Vermont was undertaken during the summers of 1978, 1981, and 1984-1991. Appendix A lists the locations of the sites by number, and Fig. 1 illustrates site locations. In the text that follows, these sites are also given by number.

Ten of the sampled sites yielded no snails. Five of them (Dillon Pond, site number 355; Limekiln Lake, 359; Big Moose Lake, 362; Nicks Lake, 365; and Moss Lake, 413) had pH values of 5.2-6.0, very low conductivities of 23-38 μmhos/cm, and calcium concentrations of 2 ppm or less. It could be assumed that the low calcium concentrations and low buffering capacities of these lakes are the factors causing the lack of snails. A stream, Geyser Brook (267) in Saratoga Springs, had an abundance of stoneflies and mayflies but no snails. The water contained more than sufficient calcium, 35 ppm, but apparently it contains natural radium. Another site, Rushford Lake (414), showed evidence of drawdown. The three remaining sites (364, 418, 419) had no readily perceptible negative features and would have to be examined in greater detail in order to explain the lack of snail populations.

The following native species should be considered as rare or extirpated in New York State: Valvatidae: *Valvata sincera* and *V. lewisi* (both rare); Viviparidae: *Lioplax subcarinata* (extirpated?); Hydrobiidae: *Probythinella lacustris* (extirpated?), *Gillia altilis* (rare), *Birgella subglobosa* (rare); *Cincinnatia cincinnatiensis* (rare), *Pyrgulopsis letsoni* (extirpated or limited to far the western section of the State); Pomatiopsidae: *Pomatiopsis lapidaria* (rare); Pleuroceridae: *Leptoxis carinata* (rare, apparently limited to the Susquehanna watershed); Lymnaeidae: *Lymnaea stagnalis* (rare), *Stagnicola emarginata* (rare), *S. caperata* (rare), *Acella haldemani* (rare), *Bulimnea megasoma* (extirpated), *Fossaria parva* (rare); Planorbidae: *Gyraulus circumstriatus* (rare), *Planorbula armigera* (rare). Several of the pulmonates, e.g., *S. caperata*, *F. parva*, *G. circumstriatus*, and *P. armigera*, tend to inhabit small bodies of water, such as temporary ponds, and they might appear rare due to undersampling of these ephemeral habitats. The other species, however, are inhabitants of permanent bodies of water, and their scarcity is probably real.

MATERIALS AND METHODS

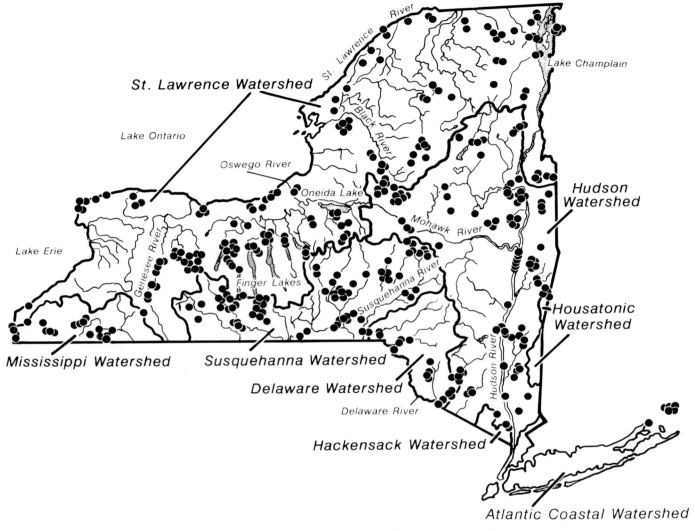

Fig. 1. Watersheds of New York State and collecting sites visited during the present survey.

Methods for finding snails included visual examination of vegetation, detritus, and bottom material; sweep netting aquatic vegetation; and digging for sediment-dwelling species. Usually, several sites per habitat were investigated. The snails were anaesthetized overnight in sodium nembutol (van der Schalie 1953) and preserved in 70% ethanol. Identifications are based on Clarke (1973), Baker (1928a), Berry (1943), Clench & Fuller (1965), Te (1975, 1978), Burch (1982), Harman & Berg (1971), Taylor & Jokinen (1984), and Jokinen (1983).

The following data are available on an electronic database from the New York State Museum for each specimen lot: catalog number, preservation method, species name, collection date and locality, major drainage basin (system draining into the Atlantic Ocean, e.g., Hudson River, St. Lawrence River, etc.), subdrainage system (system draining directly into the major drainage basin, e.g., the Mohawk River for the Hudson River system), water body type (lake, stream, marsh, canal, ditch, etc.), lake or pond surface area, altitude, water chemistry parameters (pH, conductivity, cations), number of specimens in lot, collector's remarks, and, for cross-reference, the collector's site number. Interested researchers can access information under any of the above categories for any species. For example, a species list with accession numbers can be generated for snails of Oneida Lake, snails for Orange County, and so on.

Water samples were taken at each site and chemical analyses were made by the following methods at a standard laboratory temperature of 25°C:

- pH: Corning Model 10 pH meter and combination electrode;

- Conductivity (µmhos/cm): YSI Model 31 Conductivity Bridge, cell constant = 0.1;

- Cations (Ca^{++}, Mg^{++}, Na^+ and K^+ in parts per million): by atomic absorption and emission with a Perkin Elmer Atomic Absorption Spectrophotometer Model 306. Direct measurements of divalent cation concentrations, especially for calcium, replace standard alkalinity data; they are more reliable at all pH values and are independent of temperature.

Appendix B is an alphabetical list of the collecting sites giving their water chemistry parameters. Parameter ranges, means, and standard errors of the mean are given with the discussions of the species.

Aquatic snails live in nearly all standing or flowing waters, including temporary pools, ditches, watering troughs, ponds and lakes, intermittent and permanent streams, rivers, and marshes. They are commonly found near shore on submerged terrestrial litter, such as branches and leaves. Other habitats include cobble and boulders, clam shells, undersides and stems of aquatic macrophytic vegetation, filamentous green and blue-green algae, old bottles and cans, sand (where they can be completely buried), and out of water on mud, leaf litter, or rocks near water's edge. Often, they can be easily collected by hand. Netting the substratum also is effective, and a quick way to find snails is to net live vegetation, litter, or other material and shake it over white pans or into the net while holding it under water. Most individuals will drop to the bottom, where they are easily seen. Deep water collecting can be done with an Eckman dredge or with the aid of SCUBA or snorkeling equipment.

If snails are to be brought back alive from the field, they should be carried in a small amount of water with a good air space between the water and the jar lid. When they are enclosed without an air space they soon deplete the dissolved oxygen and die. In warm weather, keeping the snails in a picnic or camp cooler while traveling is recommended.

Accurate identification of some species relies on the anatomy of soft tissues, so it is necessary to preserve the soft tissues as well as the shell. If snails are dropped directly into preservative they withdraw into their shells, and dissection or examination of soft tissues is difficult. Therefore, they should be narcotized, or relaxed, before preservation. Relaxants include sodium nembutol (van der Schalie 1953), pentobarbital (Meier-Brook 1976a, 1976b), propylene phenoxytol (McKay & Hartzband 1970), and menthol crystals. Usually, leaving pulmonate and small prosobranch snails in relaxant overnight is sufficient for relax-

ation. Menthol crystals, which are often available at a pharmacy, are useful for relaxing many species. They should be sprinkled into the container with the snails. If nothing else is available, tobacco from menthol cigarettes also will act as a narcotizing agent when sprinkled on top of the water. The snails are relaxed when they are lying inactive and their bodies are not withdrawn into the shells. They should not react when gently prodded.

Snails can be placed in preservative once they are relaxed. The preservative of choice is 70% ethyl alcohol. It is recommended that the alcohol solution include 5% glycerine to prevent the snails from drying out if the alcohol should evaporate. Fifty percent isopropyl alcohol (rubbing alcohol) can be used until a more appropriate preservative can be substituted.

Snail tissues to be used for histological examination require special fixatives following narcotization. A common tissue fixative for snails is FAA (10 parts saturated formalin solution (39-40% formaldehyde), 2 parts glacial acetic acid, 50 parts 95% ethyl alcohol, 40 parts water). Appropriate histological references should be consulted (e.g., Humason 1972).

Specimens must be properly labeled with collection data. Labels and field notes should be recorded immediately after making a collection. Containers can be labeled with a waterproof marker until the snails are preserved. Also, waterproof paper labels can be attached to the outside. Paper labels should not be placed inside a container with live snails. Penciled labels can still be read if they get wet.

Permanent paper labels placed in the jars with the preserved snails are written on 100% rag paper with waterproof India ink. The ink is allowed to dry for several hours before placing the label in the preservative.

Data taken at the time of collection include the name of the body of water, collecting date, and locality. Other helpful data include type of microhabitat (specific location within the habitat), associated vegetation (both terrestrial and aquatic), latitude and longitude, and water depth. Any habitat or ecological data could be useful. Of special value in relocating sites is the name of the pertinent United States Geological Survey topographic map.

Many snails can be identified to species by shell characteristics alone. Others, including hydrobiids and physids, can be identified only to genus or family by shell characteristics, and inspection of soft tissues is necessary for species identification. Details are presented in the appropriate keys.

Some shell features, such as spiral striae and hirsuteness, are best viewed on a dry shell, with the body removed. Shell details (color, texture, ornamentation) mentioned in most shell keys or manuals are described from clean, dry shells free of soft tissues. Shells can be cleaned with a small brush under gently running water. Soap or a mild base can be used (e.g., a weak solution of Clorox®). The shell will dissolve if it is placed in acid. Shells should be housed in stiff boxes or glass shell vials with light cotton packing to protect them from breakage.

HISTORY OF FRESHWATER MALACOLOGY IN NEW YORK STATE

The study of snails and clams in New York State was initiated in 1843 with the publication of James E. De Kay's *Mollusca*. De Kay (1792-1851) was trained as a physician, but his primary interest was paleontology. He worked on the early New York State Geological and Natural History Survey (1836-1844) and authored the "Zoology of New York," six parts in five volumes, one of which was the *Mollusca* (Johnson 1904, Elliot 1979). In his introduction, De Kay credited Augustus A. Gould's *Invertebrata of Massachusetts* (1841) as the basis for identification of the New York fauna (De Kay 1843). Gould's type collection, purchased by the New York State Museum in 1867, is now housed at Harvard University (Anonymous 1875a, Johnson 1984).

De Kay's publication appeared during an era when exhibition of natural objects in public and private museums was gaining popularity. Shell collecting was a popular avocation of educated citizens, along with the consequent cataloguing, trading, and writing of articles for such scientific periodicals as the *American Journal of Conchology* and the *Proceedings of the Academy of Natural Sciences*. One of the most active collectors and writers during the 1850s and 1860s was Dr. James Lewis, a physician from Mohawk, New York. Lewis collected extensively from the Erie Canal and throughout the region of Mohawk, in Herkimer and Otsego Counties. He had an intense interest in evolution and urged colleagues to pay attention to intraspecific variability of shell characters in relation to environment. Lewis affirmed Darwin's theories, urged conservative taxonomy as opposed to naming each variant population as a separate species, and he proposed that pulmonates were of later evolutionary origin than prosobranchs. He experimented with transplantation of populations by placing *Viviparus georgianus* from Illinois in the Erie Canal in 1867. He also introduced several species of the clam *Unio* from Ohio (Lewis 1856b, 1860, 1868, 1872, 1874). Lewis's collection of molluscs was deposited in the New York State Museum in 1875 (Anonymous 1882).

In 1866 and 1867, Truman Aldrich, of Rensselaer Polytechnic Institute, collected aquatic and terrestrial molluscs in the Hudson River, Mohawk basin, and the Erie Canal within a six mile radius of Troy (Aldrich 1869). His collection was presented to the New York State Museum (Anonymous 1875b).

Staten Island and Long Island were sampled by Sanderson Smith (1832-1915), curator of shells at the American Museum of Natural History, and Temple Prime (1832-1903), a lifelong resident of Huntington, Long Island (Hubbard & Smith 1865, Smith & Prime 1870). Although Prime did not publish much on snails, he was an expert on corbiculid clams and named numerous species (Johnson 1959, Abbott & Young 1973, Elliott 1979). In 1872, Prime donated specimens of 106 species to the New York State Museum and a similar set to the Long Island Historical Society (Anonymous 1873). His main collection was deposited in the Museum of Comparative Zoology at Harvard University in 1895 (Elliott 1979). Later publications on Long Island, Staten Island, and Brooklyn molluscs were authored by S.C. Wheat (1907a, b), a resident of Brooklyn and a member of the Brooklyn Conchological Club.

In the 1880s, collections in Onondaga County and other parts of New York were being made by the Reverend William Beauchamp (1830-1925), Episcopal priest, published amateur conchologist, and expert on the language, history, and culture of the Iroquois (Smith 1926, Abbott & Young 1973). Beauchamp (1886a, 1887, 1891) published articles in *The Nautilus* (the first few volumes were named the *Conchologists' Exchange*). As a result of ten years' work, Beauchamp (1886b) privately published a booklet on terrestrial and aquatic shells of New York State, primarily those of Onondaga County. That publication is not merely a list of species; it includes instructions on where and how to collect specimens and preserve them.

A major contributor of freshwater and terrestrial specimens to the New York State Museum was Charles Beecher (1856-1904), who was also an expert on trilobites and brachiopods. While serving as a paleontological assistant to James Hall at the State Museum, Beecher contributed approximately 20,000 primary specimens, plus a similar number of duplicates. The shells came from Albany, New York; Ann Arbor, Michigan (where Beecher received his Bachelor of Science degree); and Warren, Pennsylvania. All were collected by Beecher himself. In 1899, Beecher was appointed curator of geological collections at the Peabody Museum, Yale University. It was to the Peabody that Beecher donated a second collection of over 100,000 specimens (Schuchert 1904, Abbott & Young 1973, Elliott 1979).

In the 1890s, William Marshall (1865-ca. 1958), as assistant zoologist of the New York State Museum, catalogued and reported on the freshwater and terrestrial molluscs deposited in the museum and exhibited at the 1893 World's Columbian Exposition in Chicago. By this time, collections from C.E. Beecher, W.M. Beauchamp, W.S. Teator, A. Baily, and others had been acquired by the Museum (Marshall 1894, 1895). Marshall (1892) also followed up on Lewis' successful transplantation of *Viviparus georgianus* into the Erie Canal and Mohawk River. Also during that period, Mearns (1898) reported on terrestrial and aquatic molluscs of the Hudson Highlands in Ulster, Orange, and Greene Counties, and William S. Teator (1860-1930), a farmer and naturalist, was collecting molluscs from near his home in the Hudson Valley at Upper Red Hook, Dutchess County (Garlinghouse 1976). Recently, a part of the Teator collection was donated to the American Museum of Natural History.

Molluscan studies in eastern New York State were concentrated around New York City, Albany, Rensselaer, and Herkimer Counties, but explorations were also occurring in western parts of the State. John Walton published an extensive and well-illustrated list of freshwater and terrestrial molluscs from Monroe County (Walton 1891, 1898).

The first instructional handbook for shell collectors was published in 1898 by paleoecologist Carlotta J. Maury (1874-1938). The three-chapter handbook was based on Chautauqua Lake shells. Included were sections on collecting, aquarium-keeping, molluscan habits, in-lake distribution, and the history of post-glacial clam migration from the Mississippi Valley. Paleontological works include Maury (1908). Maury (1916) later published a list of the shells from Cayuga, Cayuta, Chautauqua, Canandaigua, Conesus, and Owasco Lakes that she had given to Cornell University. Baker (1928b) later compared data from Maury's Chautauqua Lake collection with his own observations.

The western part of the State was also explored for freshwater molluscs by Elizabeth J. Letson Bryan (1874-1919), a member and a director of the Buffalo Society of Natural Sciences. Letson published on shells from the Niagara Frontier, including post-Pliocene fossils of the Niagara River gravels (Letson 1901, 1909). She also published a "Check List of the Mollusca of New York" (Letson 1905) and several articles in *The Nautilus*. After marrying William Bryan of the College of Hawaii, she moved to Hawaii, where she and her husband amassed the largest collection of Hawaiian marine shells of the time (Pilsbry 1919). Part of her collection of New York specimens is housed in the New York State Museum (Letson 1905).

One of the most prolific contributors to New York's early 20th century malacology was Frank Collins Baker (1894-1942), best known for his publications on Wisconsin freshwater molluscs (Baker 1928a). As a young man, Baker worked for Ward's Scientific Establishment in Rochester before he was appointed curator at the Chicago Academy of Science in 1894. Baker returned to New York for the years 1915-1917, when he carried on research at Oneida Lake for the New York College of Forestry (Baker 1916a, b; 1918a, b, c; 1919a; van Cleave 1943; Abbott & Young 1973). Baker's work on Oneida Lake's benthic community was quantitative, qualitative, and highly detailed, and it was an impressive forerunner to the ecological studies of later researchers. Between 1899 and 1928, Baker wrote numerous papers on New York's and New Jersey's extant and Pleistocene freshwater molluscs. Many of these publications were the result of explorations made during his summer vacations near Rochester (Baker 1898, 1900b, 1901, 1913). Later publications on Oneida Lake's molluscs include those of Henry Pratt (1923) and Harman & Forney (1970).

From the 1940s to the 1970s, Morris K. Jacobson (1906-1980), a high school foreign languages instructor, was an active amateur malacologist. He founded the New York Shell Club in 1949, and he authored nine books and over 65 papers on molluscs and other invertebrates. Several of his publications deal with molluscs of the vicinity of New York City (e.g., Jacobson 1945, 1951, 1965, 1969), and in 1961, under joint authorship with William Emerson of the American Museum of Natural History (Jacobson & Emerson 1961), the book *Shells of the New York City Area* appeared (Abbott 1980). Additional studies of snails in the vicinity of New York City were published by Dorothy Freas (1950a, b; 1951), and by Roger Bretet and Edwin Carswell (Bretet & Carswell 1952).

One of the major contributors to current New York malacology, especially in central New York, is Willard Harman, who began publishing as a graduate student of Clifford Berg's at Cornell University. Berg's main interest in molluscs was the fact that they are the food source of the larvae of the predatory and parasitoid snail-killing flies (Diptera: Sciomyzidae) (Berg & Knutson 1978). Harman's studies include gastropod surveys of central New York (Harman & Berg 1970, 1971; Harman 1982), Green Lake (Harman & Jackson 1967), Otsego Lake (Harman 1971, MacNamara & Harman 1975), Canadarago Lake (Harman 1973), and Oneida Lake (Harman & Forney 1970). In addition to survey work, Harman has published on various aspects of gastropod natural history and ecology (e.g., Lanciani & Harman 1968; Harman 1968a, b; 1970, 1972).

Recently, Douglas Smith (1983) and David Strayer (1987) have published on the molluscan fauna of the Hudson River basin. Jean Q. Wade and Carey E. Vasey are conducting studies on molluscs of Livingston County, especially the community in Conesus Lake (e.g., Wade 1980, 1987; Wade & Vasey 1976).

HYDROLOGY, CLIMATE, AND GEOLOGY OF NEW YORK STATE

The State of New York encompasses an area of 127,190 square kilometers, approximately 10% (13,876 square kilometers) of which is water surface. There are over 4000 lakes and ponds with more than 260 square kilometers of surface area, and there are 130,000 kilometers of rivers and streams. The climate is humid, cloudy, and cool. The Great Lakes, especially Lakes Erie and Ontario, influence temperature and snowfall. Annual precipitation ranges from 76 cm in western New York to 127 cm north of New York City and in the Adirondack Mountains. Information in

this section is based on Berg (1963), Broughton *et al.* (1966), Van Diver (1985), and van der Leeden *et al.* (1990).

New York is drained by several primary watersheds (Fig. 1). The St. Lawrence River watershed, originating with the Great Lakes, drains water from the northern part of the State into the Atlantic Ocean at the Bay of St. Lawrence. The Hudson River watershed drains water from approximately 34,000 square kilometers of the eastern and central regions into the Atlantic Ocean at New York City Harbor. The Delaware River watershed directs water south

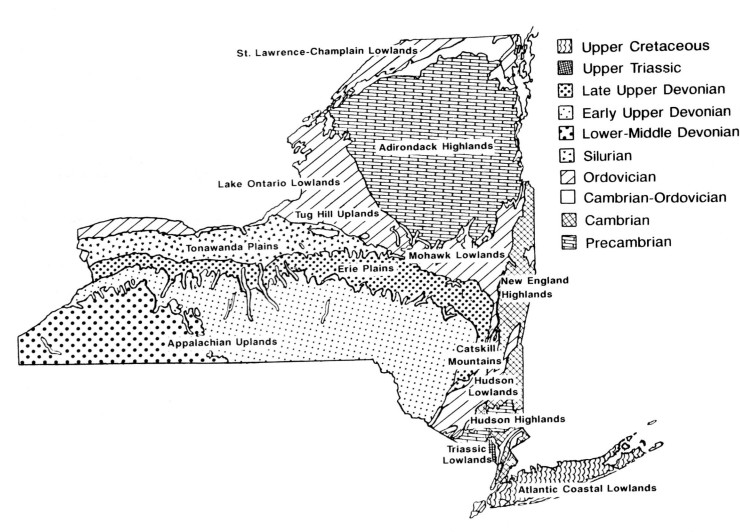

Fig. 2. Geological regions of New York State. Symbols represent exposed bedrock formations. Precambrian formations tend to be low in calcium-bearing rock, thereby yielding soft waters with low pH.

from the southeastern region of the State, west of the Hudson River, into the Atlantic Ocean at Delaware Bay. The Susquehanna River watershed, in south-central New York, directs water into the Atlantic Ocean at Chesapeake Bay. The Mississippi River watershed, represented in southwestern New York by the Allegheny River, flows into the Gulf of Mexico. The northern section of the Housatonic River, draining water from western Connecticut, southwestern Massachusetts, and a small section of southeastern New York, flows into Long Island Sound. The Hackensack River, draining a small section west of the Hudson, empties into Newark Bay and the Hudson River Estuary. The Atlantic Coastal Plain rivers are small drainage systems from eastern Fishers Island in Long Island Sound south to New Jersey.

The Adirondack Highlands (Fig. 2) are a southeasterly extension of the Grenville Province of the Precambrian Canadian Shield. The High Peaks, up to 1524 m above sea level (average relief: 610 m), have the greatest elevations in the State. East of the High Peaks, elevations drop abruptly to 29 m at Lake Champlain. Most of the rocks of the Adirondacks are metamorphic and poor in calcium: amphibolite, anorthosite, granitic gneisses, and small amounts of metasedimentary rock (marble, calci-silicates, quartzite, and paragneisses). Water from the region is drained to the west, east, and north by St. Lawrence River tributaries and to the south by the Mohawk and upper Hudson River systems. Most lakes were glacially produced, are low in calcium (less than 5 ppm), and are naturally oligotrophic. The poor buffering capacities of Adirondack waters have made them especially susceptible to the effects of acid rain and intolerable to the majority of freshwater molluscs (Jokinen 1991).

The St. Lawrence-Champlain Lowlands, including the St. Lawrence River Valley and Lake Champlain, lie north and east of the Adirondacks. The average elevation is 31 m, and water drains into the St. Lawrence River system. The underlying rocks are Cambrian and Ordovician sandstones, dolomites, and limestones. Because of the limestone, the waters of this region have higher calcium levels, lower acidity, and greater buffering capacities than those of the Adirondacks.

The Lake Ontario Lowlands border Lake Ontario and extend up the Black River Valley. Elevations range from 74 m at the lake to 457 m inland in the eastern portion. Surficial deposits consist of calcareous silts and clays derived from Ordovician limestone and dolomite. In the eastern section of the Lowlands are the Tug Hill Uplands, consisting of sedimentary sandstone. The elevation is 549-610 m, and relief is low. Below the sandstone is a series of sandy shales underlain by limestone, which forms a series of rock terraces along the west side of the Black River Valley. Poor drainage has resulted in the presence of many swamps, and the limestone has produced waters high in calcium.

The northwestern portion of the Lake Ontario Lowlands has hard water ponds and rivers (greater than 20 ppm calcium). The southern border of the western Lake Ontario Lowland is the 76 m high Niagara Escarpment, which forms the northern edge of the Tonawanda Plain of Silurian dolostone, limestone, shale, salt beds, sandstone, and conglomerate. The surficial landscape includes one of the largest drumlin fields in the world. The waters of the Plain are high in calcium.

The greater part of the southern half of New York is made up of the Appalachian Uplands, which consist of three sections of Devonian sedimentary rocks now dipping to the south. The Uplands consist of shale, siltstone, and sandstone mixed with limestone. The Finger Lakes are located in the center of this section. The eastern end contains the Catskill Mountains, which end abruptly at an escarpment rising 610 m above the Hudson River. Catskill waters drain into the Delaware River.

Some waterways, such as the Genesee River and its tributaries, drain west to north to the St. Lawrence system, but the dominant watersheds are the Susquehanna and Delaware. The Susquehanna and Oswego Rivers drain a number of glacially formed swamps and marshes in common, and some snail migration might have been via this connection (Harman & Berg 1971). The waters have low to high calcium values, and river systems dominate over lakes south of the Finger Lakes.

In the southwest section, the only large standing body of water is Lake Chautauqua, Chautauqua County. Most of the waters are of high calcium, and drainage is primarily via the Allegheny River system south to the Ohio River and eventually to the Mississippi. The western section, adjacent to Lake Erie, drains into the St. Lawrence River system.

A small triangle, an extension of the Allegheny Plateau, occupies a region bordering on Pennsylvania and is the only section of New York that remained unglaciated. The waters here are very low in calcium.

The Hudson-Mohawk Lowlands, drained by the Hudson and Mohawk Rivers, lie south of the Adirondacks and extend south to Pennsylvania. The Mohawk Lowlands are bordered on the south by the Helderberg Escarpment, and the surficial deposits consist of glacial till derived from limestone and alkaline shales of Silurian origin. The Hudson Lowlands lie between the Catskill Mountains on the west and the Taconic Mountains, part of the New England Highlands, on the east and consist of Cambrian-Ordovician slate, shale, schist, gneiss, limestone, dolomite, quartzite, marble, and graywacke. Calcium values are high.

East of the Hudson Lowlands are the New England Highlands, a geologically complex province consisting of the Hudson Highlands, New York City Group, and the Taconic Mountains. The highest relief is in the Hudson Highlands where the elevations exceed 457 m. The majority of the ridges and valleys of the highlands follow a northeast to southwest direction and consist of Precambrian metamorphic gneisses and quartzites. Waters of this region are very low in calcium.

The Taconic Mountains lie in a north-south direction and consist of schist uplands, limestone valleys, and the Rensselaer Plateau formed by Rensselaer Graywacke. The calcium content of the waters is relatively high.

At the southwestern edge of the Hudson Lowlands is the Triassic Lowland, lying within the borders of Rockland County. The bedrock consists of conglomerates, red sandstones, red shales, and diabase. The most obvious feature of the Triassic Lowland is the Palisades, a north-south escarpment on the west bank of the Hudson River extending from Nyack to Staten Island.

The Atlantic Coastal Lowlands, of Cretaceous sedimentary rocks overlain by glacial drift, make up Staten Island and Long Island. Drift consists of unconsolidated gravels, sands, and clays. Elevations and relief are low, as are soil nutrients and lime.

Almost all of New York State was heavily glaciated during the Wisconsinan Glaciation. The shapes, sizes, and flow direction of the water bodies were all profoundly influenced by the ice sheet. Berg (1963) summarized the major basin-forming processes as uplift and tilting by rebound following deglaciation, excavation of plunge pools, and formation of kettle lakes. The Finger Lakes were formed from gouged river valleys, and Seneca and Cayuga have lake bottoms below sea level. Waterfalls, such as those at Taughannock and Watkins Glens, originated from valleys of tributary streams left hanging high above newly scoured valley floors. Long Island and associated islands in Long Island Sound consist of end moraines dropped by the glacier as it began to recede.

The primary geological factor of importance in the distribution of snail species is bedrock chemistry. Snails differ in their abilities to extract calcium from their environment. Some species (e.g., *Stagnicola elodes*) appear to require relatively high levels of dissolved calcium (greater than 6 ppm) to maintain populations. Other species (e.g., *Amnicola limosa* and *Micromenetus dilatatus*) are tolerant of low dissolved calcium (less than 5 ppm) and maintain viable populations in soft, acidic water. Areas where the bedrock is of acidic, low calcium material have lower species diversity than do areas where the rock is limy. Within New York State, the Adirondack Mountains contain a large number of aquatic habitats of very low calcium content and therefore, have fewer species and lower diversity communities in lakes and streams (Jokinen 1991).

Another important aspect of geology in regard to snail distribution is topography, with its resultant drainage types. For example, areas of moderate drainage will have intermittent ponds and streams in early spring, but these dry up during late summer. Animals existing in these ephemeral habitats need survival mechanisms to tolerate dry periods. Most snails need permanent water, but species such as *S. elodes*, *Gyraulus parvus*, *G. circumstriatus*, and *Aplexa elongata* are able to aestivate over drought and maintain populations in habitats otherwise inaccessible to most aquatic gastropods.

In areas of high relief rivers can predominate over lakes as aquatic habitats. Species of Pleuroceridae and the ancylid *Ferrissia rivularis* might be the only gastropods found in rapids areas. In fact, *F. rivularis* appears to require the high oxygen levels found in swift waters and is not common in still waters. The river pools and backwaters have communities similar to those found in lakes.

Glaciated areas tend to have numerous lakes formed from kettles and drift-dammed streams. Consequently, molluscan diversity can be higher than in areas where lakes and ponds are rare. Areas of poor drainage can contain swamps and marshes, which act as connections between drainages and conduits for snail migration. Geological effects on the distribution of aquatic molluscs are complex and involve an array of chemical and physical factors.

CANAL SYSTEM OF NEW YORK STATE

The 19th century in New York State was an era of building canals for the transportation of goods to many American and Canadian ports. The major canal was the Erie, which was completed in 1825. It connected Albany on the east with Buffalo on the west. A number of additional canals, called laterals, were built to connect the Erie with regions north and south. The canal system connected a number of major watersheds and allowed the migration of aquatic snail species from one to the other.

Many sections of the canals were located in major river valleys. Drainage originated at the summit of the canal and flowed in two directions toward and down the connected valleys. A number of streams were captured and lakes dammed as reservoirs to act as feeders supplying the canals with enough water to maintain proper depth during low-flow periods. Even after the lateral canals were abandoned, a number of feeders were maintained as water sources for the Erie (Whitford 1906). Because of canal, feed-

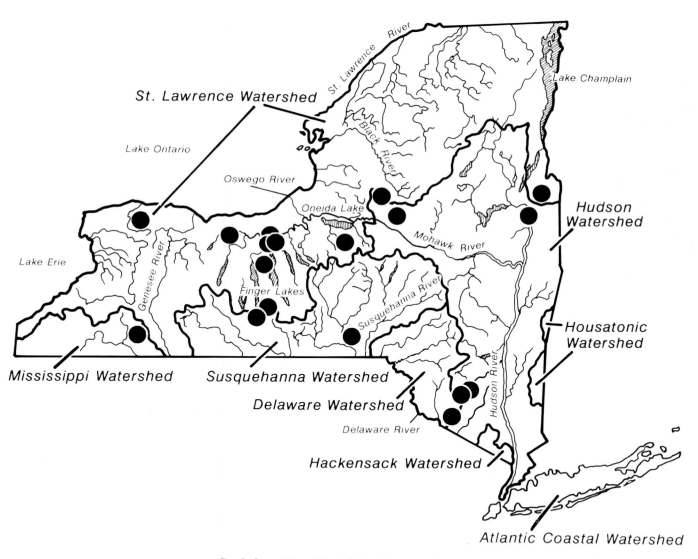

Fig. 3. Canal sites visited during the present survey.

er, and reservoir construction, abandonment and filling of many canal sections, but not others, and natural flood events of the rivers, the drainage history of New York State along canal routes is complex and confusing, but it undoubtedly had effects on freshwater snail distributions. Because of the importance of the canals, the following history is provided. Comments on snail presence (see Fig. 3) and abundance in portions of these canals are included.

The Champlain Canal, connecting the Hudson River at Waterford with Lake Champlain near Whitehall, Washington County, was completed in 1823. This 66-mile-long canal carried lumber from the Lake George-Lake Champlain region to New York City. The Canal followed the bed of Wood Creek into Lake Champlain for several miles. In 1837, a 12-mile-long feeder from Glens Falls to the canal was completed. Improvement authorized in 1900 made the Champlain Canal part of the Barge Canal project, and the Canal is still operative (Whitford 1906, Papp 1977).

During or just prior to 1878, *Bithynia tentaculata* was found in two places in New York State, Lake Ontario at Oswego, Oswego County, and the Champlain Canal at West Troy, Rensselaer County (Beauchamp 1886b, Marshall 1894). The present survey included two sites in the Champlain Canal system, the Canal itself at Fort Ann (site number 312) and the Glens Falls feeder at Glens Falls (299). Small populations of three species (*Amnicola limosa*, *Physa heterostropha*, and *Helisoma trivolvis*) were found.

The Erie Canal, extending 363 miles from Albany to Buffalo, was completed in 1825. Water flow was from Niagara toward Rome toward Oneida Lake, and Rome east toward Albany and the Hudson River. The history of the Erie Canal, its improvements, and the construction of the parallel Barge Canal, begun in 1905, is complex, and sources such as Whitford (1906), Finch (1925), Payne (1959), and Papp (1977) can be consulted for details.

Due to the experiments of Dr. James Lewis in Mohawk, Herkimer County, the establishment of molluscs in the Erie Canal is better documented than for any other New York canal. By 1860 a molluscan community had become well-established in the Canal in the vicinity of Mohawk. In addition to several clam species, the following snail species had populations in the Canal: *Campeloma decisum*, plentiful; *Goniobasis virginica*, local, recently introduced; *Amnicola limosa*, plentiful; *A. walkeri* (?, as *A. lustrica*), plentiful; *Valvata tricarinata*; *Stagnicola elodes*; and *S. catascopium*, abundant (Lewis 1860). A decade later, Lewis (1872) noted additional species, including *Cincinnatia cincinnatiensis*; *Fontigens nickliniana* (as *Bythinella obtusa*); *Goniobasis livescens*, introduced from western waters; *Helisoma anceps*; *H. trivolvis*; *Birgella subglobosa*, introduced from the west since 1860 and numerically more abundant than any other mollusc in the canal; and *Viviparus georgianus*, a colony from Illinois planted in the canal in the fall of 1867, now thriving. By 1892, *V. georgianus* had migrated east to Amsterdam, Montgomery County (Strayer 1987) and Albany, Albany County (Marshall 1894).

Four sites were sampled on the Erie Canal system during the present survey: Ridgeway Township, Orleans County (443), which yielded the species *Physa gyrina* and *Helisoma trivolvis*; Widewaters at Arcadia Township, Wayne County (504), which yielded *Physa integra* (?) and *Goniobasis livescens*; the Old Erie Canal at Sullivan Township, Madison County (565), which yielded *Fossaria rustica* and *Physa heterostropha*; and the feeder canal from West Canada Creek, Trenton Township, Oneida County (380), which yielded the river ancylid, *Ferrissia rivularis*.

The Cayuga and Seneca Canal, completed in 1821, connected Cayuga and Seneca Lakes for shipment of flour, salt, gypsum, and grain. In 1828, the 20-mile canal connected the Erie Canal at Montezuma with Seneca Lake, at or near Geneva (Whitford 1906).

Four sites along the Cayuga and Seneca Canal system were sampled during this survey: Waterloo Township, Seneca County (527); Mud Lock, Aurelius Township, Cayuga County (531); Tyre Township, Seneca County (534); and a portion of the abandoned canal near the Mud Lock portion of the Canal, Aurelius Township, Cayuga County (532). The diversity and abundance of snails collected in the active Canal (527, 531, 534) were fairly high. Species found included *Amnicola limosa*, *Bithynia tentaculata*, *Goniobasis livescens*, *G. virginica*, *Pleurocera acuta*, *Physa gyrina*, *P. integra*, *Helisoma trivolvis*, *Gyraulus parvus*, *Laevapex fuscus*, *Ferrissia rivularis*, and *F. parallela*. In marl deposits at Aurelius, shells of *Helisoma campanulatum*, *Helisoma anceps*, *Stagnicola elodes*, and *S. catascopium* were found. The marl at Tyre included shells of *Pomatiopsis lapidaria*, *H. anceps*, *S. catascopium*, and *G. parvus*. The marls contained different species from those found alive, indicating a change in community structure over the last century. The modern absence of lynmaeids is notable. The portion of the abandoned canal at Mud Lock was filled with the macroalga *Chara* sp. *Stagnicola elodes* and *Physa gyrina* were abundant in a flowing portion containing sulfur bacteria.

The story of the Delaware and Hudson Canal is linked with the development of a market for coal. The Canal, opened in 1827, ran for 59 miles from Kingston, on the Hudson River, to Port Jervis, on the Delaware. It continued 22 miles up the Delaware, and 25 miles up the Lackawaxen River to the Honesdale terminus. In 1899 the entire bed of the Canal was sold to private parties, and later it was sold to the railroads (Whitford 1906).

Lewis (in Marshall 1894) theorized that *Lioplax subcarinata* entered the lower Hudson via the Delaware and Hudson Canal, but evidence does not exist to substantiate that claim.

During this survey, four sites on the Delaware and Hudson Canal were sampled: Deerplace Township, Orange County (455); Mamakating Township, Sullivan County (460, 463), and Summitville Township, Sullivan County (462). Sampling yielded a moderately high diversity of pulmonates in moderate densities, but no prosobranchs. Species included *Fossaria modicella*, *Stagnicola emarginata*, *Pseudosuccinea columella, Physa ancillaria, P. gyrina, P. heterostropha, Helisoma trivolvis, Gyraulus parvus, G. deflectus, Micromenetus dilatatus,* and *Planorbula armigera.*

The Chemung Canal, completed in 1831, was 39 miles long and designed to connect the New York State waterways from Elmira, Tioga County, with the Chemung River, a branch of the Susquehanna River, and from there to the bituminous coal fields of western Pennsylvania. The two important feeder sources were the Chemung River and Catharine Creek. By the 1870s, the Fall Brook Railroad, which ran nearly parallel with the canal and extended into the coal fields, outcompeted the canal and caused its closure in 1878. A portion at Montour Falls was reopened later as a waterway through Seneca Lake and the Seneca and Cayuga Canal (Whitford 1906). The Canal's effect on molluscan migration has not been established (Clarke & Berg 1959).

During this survey, two sites from the Chemung system were sampled: the diversion channel from Catharine Creek to the Barge Canal (394), and the Barge Canal (395) (Catharine Creek) to Seneca Lake, Montour Falls, Schuyler County. Although snail diversity was low (three species), the population levels of two species were high in the diversion channel. Large numbers of *Stagnicola elodes* and *Physa heterostropha* and a small number of *Helisoma anceps* were found. Only *P. heterostropha* was found in the Barge Canal.

In 1836 the Chenango Canal was completed. It extended for 97 miles from Binghamton, Broome County, up the valley of the Chenango River, a tributary of the Susquehanna, to its headwaters, and then north to the Erie Canal at Utica. An extension was built from Binghamton, along the valley of the Susquehanna, to the State border near Tioga Point. By 1877, competition from the railroads prompted the Canal's abandonment, except for the reservoirs that flowed north and could supply water to the Erie Canal at Oriskany and Utica (Whitford 1906).

Only one site along the Chenango Canal was sampled. It is in Fenton Township, Broome County (554). Three species of low to moderate population density were found: *Fossaria modicella, Physa heterostropha,* and *Ferrissia rivularis.*

The 50-mile-long Black River Canal was opened to navigation in 1849. It was designed to connect the Black River of the eastern Adirondack Mountains and the lowlands of Herkimer, Oneida, Lewis, and Jefferson Counties with the Erie Canal. Several lakes, including those in the Fulton chain, were dammed as reservoirs, and water was shunt-ed into the Lansing Kill and the Mohawk River, where it entered the Erie Canal by the feeder at Rome. Later, additional reservoirs on the Black, Beaver, and Moose Rivers were constructed to supply water to the Black River. They compensated mill owners at Watertown and Carthage for waters diverted into the Erie Canal. The Black River Canal was enduring and successful as a supplier of water for the Erie Canal (Whitford 1906).

A sampling site (367) on a remnant of the Black River Canal at Boonville yielded an extraordinary snail community of high diversity and density. Only two or three net sweeps yielded 690 individuals of *Amnicola limosa.* Other species included *Campeloma decisum, Fossaria modicella, Pseudosuccinea columella, Physa gyrina* (320 in number), *Gyraulus parvus, Helisoma trivolvis* (184 in number), and *Ferrissia walkeri.* The Canal remnant is isolated and has fairly swiftly running water. There does not appear to be a well-defined predator habitat. High oxygen, good vegetation, and low predation possibly allowed the snail populations to become extremely dense.

The Genesee Valley Canal extended 125 miles from the Erie Canal in Rochester, through the valley of the Genesee River to Mount Morris, and then to the Allegheny River at Olean. It did not open completely until 1861, although by 1840 the section between Rochester and the Genesee dam near Mount Morris was in use. A branch was built from Mount Morris up the valley of Canaseraga Creek to Dansville. By 1847 the Genesee and Erie Canals were taking so much water from the Genesee River that they impinged on water privileges of manufacturing interests in and below Rochester. Consequently, Conesus Lake in Livingston County was made into a reservoir. By 1880, roads and railways served as trade routes, and the main Canal line was abandoned and deeded to the Genesee Valley Canal Railway Company (Whitford 1906).

During this survey, a site at the summit of the Genesee Valley Canal, Cuba Township, Allegany County (415) was sampled. Diversity and abundance of snails were moderate. All species were pulmomates, including *Fossaria exigua, Physa gyrina, Helisoma anceps, H. trivolvis,* a *Gyraulus* sp., and *Ferrissia parallela.*

Species from Conesus Lake (505), a reservoir for the Canal, were abundant and included *Viviparus georgianus, Goniobasis livescens, Amnicola limosa, Pyrgulopsis lustrica, Physa integra, Gyraulus parvus,* and *Laevapex fuscus.* Shells of *Valvata tricarinata* and *V. sincera* were found in the marl, but live populations were apparently absent.

KEY TO THE FAMILIES OF FRESHWATER SNAILS

1a. Shell not coiled, shaped like a Chinese hat ....
....Ancylidae, limpets

1b. Shell coiled..2

2a. Shell without spire, flatly coiled 3

2b. Shell with spire 4

3a. Shell brown ....Planorbidae, rams-horn snails

3b. Shell white to light tan...................Valvatidae, valvatids

4a. Shell sinistral; aperture on left when spire upright ....
....Physidae, physid snails

4b. Shell dextral; aperture on right when spire upright..........
....5

5a. Shell with operculum covering aperture 6

5b. Shell without operculum ....Lymnaeidae, pondsnails

6a. Shell long and tapered, at least twice as long as wide
....7

6b. Shell of various shapes, not long and tapered............8

7a. Sides of whorls flattened, sometimes with spiral ridges,
adults over 15 mm high ......Pleuroceridae, elimia snails

7b. Sides of whorls rounded, shells < 15 mm high ....
...Pomatiopsidae, walker snails (Pomatiopsis lapidaria)

8a. Operculum concentric 9

8b. Operculum spiral 10

9a. Operculum chitinous, thin; shell globose to conical......
.... Viviparidae, mystery snails

9b. Operculum calcareous, thick; shell moderately elon-
gate ....
..........Bithyniidae, faucet snails *(Bithynia tentaculata)*

10a. Operculum multispiral throughout................................
....Valvatidae, valvatid snails

10b.Operculum paucispiral or multispiral only in center........
....11

11a. Whorls rounded ....
.......................Hydrobiidae, amnicolas and duskysnails

11b. Whorls flattened ....Pleuroceridae, elimia snails

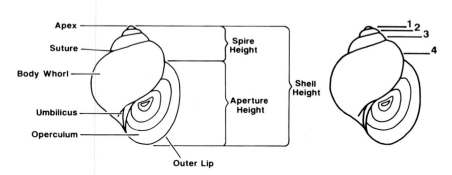

Fig. 4. Shell structure terminology. Numbers indicate whorl count (from Jokinen 1983).

DESCRIPTIONS, DISTRIBUTIONS, AND ECOLOGY OF THE SPECIES

Subclass Prosobranchia

Gill complex located anteriorly in mantle cavity; sexes usually separate (except Valvatidae); shell usually developed and provided with operculum covering shell aperture (Baker 1928a, Hyman 1967).

Order Mesogastropoda

Siphon, operculum, and penis usually present; radula usually of taenioglossate type (seven teeth in each transverse row, Fig. 5a); 1 auricle, 1 gill, and 1 kidney present (Hyman 1967).

Family Valvatidae

Shell small, spiral, dextral, turbinate to subdiscoidal; whorls rounded or carinate; aperture entire, circular; lip simple, sharp; operculum circular, multispiral. Gills external; left one feather-like, extended over back; right one rudimentary, forming slender appendage (Baker 1928a). Snails simultaneously hermaphroditic, not self-fertilizing (Hyman 1967); external verge long, slender, nonretractile (Baker 1928a); egg capsules 1-2 mm in diameter, globose, attached to substratum by capsule base; embryos inside capsule embedded in albumin covered by mucoid coat (Fretter & Graham 1962).

Key to the Valvatidae

1a. Shell with 2-3 prominent spiral ridges...............................
....*Valvata tricarinata*

1b. Shell without spiral ridges...2

2a. Shell high-turbinate, about as high as wide; umbilicus narrow ....*Valvata piscinalis*

2b. Shell depressed to low-turbinate, wider than high; umbilicus wide...3

3a. Shell depressed, with coarse striae; spire very short ......
....*Valvata lewisi*

3b. Shell low-turbinate, with fine striae; spire elevated.........
....*Valvata sincera*

Valvata tricarinata (Say, 1817)

Threeridge valvata
Figs. 6a, 7

Shell turbinate, 6 mm wide, translucent, shiny; umbilicus deep, funnel shaped; whorls 4.0, rapidly enlarging, typically with 3 sharp carinae on body whorl: dorsally (on shoulder), peripherally, and ventrally (on base); shell flattened between carinae, sloping upward from dorsal carina to suture on upper surface; sutures distinct; lip simple, sharp, continuous, appressed to body whorl.

Some carinae can be absent in certain individuals that are considered to represent various subspecies or morphs (see Baker 1928a; Burch 1989).

This species occurs in the eastern and midwestern United States south to Virginia, west to Nebraska and Washington, and it occurs in Canada from New Brunswick to eastern British Columbia and to the Northwest Territories south of the tree line (Baker 1928a; Richards 1934; Dawley 1947; McKillop & Harrison 1972; Clarke 1973, 1981; Tudorancea *et al.* 1979; Cvancara 1983; Jokinen 1983; Smith 1987; Taylor & Bright 1987).

Populations were found in 22 collection sites in the Hudson River watershed (265, 269, 291, 453, 459, 604, 616); Ohio-Mississippi River watershed (431); St. Lawrence River watershed (141D, 338, 390, 408, 449, 493, 497, 499, 500,

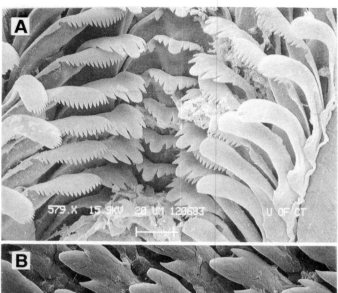

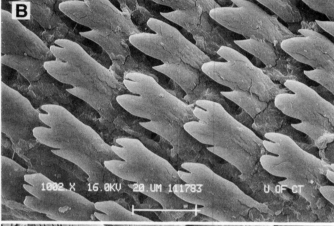

Fig. 5. Types of radulae of freshwater snails: a, taenioglossate radula, with seven teeth per row (Hydrobiidae); b, radula with many teeth per row (Lymnaeidae); c, radula with many, small, serrated teeth per row (Physidae).

505, 520, 523, 535); and Susquehanna River watershed (400). Populations are known to be common in the Oswego (St. Lawrence), Allegheny (Ohio-Mississippi), and Hudson River watersheds (Harman & Berg 1971, Strayer 1987).

Valvata tricarinata was first reported from New York by De Kay (1843). During the 19th century, the species was noted to exist in scattered localities across the State, from Albany County (Marshall 1895), west to Herkimer, Otsego, Onondaga, Cayuga, Monroe and Chautauqua Counties (Lewis 1856 a, b; 1860; 1872; Beauchamp 1886b; Walton 1891, 1898; Marshall 1894; Maury 1898; Baker 1899). Over the next 35 years, additional sites were added from Madison, Oswego, Cayuga, Schuyler, Niagara, Erie, and Chautauqua Counties (Baker 1900b, 1916a, b, 1918a, 1928b; Evermann & Goldsborough 1902; Henderson 1907; Letson 1909; Maury 1916; Pratt 1923; Fluck 1933). During this time, fossils of *V. tricarinata* were found in peat in Bronx County (Humphreys 1910) and in the Cayuga Valley (Maury 1916). Eastern sites were added for Warren, Greene, Dutchess, Manchester and Rockland Counties (Townes 1936, Jacobson 1945, Jacobson & Emerson 1961, Bretet & Carswell 1952). In western New York, Townes (1937) found the snail still present in Lake Chautauqua and in Findley, Bear, and Upper and Middle Cassadaga Lakes. Burdick (1939) noted *V. tricarinata* as common in Lake Ontario. Otsego, Onondaga, Cayuga, Seneca, Yates, Steuben, and Livingston Counties in central New York and Jefferson County in northern New York have been cited as having populations (Harman & Berg 1971; Harman 1970, 1971; MacNamara & Harman 1975; Wade & Vasey 1976; Buckley 1977; Wade 1987). Strayer's (1987) extensive survey has demonstrated this species to be common and widespread in the Hudson River basin.

Of the 22 sites sampled during this survey, eight were river and stream sites, nine were lakes, four were permanent ponds, and one was a marsh. In Connecticut and Massachusetts, *V. tricarinata* is found only in larger lakes and ponds (Jokinen 1983, Smith 1987). In other parts of its range, it also can inhabit slow rivers, small streams, intermittent streams, freshwater tidal marshes, stream backwaters, and muskeg pools (Goodrich 1932, Clarke 1981, Cvancara 1983, Strayer 1987). Populations can survive in shallow to deep water on many types of substrata, including aquatic vegetation, such as the algae *Cladophora* sp. and *Oedogonium* sp., and macrophytes and decaying terrestrial leaf litter (Baker 1918a, 1928b; Clarke 1973; Jokinen 1983).

The life cycle of *V. tricarinata* is annual. Eggs appear from March to July (Baker 1928b, McKillop 1985), with the time probably dependent on geographic location. Ten to 30 eggs in a gelatinous mass with a diameter of 1 mm are deposited on aquatic plants or stones (Baker 1928b,

15

Heard 1963). Newly hatched young float on the undersurface of the water film (Baker 1928a). Populations of *V. tricarinata* can be dense enough to be a dominant element in a lake's faunal biomass (Tudorancea *et al.* 1979).

Water chemistry values in New York State were: pH: 6.9-8.2 (7.5 ± 0.1), conductivity: 139-2320 μmhos/cm (433 ± 102), Ca^{++}: 4-89 ppm (28 ± 4), and Na^+: 1-291 ppm (36 ± 14). These values, as well as those from Connecticut (Jokinen 1983), southeast Manitoba (McKillop 1985), central New York (Harman & Berg 1971), and North Dakota (Cvancara 1983) indicate that *V. tricarinata* populations are limited to high calcium habitats.

Valvata sincera Say, 1824

Mossy valvata
Figs. 6b, 7

Shell yellowish-brown, subglobose-conic, 5 mm wide, solid; sculpture of fine and regular striae; umbilicus round, deep, exhibiting volutions almost to apex; whorls 4.0, evenly rounded, regularly increasing in diameter; sutures well-impressed; aperture circular; lip continuous, touching but not appressed to whorl above (Baker 1928a).

The various subspecies (*V. sincera sincera* Say, *V. sincera ontariensis* Baker, *V. sincera helicoidea* Dall) are distributed as a group from the Arctic Circle south to Connecticut and west to Minnesota (Baker 1928a; Bright 1981; Clarke 1973, 1981; Jokinen 1983; Smith 1987).

Only four living populations were located during this survey, all within the St. Lawrence River watershed (259A, 261, 263, 495). Sites 259A and 263 were different localities within Dead Creek, a marshy tributary of Lake Champlain. Lake Champlain was site 261, and 495 was the Oswego River, Oswego County. An additional site, Conesus Lake (505), Livingston County, St. Lawrence River watershed, had no living populations, but shells were found in the marl. Conesus Lake, used as a reservoir for the Genesee Valley Canal, was subject to repeated drawdown, which could have destroyed the valvatids.

Although *V. sincera* appears to be relatively rare in New York State, De Kay (1843) reported populations from Oneida Lake, Onondaga County; Lake Chautauqua, Chautauqua County; and Lake Champlain, Clinton County. Lewis (1856a, 1860, 1872) noted the species as rare and only present in the marshy borders and sediments of the "Little Lakes" in Herkimer and adjacent counties. During the late 19th and early 20th centuries, *V. sincera* was reported from Winfield in Herkimer County; the Erie Canal and "Wide Waters," Monroe County; Irondequoit Bay in Lake Ontario, Monroe County; Lime Lake in Cattaraugus County; Seneca River and Oneida Lake in Onondaga County; Cayuga Lake in Cayuga County; and Lake Chautauqua, Chautauqua County (Beauchamp 1886b; Marshall 1894; Walton 1898; Letson 1909; Maury 1916; Baker 1900b, 1918a, 1928b). More recently, additional popula-

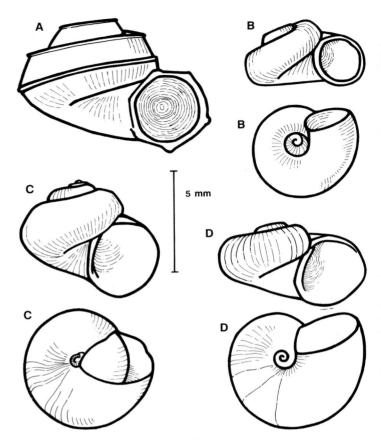

Fig. 6. Family Valvatidae, shells: a, *Valvata tricarinata*; b, *V. sincera*, two views; c, *V. piscinalis*, two views; d, *V. lewisi*, two views. All illustrations are drawn to the same scale.

tions were reported from Lake Ontario at Sodus Bay, Wayne County, and Little Sodus Bay, Cayuga County; Schroon River, Warren County; Hudson River, Greene County; Otsego Lake, Otsego County; Fifth Lake, Hamilton County; and the lower Hudson River in the vicinity of Dutchess County (Townes 1936, Burdick 1939, Jacobson 1945, Harman 1971, MacNamara & Harman 1975, Buckley 1977, Strayer 1987).

This species, in southern New England and New York, is limited to large lakes and rivers (Jokinen 1983, Smith 1987, Strayer 1987, this study). In Canada, it also inhabits muskeg pools (Clarke 1981).

V. sincera is listed as endangered in Massachusetts (Smith 1987), and the present distribution in southern New England and New York is probably a relict of a broader early Holocene distribution (Smith 1987, Strayer 1987).

Populations can live at considerable depths and are associated with submerged aquatic vegetation (Clarke 1981). Of the five sites in New York, one is a river, three are lakes, and one is a marshy creek feeding into Lake Champlain.

The snails produce egg capsules, each containing two to six eggs, on aquatic plants (Lang & Dronen 1970). In Manitoba, young are present from May to July, and the species has an annual life cycle (McKillop 1985). *V. sincera* forms part of the diet of whitefish, *Coregonus clupeaformis* (Mitchill), and perch, *Perca flavescens* (Mitchill) (Goodrich 1932, Clarke 1981).

Except for Fifth Lake in the Black River basin (Buckley 1977), this species usually lives in high calcium habitats. Water chemistry values for the five sites sampled during this survey are: pH: 6.9-7.4 (7.2 ± 0.1), conductivity: 142-905 µmhos/cm (431 ± 126), Ca^{++}: 13-44 ppm (35 ± 6), and Na^{+}: 7-117 ppm (34 ± 21). These values are similar to those in Connecticut (Jokinen 1983), central New York (Harman & Berg 1971), and Manitoba (McKillop 1985). It appears that in Canada *V. sincera* is limited to oligotrophic and mesotrophic lakes (Clarke 1979), but in Connecticut (Jokinen 1983) and New York, habitats can be eutrophic.

Valvata piscinalis (Müller, 1774)
European stream valvata
Figs. 6c, 7

Shell yellowish brown to greenish, shining, rather solid, 5 mm wide, about as high as wide; sculpture consisting of collabral threads; umbilicus narrow, deep; whorls up to 5.0, rounded; spire conical, apex obtuse; aperture circular, appressed to body whorl; inner lip reflected slightly over umbilicus (Clarke 1981).

This is an introduced Eurasian species that has spread throughout Lake Ontario, Lake Erie, the upper St. Lawrence River and its tributaries, and the lower Hudson River (Baker 1900b, Oughton 1938, Clarke 1981, Strayer 1987).

In New York, Baker (1900b), noting that the species had been seen first in 1897, recorded *V. piscinalis* (as "*obtusa*") as abundant in beach wash of Lake Ontario, Monroe County. Burdick (1939) later noted the species at a depth of 6-9.5 m in Oswego Harbor, Lake Ontario, Oswego County. Cayuga Lake, Tompkins County, also has a population (Harman 1968b, Harman & Berg, 1971).

Three populations were located during this survey, two in the Hudson River (96E, 286) and one in the St. Lawrence watershed (141). Strayer (1987) collected a few specimens from the tidal Hudson River in Dutchess County.

Valvata piscinalis occurs in lakes and slow moving rivers (Clarke 1981). Immediately prior to egg laying the snails leave the substratum and move to aquatic vegetation to deposit egg capsules containing 4-60 eggs. The young emerge in 15-30 days and feed on periphyton before they migrate down to the substratum (Cleland 1954, Clarke 1981).

Water chemistry values for sites 141 and 286 were: pH: 6.9 and 7.9, conductivity: 162 and 208 µmhos/cm, Ca^{++}: 13 and 29 ppm, and Na^{+}: 7 ppm at both sites.

Valvata lewisi Currier, 1868
Fringed valvata
Figs. 6d, 7

Shell turbinate, thin, 5 mm wide, regularly striate; spire depressed, apex flattened; whorls 3.5, rapidly enlarging; lip thin, continuous, appressed to body whorl above; umbilicus wide, deep, exhibiting interior whorls (Baker 1928a).

This species occurs in southern Canada from Quebec to British Columbia and in the United States from New York west to Minnesota (Goodrich 1932, Burch 1982).

Only one population of this species was located during this survey. It was in a ditch at Oneida Shores County Park, Onondaga County, St. Lawrence River watershed (450). The only population found by Harman & Berg (1971) in central New York was in Oneida Lake.

In Oneida Lake, *V. lewisi* was relatively scarce, living on sand down to depths of 7 m (Harman & Berg 1971). Other substrata include mud and aquatic vegetation (Baker 1928a).

Family Viviparidae

Shell turbinate, moderately large, imperforate or subperforate; whorls convex, often carinate; aperture entire, subcircular or somewhat applied above; lip simple; operculum convex, concentric; nucleus subcentral; rostrum long; tentacles long, slender; male right tentacle short, wide, forming penis sheath; uterus large, filling much of last whorl; females ovoviviparous; snails in mid-neanic stage when born (Baker 1928a); shells of developing viviparids marked by spiral rows of periostracal hairs and/or ridges (Jokinen 1984).

Key to the Viviparidae

1a. Shell with distinct angulations or ridges on whorls...........
....*Lioplax subcarinata*

1b. Shell without distinct, sharp angulations.......................2

2a. Inner lip not reflected, not forming an umbilicus ....
....*Campeloma decisum*

2b. Inner lip reflected, forming a slit-like umbilicus 3

3a. Shell striped with chestnut-colored bands, sometimes visible only inside shell aperture ....
....*Viviparus georgianus*

3b. Shell not striped ....*Cipangopaludina* spp., 4

4a. Shell apex obtuse, without spiral angulations, often with surface malleation ....
....*Cipangoplaudina chinensis*

4b. Shell apex acute, with low angulations on whorls, without malleations ....*Cipangopaludina japonica*

Viviparus georgianus (Lea, 1834)
Banded mysterysnail
Figs. 7, 8a

Shell subglobose, moderately large, up to 45 mm high, imperforate or with narrow, slit-like umbilicus; whorls 4.0-5.0 with 4 spiral, chestnut-colored bands (possibly obliterated outside but always visible inside); sutures deep; outer lip thin; parietal lip a thickened glaze; operculum roundly ovate, concentric (Baker 1928a, Clench 1962, Clench & Fuller 1965); newly released young with 3 spiral rows of hooked hairs on apical and second whorls and 11-13 rows on third whorl (Jokinen 1984).

A common synonym is *Viviparus contectoides* (Binney 1863).

This species occurs east of the Mississippi River, from southeastern Canada to Florida and the Gulf of Mexico. It has extended its range northeasterly since the middle of the 19th century (Richards 1934, Clench 1962, Harman & Berg 1971, Clarke 1981, Jokinen 1983, Smith 1987, Strayer 1990).

Thirty-two populations of *V. georgianus* were found in all major New York drainage basins except the Delaware. Localities were in the Hudson River watershed (280, 284, 293, 318, 319, 320, 610); Mississippi-Ohio River watershed (427B); St. Lawrence River watershed (141A, 141C, 262, 307, 338, 339, 341, 353, 358, 377, 407, 408, 409, 410, 448A, 502A, 505, 510, 512, 513, 521, 562); Susquehanna River watershed (592); and Housatonic River watershed (294). Populations also have been reported from scattered localities in the Susquehanna, Oswego and Genesee (St. Lawrence), and Mohawk River watersheds (Harman & Berg 1971, Wade & Vasey 1976, Strayer 1987).

De Kay (1843) did not list *V. georgianus* as occurring in New York State. The species was introduced into New York in 1867 when J. Lewis deposited 200 individuals from Illinois into the Erie Canal and Mohawk River in Herkimer County (Lewis 1872, Clench 1962). As of 1961, it had not yet migrated to Peekskill or Long Island, but it had extensively populated a pond in New York City's Central Park, New York County (Jacobson & Emerson 1961). Robertson (1933) reported the species from Buffalo. The New York State Museum has specimens collected during the 1950s and 1960s from Cayuga, Genesee, Herkimer, Madison, Monroe, Oneida, Onondaga, Ontario, Oswego, Tompkins, and Wayne Counties.

Of the 32 populations located during this survey, six were in river and stream sites, 14 in lakes, nine in permanent ponds, two in marshes, and one in a ditch. None of the habitats were ephemeral.

In temperate lakes, females bear young their second summer and live to three years. They grow larger than males, which die during their second summer after a period of reproduction. The snails migrate to shallow water in midsummer and to deeper water in October (Jokinen et al. 1982). Fecundity varies from 4-81 embryos/female (Vail 1978, Browne 1978, Jokinen et al. 1982).

The New York populations existed in water with pH: 6.3-8.5 (7.3 ± 0.1), conductivity: 42-452 μmhos/cm (225 ± 21), Ca^{++}: 3-36 ppm (18 ± 2), and Na^{+}: 2-40 ppm (12 ± 2). This species appears to have a relatively wide tolerance range for soft and hard water habitats.

Cipangopaludina japonica (von Martens, 1861)
Japanese mysterysnail
Figs. 7, 8b

Shell somewhat extended, up to 65 mm high, olivaceous green to dark brownish green, without banding, rimately umbilicate; whorls 7.0-8.0, strongly convex; spire extended, produced at 50-55° angle; outer lip thin; parietal lip with thin glaze; operculum thin, nucleus submarginal (Clench & Fuller 1965).

This is an oriental species found in Japanese mesotrophic and eutrophic lakes and ponds (Taki 1981). It was introduced into North America, where there are now scattered populations (see review in Jokinen 1982).

18

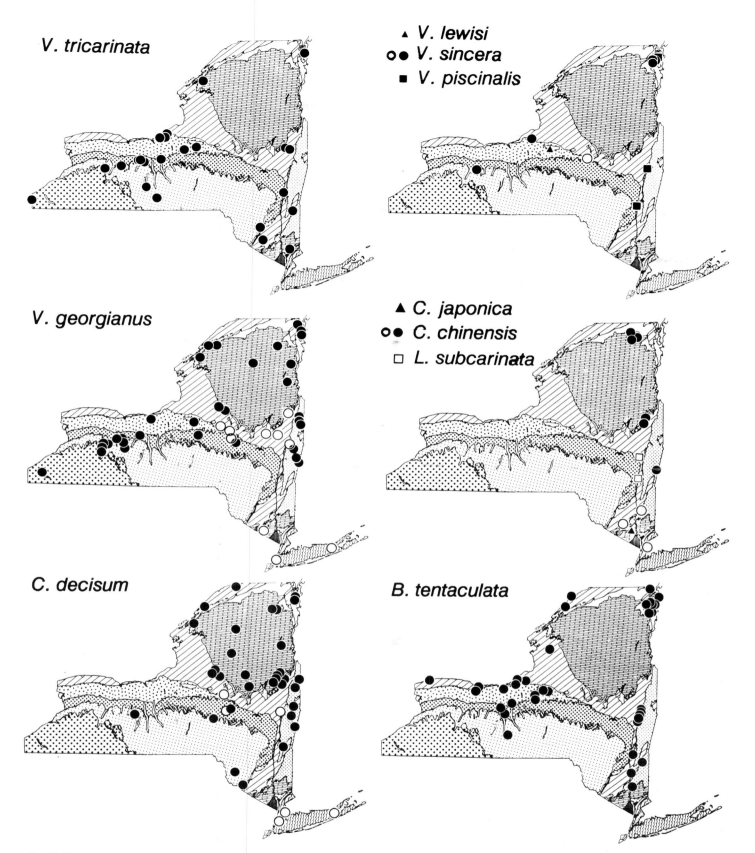

Fig. 7. Known distributions of species of Valvatidae, Viviparidae, and Bithyniidae in New York State. Closed circles indicate records from the present survey, and open circles indicate records from museum specimens.

Lake Tiorati (site 607, Hudson River watershed), a soft water lake in the Palisades Interstate Park, Orange County, has the only population found during this survey.

Females can survive up to eight years and carry 10-120 developing embryos. Young are released from late April, when water temperatures reach 15°C, until October. In Japan, the snails hibernate in mud from December through February (Taki 1981).

Little is known of the habitat parameters of this species. Lake Tiorati has soft water: pH: 6.3, conductivity: 62 μmhos/cm, Ca^{++}: 11 ppm, and Na^+: 16 ppm. A Connecticut population lives in a lake of medium hard water: pH: 7.3, conductivity: 194 μmhos/cm, Ca^{++}: 11 ppm (Jokinen 1983).

Cipangopaludina japonica was synonymized with *C. chinensis* by Dundee (1974), and Clarke (1978), and Strayer (1990) agreed. Others have not synonymized these species (Clench & Fuller 1965, Smith 1987), or have recognized them as different phenotypes (Jokinen 1982).

Cipangopaludina chinensis (Gray, 1863)

Chinese mysterysnail
Figs. 7, 8c

Shell large, to 60 mm high, uniform light to dark olive-green to brown, without banding; sculpture of fine growth lines, spiral lines, and malleations; umbilicus small, round, covered in part by reflected parietal lip; whorls 6.0-7.0, slightly shouldered; spire moderately extended, produced at 65-70° angle; sutures deep; outer lip slightly reflected, entire lip colored black; operculum corneous, thin, with concentric growth lines, nucleus submarginal (Clench & Fuller 1965); *spiral lines of periostracal hairs conspicuous in young* (Jokinen 1984), *resulting in rows of pits on many adult shells. Growth allometric, young with lower height to width ratio and sharply angled body whorl* (Jokinen 1982).

A commonly used synonym is *Viviparus malleatus* (Reeve 1863).

This is an Asian species introduced into North America in the Chinese markets of San Francisco as a food item (Abbott 1950). It has spread across the United States, north to Montreal, and it is abundant on the northeast coast up to New Hampshire (Jokinen 1982). Accounts of *C. chinensis* in New York and New England are found in Jacobson & Emerson (1961), Clench & Fuller (1965), Dundee (1974), Jokinen (1983), Smith (1987), and Strayer (1990). Harman and Berg's (1971) survey of central New York State did not reveal any populations.

Six populations of *C. chinensis* were found during this survey in the Hudson River watershed (295, 297) and the eastern St. Lawrence River watershed (298, 311, 349, 351). Additional populations have been reported from the Black River (Buckley 1977) and Hudson River basins (Buckley 1977, Strayer 1987). Sites in Westchester, Orange, Dutchess, Queens, and Nassau Counties are noted in Clench and Fuller (1965).

No populations were reported in New York prior to 1942, at which time the snail was found in the Niagara River, Niagara County (Schmeck 1942). The species had not populated central New York by the early 1970s (Harman & Berg 1971) but had been introduced into Oneida Lake by 1978 (Clarke 1978).

Female snails have a five year life span, but most males die after three years, with a few surviving to four years. Growth continues throughout life; and females grow larger than males. They begin to produce young ovoviviparously at the end of their first year, but maximum productivity is not reached until the fourth and fifth years. Newborn appear from June through October (Stańzykowska *et al.* 1971). The snails are found in shallow water during summer, where they feed primarily on epibenthic diatoms on muddy to sandy sediments (Stańzykowska *et al.* 1972). The animals migrate to deeper water in the autumn (Stańzykowska *et al.* 1971).

This species lives in permanent lakes and quiet embayments of rivers (Jokinen 1982). Three New York populations occurred in lakes and three in ponds. Chemical conditions were: pH: 6.5-7.8 (7.0 ± 0.2); conductivity: 63-400 μmhos/cm (165 ± 56); Ca^{++}: 5-16 ppm (10 ± 2); and Na^+: 2-49 ppm (13 ± 7). These are similar to the parameters for Connecticut populations (Jokinen 1983). *C. chinensis* appears to be limited to waters of medium to high calcium and pH values.

Campeloma decisum (Say, 1816)

Pointed campeloma
Figs. 7, 8d

Shell elongate-oval, 40 mm high, thin, dark green or olive to brown; imperforate; whorls 6.0, early ones usually eroded; spire long and pointed, sharply conic; operculum thick, entirely concentric (Baker 1928a).

Clarke (1981) and Burch (1986) list *C. integrum* (Say 1821) as a synonym.

This species ranges from Nova Scotia and New England west to Manitoba and Minnesota, south to Kentucky, Tennessee, Virginia, and Louisiana (Baker 1928a, Goodrich 1932, Richards 1934, Clench 1962, Clarke 1981, Jokinen 1983, Branson *et al.* 1987, Smith 1987, Brown *et al.* 1989). The range might extend into North Dakota, but only shells have been collected (Cvancara 1983).

In New York State, *C. decisum* occurs in the Delaware River watershed (457, 466); Hudson River watershed (212, 284, 292, 293, 297, 303, 304, 305, 317, 320, 321, 367, 384, 386, 612); St. Lawrence River watershed (141C, 141D, 262, 298, 338, 339, 345, 352, 353, 354, 363, 366, 377, 517); and the Susquehanna River watershed (583, 591). Older specimens in the New York State Museum are from Riverhead and Greenport, Suffolk County, Long Island (NYSM 27825-27828, 29942, 29943), Oneida County (NYSM 29944, 29946), Schuylers Lake, Otsego County (NYSM 31040), and Lake

Erie (NYSM 31041). Populations were found in all major drainages of New York except the Allegheny (Mississippi-Ohio), but they appear to be more plentiful in the northeastern part of the State. This species is abundant in the basins of the Mohawk and Hudson Rivers (Strayer 1987) and the Oswego-St.Lawrence basin, with only scattered accounts from the Susquehanna watershed (Harman & Berg 1971).

The first mention of *C. decisum* in New York was made by De Kay (1843), who noted it to be the most common species in the State. Lewis (1856a, b; 1860; 1868; 1872; 1874) found populations in the Erie Canal and in rivers and lakes of Herkimer and Otsego Counties. In a series of papers from the late 19th through the early 20th centuries populations were recorded from the Erie Canal, Oneida and Monroe Counties (Baily 1891; Walton 1891, 1898; Marshall 1886); Canandaigua Lake, Ontario and Yates Counties (Mitchell 1899; Maury 1916); Chautauqua Lake, Chautauqua County (Maury 1898, 1916; Evermann & Goldsborough 1902; Townes 1937); Owasco Lake and Owasco River, Cayuga County (Baker 1899); Hudson River, Washington County (Pilsbry 1897); Onondaga County (Beauchamp 1886b); Albany, Albany County, and Troy, Rensselaer County (Marshall 1895); Genesee River, Monroe County (Baker 1900b, 1901); Riverhead, Suffolk County, Long Island (Smith & Prime 1870); Niagara River, Niagara County, and Lake Erie (Letson 1909), Oneida Lake (Baker 1916a, 1916b, 1918a; Pratt 1923); Cayuga Lake, Cayuga County; and Conesus Lake, Livingston County (Maury 1916).

More recent records of *C. decisum* are from Conesus Lake, Livingston County (Robertson & Blakeslee 1948; Wade 1980, 1987; Wade & Vasey 1976); Lake Ontario (Burdick 1939); Warren County (Jacobson 1945); Hudson River from Hudson, Greene County, to Port Ewen, Ulster County (Townes 1937); Mohawk River (Strayer 1987); lakes in the Allegheny watershed, Chautauqua County (Townes 1937); Finger Lakes (Harman & Berg 1971); and the Black River, Lewis, Jefferson, and Oneida Counties (Buckley 1977). The New York State Museum has lots collected from 1955-1966 from Cayuga, Essex, Madison, Monroe, Onondaga, Ontario, Schuyler, Seneca, Tioga, Tompkins, and Wayne Counties.

Of the 33 populations found during this survey, six were in river and steam sites, 20 in lakes, five in permanent ponds, one in a marsh, and one in a canal. *C. decisum* is a burrowing snail, and it is usually located within the top several centimeters of soft sediments such as sand, clay, silt and detritus (Baker 1918a, 1928a; Goodrich 1932; Dawley 1947; Clench 1962; Harman & Berg 1971; Clarke 1973; Jokinen 1983; Smith 1987; Strayer 1987).

The animals appear to feed by ingesting sediment containing decaying organic matter (Chamberlain 1958, Imlay *et al.* 1981). Newly born snails are often found wedged in rock crevices rather than in sediment (Jokinen 1983). Temperate zone populations contain no males, and reproduction is by ovoviviparous parthenogenesis (Mattox 1938, van der Schalie 1965, Selander *et al.* 1977).

Individuals from temperate zone populations have life spans of three to five years, with reproduction beginning in the second year (Medcof 1940, Chamberlain 1958, Imlay *et al.* 1981). Subtropical populations in Louisiana have shorter life spans, usually two years, with some females surviving to three years. By age 1.5 years, females are brooding embryos that are released by the second year. Males, smaller than females of the same age, exist in the subtropical populations but are outnumbered by females three to one (Brown *et al.* 1989). In the subtropical populations, *C. decisum* has demonstrated very high secondary productivity as expressed by biomass (Richardson & Brown 1989).

This species is common in lakes and rivers in the northeastern United States, and it lives within a wide range of chemical parameters. Water chemistry values for 31 sites sampled during this survey are: pH: 5.8-9.2 (7.0 ± 0.1), conductivity: 28-368 µmhos/cm (125 ± 16), Ca^{++}: 1-37 ppm (11 ± 2), and Na^+: 1-40 ppm (7 ± 2). In central New York, pH values for 21 sites were 7.3-8.5 (7.9) (Harman & Berg 1971). Connecticut values for 40 sites were: pH: 5.8-10.0, conductivity: 38-286 µmhos/cm, Ca^{++}: 1-27 ppm, and Na^+: 1-22 ppm (Jokinen 1983).

Lioplax subcarinata (Say, 1816)
Ridged lioplax
Figs. 7, 8e

Shell ovate, 20 mm high, thin to thick, pale brownish green to olivaceous; finely umbilicate; whorls 6.0; spire whorls usually carinate, body whorl not carinate; spire and aperture equal in length; apex sharp in young, truncated in older shells; sutures deep; outer lip thin; inner lip callus on parietal wall; operculum distinct with spiral nucleus and concentric periphery (Baker 1928a, Clench & Turner 1955).

This species is found on the Atlantic coast from New York south to North Carolina (Richards 1934, Clench 1962, Clench & Turner 1955, Branson *et al.* 1987).

Populations were not located during a recent survey of the Hudson River basin (Strayer 1987), nor during this survey.

Lioplax subcarinata was first collected in New York State by Beecher in 1878 at the mouth of the Normans Kill, Albany County (Marshall 1895) (NYSM 31043). This species might have migrated into the Hudson from the Delaware River via the Delaware and Hudson Canal (Lewis 1874). Beauchamp (1886b) located it in the Erie Canal, Onondaga County, and in the Hudson River. The most recent collection was that of Townes (1936), who found the snails to be common on the mud bottom of the Hudson River from Hudson, Greene County, to Port Ewen, Ulster County. The University of Michigan Museum of Zoology, Museum of Comparative Zoology at Harvard University, and The

Academy of Natural Sciences of Philadelphia have specimens from the Hudson River in Greene and Dutchess Counties and from the Normans Kill (Hudson River watershed), Albany County.

Populations of *L. subcarinata* dwell in lakes and rivers on mud, sand, and gravel in water depths up to 1 m and in a wide range of current speeds (Clench & Turner 1955; Clench 1962).

Little is known of the life history of this snail, but data are available for a midwestern *Lioplax* species, *L. sulculosa* Menke. Females live two years, begin to bear young the first year, and release one brood a year. Males are smaller than females of the same age and live only one year (van Cleave & Chambers 1935).

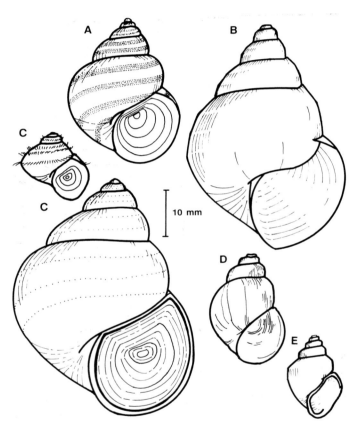

Fig. 8. Family Viviparidae, shells: a, *Viviparus georgianus*; b, *Cipangopaludina japonica*; c, *C. chinensis*, with immature individual shown to the upper left; d, *Campeloma decisum*; e, *Lioplax subcarinata*. All illustrations except for the immature are drawn to the same scale.

Family Bithyniidae

Shell ovate, conical or turbinate, up to 12 mm long; spire produced; umbilicus imperforate; whorls 5.0-6.0, somewhat flattened; aperture oval, continuous; lip thickened; operculum calcareous, spiral when young, concentric when adult, never withdrawn into body whorl; foot simple, with right cervical lobe forming water conduit; tentacles long, pointed, tapering; dioecious; verge bifid; eggs deposited in double-rowed clusters (Baker 1928a, Berry 1943, Fretter & Graham 1962).

Bithynia tentaculata (Linnaeus, 1758)
Mud Bithynia
Figs. 7, 9a

Synonyms include *Bythinia tentaculata* (L.) and *Bulimus tentaculatus* (L.).

This species was introduced into North America from Europe and is now distributed in the Great Lakes - St. Lawrence drainage system, from Quebec west to Wisconsin (Baker 1928a, Berry 1943, Clarke 1981) and in the Mohawk and Hudson Rivers (Strayer 1987). It does not occur in southern New England (Jokinen 1983, Smith 1987) or Lake Superior (Berry 1943; Jokinen, unpublished data).

Populations of *B. tentaculata* were found at 39 sites during this survey: Hudson River watershed (96A, 96D, 96E, 96F, 96G, 96H, 96I, 286, 290, 603), and St. Lawrence River watershed (141A, 259A, 259B, 260, 261, 262, 263, 264, 308, 332, 340, 343, 398, 441, 445A, 445C, 448A, 448B, 450, 493, 494, 495, 497, 499, 502A, 524A, 524B, 527, 531).

It is possible that this species had a double origin in North America. Baker (1928a) notes "there is no doubt that this common European species was introduced into America from Europe in the ballast of the timber ships...." However, Pleistocene fossils of *B. tentaculata* were unearthed in sediments of Glacial Lake Chicago, indicating the species had been in North America for thousands of years. The possibility that the American populations remained extant and interbred with the European form is not established (Baker 1928a).

Beecher collected several hundred specimens from the Champlain Canal in 1879 and deposited them in the New York State Museum (Marshall 1894). The first published report of *B. tentaculata* occurring in New York is that of Beauchamp (1886b), who noted the species had been in Lake Ontario at Oswego, Oswego County, since 1879 and was abundant in Lake Ontario at Syracuse, Onondaga County. The species was in the Champlain Canal at West Troy, Saratoga County, by the 1880s (Ancey 1887). *B. tentaculata* quickly became the most abundant species in the Erie Canal at Syracuse, Onondaga County, where it seemed to be driving out the native pleurocerids, *Goniobasis virginica* and *G. livescens* (Beauchamp 1887, 1891).

By the turn of the century, *B. tentaculata* was in Monroe County in the Erie Canal and "Wide-Waters" at Rochester, the Genesee River below the falls, Irondequoit Bay in Lake Ontario, and it was collected among beach wash at Lake Ontario (Walton 1891, 1898; Baker 1900a, 1901). It soon was reported from the western end of the Erie Canal (Letson 1909); Cayuga Lake, Cayuga and Seneca Counties;

the Seneca River at Waterloo, Seneca County (Maury 1916); Oneida Lake, Oswego and Onondaga Counties (Baker 1916a, b, 1918a; Pratt 1923); the Hudson River from Hudson to Staatsburg, Columbia County (Townes 1936); and Oswego Harbor in Lake Ontario, Oswego County (Burdick 1939). Prior to 1960, Jacobson & Emerson (1961) located populations in Canopus Creek and other local streams at Annsville, near Peekskill, Westchester County. By 1970, *B. tentaculata* was established in Seneca Lake, Yates and Seneca Counties; Cross Lake, Cayuga and Onondaga Counties (Harman & Berg 1970); and in the Black River, Jefferson County (Buckley 1977). At present, this species is abundant in the intertidal zone of the Hudson River, Dutchess and Ulster Counties (Strayer 1987).

During this survey, populations were found at 15 river and stream sites, 15 lake sites, two permanent ponds, a ditch at the edge of Oneida Lake, four marshes, and two canal sites. No populations were found in ephemeral habitats.

Bithynia tentaculata lives on a variety of substrata. In Oneida Lake, it is active on gravel, sand, clay, mud, and the exposed undersides of rocks (Baker 1918a, Mattice 1972). In any one area, most of the snails often are on macrophytic vegetation (Harman 1968a, Vincent *et al.* 1981, Bronmark 1988). Water depths are usually shallow (Vincent 1981, Vincent *et al.* 1981, Strayer 1987) but can go as deep as 5 m (Baker 1918a). Individuals living on macrophytes migrate down from the plants to the substratum from September to December but do not appear to make deep to shallow water migrations (Vincent *et al.* 1981).

The life span of this species seems to vary with climate. In Oneida Lake, New York; northwestern England; and Lac St-Louis, Montreal, the snails live 17-18 months (Mattice 1972, Dussart 1979, Pinel-Alloul & Magnin 1971). In a study of several local populations of *B. tentaculata* in the St. Lawrence River at Quebec, Vincent & Vaillancourt (1981), calculating snail age by annual growth lines and not by histograms, demonstrated a 32-39 month life span. The discrepancies could be due to environmental differences or incorrect estimates by researchers.

Ovipositing times differ among localities. Egg-laying can begin in May or June and continue into July (Pinel-Alloul & Magnin 1971, Mattice 1972, Vincent *et al.* 1981). In some populations, there is a second egg-laying period in October and November by grown females born in the spring (Pinel-Alloul & Magnin 1971). Spring oviposition begins when the water temperature reaches 20°C, and eggs are deposited on rocks, wood, and shells of living and dead molluscs (Vincent *et al.* 1981). In Oneida Lake, females lay eggs in double-rowed masses at densities of up to 155 masses/m^2 of rock substratum (Mattice 1972). Eggs masses contain 1-77 eggs, with a mean of 13 eggs (Vincent & Gaucher 1983).

Females reach minimum shell length of 6 mm before depositing eggs. All those greater than 8 mm carry eggs. Where females live more than one year (e.g., in the St. Lawrence River), fecundity is greatest in the two-year class, from which 65-74% of the eggs originate. The highest measured fecundity is 347 eggs/female. Even in the St. Lawrence River study area, considerable variation existed between populations (Vincent & Gaucher 1983).

In warmer climates, eggs hatch in three to four weeks (Mattice 1972) but can take two to three months in colder water (Vincent *et al.* 1981). Young hatch when shell length reaches 0.8 mm (Mattice 1972, Vincent *et al.* 1981), and they grow approximately 0.5 mm per week throughout the summer (Pinel-Alloul & Magnin 1971). Growth rates differ among populations, but, in general, they slow in August, and growth ceases from September through May (Vincent *et al.* 1981). In some populations, however, snails hatch in October and grow during the winter (Pinel-Alloul & Magnin 1971). In populations where snails live for three years, most linear growth is achieved in the first two years and only 10% in the third year. Weight increase is maximal during the second year (Vincent *et al.* 1981).

Densities vary from population to population, with the seasons, and from year to year (Vincent *et al.* 1981). Mattice (1972) counted up to 80 snails/m^2 in Oneida Lake. *B. tentaculata* makes up 48% of the gastropods in the Upper Estuary of the St. Lawrence River at Gentilly, Canada (Vincent 1979) and 32% of the total benthic fauna of the St. Lawrence at Quebec (Vincent 1981)

The genus *Bithynia* is capable of filter feeding. Snails draw water in between the mantle cavity and the body mass on the left side. Nutrient particles are packaged in mucous "sausages" which are extruded in a furrow between the right tentacle and the exhalant siphon. As the sausage is extruded, it is grasped by the snail's mouth and swallowed. This feeding mode allows populations to be dense on solid substrata because the snails are not dependent upon grazing (Meier-Brook & Kim 1977).

Bithynia tentaculata possibly competes with species of Pleuroceridae (Beauchamp 1887, 1891; Harman 1968a). In areas of New York State where this species has become densely populated, such as Oneida Lake, the pleurocerids have disappeared. In habitats like Cayuga Lake, where individuals are in low numbers, this species co-exists with pleurocerids (Harman 1968). Two decades after Harman's survey, *B. tentaculata* has not been found in Cayuga Lake (site 535), but the pleurocerid *Goniobasis livescens* remains.

These snails tend to live in habitats with relatively high calcium. Chemistry values for this survey were: pH: 6.6-8.4 (7.4 ± 0.1), conductivity: 87-2320 μmhos/cm (567 ± 93), Ca^{++}: 5-89 ppm (32 ± 4), and Na$^+$: 4-291 ppm (53 ± 12). *B. tentaculata* is especially tolerant of high sodium values, reflecting its ability to survive in the intertidal reaches of the lower Hudson River. The pH values are similar to those found by Harman & Berg (1971). In northwestern England, distribution correlates positively with stone substratum and potassium concentration, and it correlates negatively with nitrate concentration (Dussart 1979).

Family Hydrobiidae

Shell dextral, conical or attenuated; umbilicus perforate or imperforate; whorls 4.0-8.0; aperture entire; peristome usually continuous; operculum corneous, paucispiral or centrally multispiral with paucispiral periphery; foot longer than wide, rounded posteriorly; tentacles long, usually cylindrical, with eyes at base; dioecious; verge exerted, arising from posterior surface of head, near mantle margin, median or slightly to right (Berry 1943).

Key to the Hydrobiidae

This key is based primarily on shell characteristics (except for couplet 10). If possible, confirmations should be made using the anatomy of the verges, which are illustrated with the shells in Figs. 9 & 10).

1a. Apex truncate; nuclear whorl sunken below following whorl..*Probythinella lacustris*

1b. Apex not truncate 2

2a. Operculum multispiral in center.............................3

2b. Operculum paucispiral 4

3a. Aperture of mature snails not attached to whorl above ....*Amnicola (Lyogyrus) pupoidea*

Lyogyrus Pupoideus

3b. Aperture attached to whorl above ....
....*Amnicola (Lyogyrus) grana*

4a. Umbilicus imperforate or a narrow slit............................5

4b. Umbilicus perforate 7

5a. Whorls flattened; sutures shallow; shell 3 mm high........
....*Pyrgulopsis letsoni*

5b. Whorls rounded...6

6a. Shell elongate....................................*Fontigens nickliniana*

6b. Shell globose...*Gillia altilis*

7a. Shell elongate, < 6 mm high ....*Pyrgulopsis lustrica*

7b. Shell conical 8

8a. Apex blunt; nuclear whorl in same plane as following whorl...*Amnicola limosa*

8b. Apex pointed; nuclear whorl above following whorl ..9

9a. Body whorl very large compared to preceding whorls; shell 9 mm high ....*Birgella subglobosa*

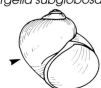

9b. Body whorl not inflated...10

10a. Shell up to 6 mm high; verge bifid with accessory lobe six times size of penis ....*Cincinnatia cincinnatiensis*

10b. Shell tiny, up to 3 mm high; verge bifid with accessory
lobe approximately same size as penis ....
....*Amnicola walkeri*

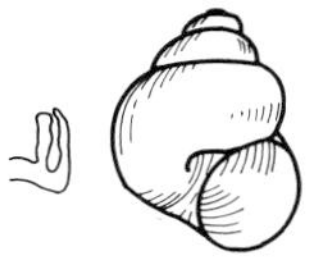

Probythinella lacustris (F.C. Baker, 1928)
Delta hydrobe
Fig. 9b

Shell globose, 3 mm high; umbilicus wide, deep, conspicuous; spire truncated; first and second whorls planorboid, sunken below third whorl; apex blunt or truncate; whorls 4.0; sutures deep; aperture subovate; peristome continuous, adnate to body whorl for short distance, occasionally detached; columella reflected; verge bilobed, without accessory duct in secondary lobe (Fig. 9b) (Baker 1928a, Berry 1943).

Synonyms include *P. binneyana* (Hannibal 1913) and *Amnicola binneyana* Hannibal 1913.

Probythinella lacustris populations occur from Quebec west to the Northwest Territories (Baker 1928a, Berry 1943, Clarke 1981, Cvancara 1983). The Hudson River basin is the southeast limit of the range (Strayer 1987).

There are few references to this species in the literature.

Lewis (1868, 1872) found a colony in the Mohawk River, Mohawk, Herkimer County. Beauchamp (1886b) found the species in the Erie Canal, Onondaga County, but noted it as rare, and Baker (1900b) collected shells in beach wash from Lake Ontario, Monroe County. Collections from the Mohawk River and Erie Canal, Herkimer County, made from 1867 through 1936 by R. Call, T. Aldrich, C. Beecher, and J. Lewis, are housed in the Harvard University's Museum of Comparative Zoology, the University of Michigan Museum of Zoology, and the University of Florida. Harman & Berg (1971) reported finding one individual, referred to as *Amnicola binneyana*, in Seneca Lake, Ontario County.

Populations of this species were not found during the present survey.

It appears that *P. lacustris* is most abundant in water greater than 3 m deep, and the specimen found by Harman and Berg (1971) was at 16 m. In the Great Lakes, this species makes up the main diet of whitefish, *Coregonus clupeaformis* (Mitchill). Substrata include sand and marl with or without vegetation (Berry 1943). In North Dakota, populations occur in permanent streams 1-37 m wide (Cvancara 1983). Canadian populations are found among vegetation in permanent lakes, ponds, and streams. At its southern range, the species tends to occur in deeper water (Clarke 1981). The diet of this species is primarily diatoms (Berry 1943).

In North Dakota, *P. lacustris* is tolerant of high alkalinity. Water chemistry parameters cited by Cvancara (1983) were: pH: 8.0-9.2, conductivity: 895-3600 μmhos/cm, and Ca^{++}: 50-320 ppm (Cvancara 1983).

Gillia altilis (I. Lea, 1841)
Buffalo pebblesnail
Fig. 9c

Shell conico-globose, 6-8 mm high, light yellow-green; umbilicus rimate to imperforate; apex usually eroded; whorls 2.0-4.0 in eroded shells of adults, 4.5 in uneroded shells; whorls shouldered below suture; aperture broadly ovate-auriculate; peristome dark rimmed, complete across parietal wall by thin callus; outer lip conspicuously arched forward in lateral profile; operculum oval, chitinous, yellow-green, paucispiral (Thompson 1984b).

This species occurs in the Atlantic drainage system of the eastern United States, from New York and Vermont south to South Carolina. It entered the Lake Ontario system and moved west via the Erie Canal (Richards 1934, Thompson 1984b).

No populations were located during this or Strayer's (1987) survey.

In the past, this species has been found in the Erie Canal, Onondaga and Herkimer Counties (Beauchamp 1886b; Walton 1891, 1898); the Albany/Troy area and the Hudson River, Albany and Rensselaer Counties (Marshall 1895); and the Hudson River from Barrytown south to Straatsburg, Dutchess County (Townes 1936). Shells have been found in beach wash from Lake Ontario, Monroe County (Baker 1900b); Oneida Lake, Oswego and Onondaga Counties (Baker 1916a, b; 1918a, b); and the Salmon River, Oswego County (Burdick 1939). Thompson (1984b) cites the following localities determined from museum lots: Hudson River, Albany, Dutchess, and Ulster Counties; Erie Canal, Herkimer and Onondaga Counties; Champlain Canal, Rensselaer County; Niagara Falls, Niagara County; Monroe County; and Wayne County. The New York State Museum has lots from the Hudson River, Albany County (NYSM 31059, 31060).

In the Hudson River, *G. altilis* lives on mud and aquatic plants in shallow water (Townes 1936).

Birgella subglobosa (Say, 1825)
Globe siltsnail
Fig. 9d, 11

Shell subglobose to globose, 10 mm high; tan to gray; umbilicus narrow, deep; spire broad, depressed, usually shorter than aperture; apex slightly raised above second whorl; whorls 4.5, convex, rapidly increasing in diameter, shouldered; body whorl large, roundly ovate; peristome sharp, thin, continuous, flattened and appressed to parietal wall; operculum paucispiral; verge compressed, bifurcate; penis dark, shorter than globose secondary lobe, without accessory duct in secondary lobe (Baker 1928a, Berry 1943, Thompson 1984b).

Some authors have placed this species in the genus *Somatogyrus*. A detailed anatomical description can be found in Thompson (1984b).

25

The distribution of *Birgella subglobosa* extends from Lake Champlain and its outlet, the Richelieu River, in New York, Vermont, and Quebec, west to Minnesota, and south to Arkansas, Alabama, and Georgia (Baker 1928a, Berry 1943, Clarke 1981, Thompson 1984b, Branson *et al.* 1987).

The only population found during this survey was in Lake Champlain, St. Lawrence River watershed (141C). Strayer (1987) did not find this species during a survey of the Hudson River drainage system. Buckley (1977) located one colony in the Black River, Jefferson County.

Lewis (1868, 1872) and Marshall (1894) reported the presence of *B. subglobosa* in the Hudson River basin, Mohawk, Herkimer County, and in the Erie Canal at Mohawk, into which it was believed introduced after 1860 to become "...numerically more abundant than any other mollusc in the canal" (Lewis 1872). It was also found in Onondaga County (Beauchamp 1886b) and as beach wash from Lake Ontario, Monroe County (Baker 1900b); the Niagara River, Niagara County (Letson 1909); Oneida Lake, Oswego County (Baker 1916a, b, 1918a, b); and the Hudson River from Hudson, Columbia County, to Hyde Park, Dutchess County (Townes 1936). Specimens deposited in Harvard's Museum of Comparative Zoology, the University of Michigan's Museum of Zoology, the Academy of Natural Sciences of Philadelphia, and the Florida State University Museum were collected from the Buffalo River; St. Albans Bay, Lake Champlain, Vermont; Hudson River, Coxsackie, Greene County; and Palmyra, Wayne County. Thompson (1984b) cites museum records from the Erie Canal and Mohawk River, Herkimer County, and from Schenectady County.

In some areas, this species is a deep water inhabitant of large lakes and rivers (Berry 1943, Clark 1981). However, in Lake Champlain (site 141C) it was found on a submerged tree trunk in shallow water. In the Hudson River it was found in mud and among aquatic plants in shallow water (Townes 1936) and on a soft silt substratum (Thompson 1984b).

Water chemistry values for the Lake Champlain site are: pH: 6.9, conductivity: 162 µmhos/cm, Ca^{++}: 13 ppm, and Na$^+$: 7 ppm.

Cincinnatia cincinnatiensis (Anthony, 1840)
Midland siltsnail
Fig. 9e

Shell globose-conical, 5.0-6.0 mm high, greenish to yellowish brown; umbilicus round, deep; spire broadly conical, elevated; nuclear whorl well-raised above second whorl; whorls 5.0-6.0, rounded, shouldered below suture, rapidly increasing in diameter; body whorl round; sutures deeply impressed; aperture roundly ovate, narrowed above, bluish-white within; peristome continuous; last whorl often separated from body whorl; basal part of columella thickened, upper part arched; verge bifid, with secondary lobe over six times size of penis, without accessory duct (Fig. 9e) (Baker 1928a, Berry 1943).

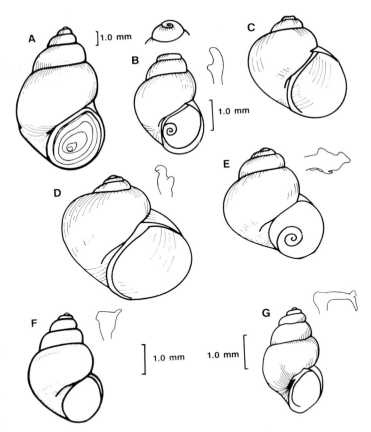

Fig. 9. a, Family Bithyniidae, shell: *Bithynia tentaculata*. b-g, Family Hydrobiidae, shells and penial structures: b, *Probythinella lacustris*, showing flattened apex; c, *Gillia altilis*; d, *Birgella subglobosa*; e, *Cincinnatia cincinnatiensis*; f, *Prygulopsis lustrica*; g, *P. letsoni*. Shell illustrations b-e are drawn to the same scale. Illustrations of penial structures are not to scale. Penial structures are redrawn from Berry (1943).

Cincinnatia integra (Say 1821) is here considered a synonym of *C. cincinnatiensis*.

This species ranges from New York and eastern Pennsylvania west to southern Manitoba, southern Saskatchewan, North Dakota and Utah, and south to Texas, Kansas, and Kentucky (Baker 1928a, Richards 1934, Berry 1943, Leonard 1959, Harman & Berg 1971, Clarke 1981, Cvancara 1983, Branson *et al.* 1987).

No populations were found during this survey. However, in the 1970s, *C. cincinnatiensis* populations were found in the Oswego River drainage system of New York State. Recently, a consulting firm found a population in the Buffalo River, Buffalo, Erie County, and submitted specimens to the author for identification (unpublished data). Specimens have been found in Seneca Lake, Seneca and Yates Counties; Otisco and Cross Lakes, Onondaga County; Oneida Lake, Onondaga and Cayuga Counties; and in the inlet of Canandaigua Lake, Yates County (Harman & Berg 1971). Shells, but no live animals, washed up in Canadarago Lake, Otsego County (Harman 1973). Additional populations were located in the Moose River, Lewis County; Kayuta Lake, Oneida County; inlet of Fifth Lake, Hamilton County, and two sites in Lewis County (Buckley 1977).

Earlier, this species was found in the Erie Canal, Onondaga County (Beauchamp 1886b), and in the Canal at Mohawk, Herkimer County (Lewis 1872, Marshall 1894). Other populations were found in Park Lake, Buffalo, Erie County (Letson 1909) and as beach wash from Lake Ontario, Monroe County (Baker 1900b); Sodus Bay, Lake Ontario, Wayne County; and the Salmon River, Oswego County (Burdick 1939). The New York State Museum has lots from the Erie Canal, Mohawk, Herkimer County (NYSM 31055), and from Ontario County (NYSM 31056).

Cincinnatia cincinnatiensis lives on muddy ooze or sand in slow creeks and lakes with little aquatic vegetation. Diatoms are their main food (Berry 1943). In North Dakota, populations are commonly associated with *Amnicola limosa*, and they inhabit large and small streams and permanent lakes and ponds (Cvancara 1983). Clarke (1979) found the species characteristic of mesotrophic lakes, and Harman & Berg (1971) noted it as a deep littoral resident of large lakes with silt and detritus substrata.

Harman & Berg (1971) reported habitat pH at 7.9-8.4.

Water chemistry data from North Dakota were pH: 7.9-9.2, conductivity 485-895 μmhos/cm, and Ca^{++}: 60-320 ppm (Cvancara 1983). *C. cincinnatiensis* might be limited to high calcium habitats, but additional data are needed to substantiate this possibility.

Pyrgulopsis lustrica (Pilsbry, 1890)
Boreal marstonia
Fig. 9f, 11

Shell conical, thin, 4.5 mm high, translucent, greenish to light brownish; umbilicus small, narrow; spire elevated, longer than aperture; apex elevated, acute; whorls 5.0, convex, regularly, but not rapidly, increasing is size, shouldered; sutures well-impressed; aperture roundly ovate, angled above, rounded below; interior waxy; peristome continuous, appressed to body whorl for short distance; columella moderately curved, verge with wide secondary lobe, without accessory duct (Baker 1928a, Berry 1943).

Some authors have placed this species in the genus Marstonia, and synonyms include *Marstonia decepta* (Baker 1928)

This species occurs from western Massachusetts, New York, Pennsylvania, and southern Ontario west to the Great Lakes states, and south to northern parts of the Mississippi River drainage (Baker 1928a, Berry 1943, Ludlam et al. 1973, Clarke 1981, Smith 1987, Strayer 1987).

During this survey, populations of *P. lustrica* were found in the Hudson River watershed (286, 287, 616); St. Lawrence River watershed (390, 498, 505, 517, 520); and Susquehanna River watershed (586). The species in not common, but it is regularly distributed across the southern half of the State.

Earlier studies noted that *P. lustrica* is widely scattered throughout central New York in larger rivers and Oneida Lake, Oswego River watershed; and in Canadarago Lake and Catatonk Creek, Susquehanna watershed (Harman & Berg 1971). It also has been found in Otsego Lake, Otsego County (MacNamara & Harman 1975); and Green Lake, Onondaga County (Harman 1970). Live populations were not found in the Finger Lakes, but shells were found in Skaneateles and Cayuga Lakes, Onondaga County (Harman & Berg 1971).

In the past, *P. lustrica* was reported from the Albany/Troy area, Albany and Rensselaer Counties (Marshall 1895); Irondequoit Bay, Lake Ontario, Monroe County (Baker 1900b); Cayuta Lake, Schuyler County (Maury 1916); Oneida Lake, Oswego County (Baker 1916a, b); and Chippewa Creek (Letson 1909). The Museum of Comparative Zoology has specimens from Seneca Lake, Yates County (MCZ 2108); Mohawk, Herkimer County (MCZ 53879); Schuyler Lake, Otsego County (MCZ 2107); Harlem River, New York City (MCZ 281981); Little Lakes, Herkimer County (uncatalogued); and the Normans Kill, Albany, Albany County (uncatalogued).

This study confirms Berry's (1943) report that *P. lustrica* is often associated with *Amnicola limosa*. Individuals live on rocks in rivers and lakes, and on vegetation, such as *Vallisneria*, *Potamogeton*, and *Chara* spp. (Berry 1943). In the Stockbridge Bowl, Massachusetts, the snails inhabit depths down to 4 m, but they are most abundant in the shallow littoral zone at 0-2 m (Ludlam et al. 1973). In contrast, populations living in Grand Traverse Bay, Michigan, on the eastern shore of Lake Michigan, were found in abundance on littoral silt and detritus in water 4-8 m deep. Highest densities, 165 snails/m^2, were in water 4 m deep (Pace et al. 1979). In central New York, this species tends to remain on inorganic substrata (Harman & Berg 1971). In association with *Valvata tricarinata* and *Goniobasis livescens* in lakes, it is found on stonewort (*Chara* sp.) on soft and hard marly substrata (Harman & Berg 1971, Smith 1987).

Nine sites for *P. lustrica* had the following water chemistry: pH: 6.6-8.0 (7.5 ± 0.1); conductivity: 208-419 μmhos/cm (329 ± 21); Ca^{++}: 5-49 ppm (27 ± 5); and Na^+: 7-28 ppm (116 ± 2). Harman & Berg (1971) reported pH values of 7.4-8.4. The snails appear to be inhabitants of medium to hard water, but they are tolerant of soft water (Ca^{++} < 6 ppm).

Pyrgulopsis letsoni (Walker, 1901)
Gravel pyrg
Fig. 9g

Shell elongate, solid, 3 mm high, dark corneous; umbilicus subimperforate or rimate; spire conical, longer than aperture; apex obtuse, blunt, dark corneous; whorls 4.5-6.0, somewhat flattened laterally, first 3 shouldered; sutures moderately impressed; aperture small, ovate, rounded below, angled above, flattened on parietal margin; peristome thick, continuous, entirely free of body whorl in adults; columella straight, oblique to axis; verge bilobed;

27

secondary lobe short, without accessory duct; penis long, black (Walker 1901, Baker 1928a, Berry 1943).

The range of this species is not well-documented. Extant populations seem to be limited to regions associated with Lake Erie, whereas Pleistocene fossil shells occur from western New York to Illinois (Berry 1943).

This species was not found during the present survey or that of Harman & Berg (1971).

Type specimens are from Pleistocene deposits from Goat Island, Niagara River, Niagara County (Letson 1909). Maury (1916) reported a population living in Chautauqua Lake, Chautauqua County. Townes (1937) also found this species in Chautauqua Lake, but he noted it as rare. It is possible that *P. letsoni* no longer lives in New York State.

These snails are difficult to collect alive. After intensive searching, Berry (1943) found them living in cavities in lime encrustations deposited by aquatic plants.

Amnicola (Amnicola) limosa (Say, 1817)
Mud amnicola
Fig. 10a, 11

Shell conical, somewhat inflated, 4-5 mm high, light yellow to tan; umbilicus narrow, deep; spire wide, obtusely conical; apex flat-topped; nuclear whorl small, on same plane as second whorl; whorls 4.5, inflated, regularly increasing in size; body whorl globose; sutures deeply impressed; aperture ovate, rounded below, slightly angled above; peristome continuous, joined to body whorl by thin callus; operculum paucispiral; verge wide, somewhat flattened, arising on right side of back beneath mantle lobe; secondary lobe short or erect, with accessory duct; penis sometimes coiling around erect secondary duct (Fig. 10a) (Baker 1928a, Berry 1943).

Berry (1943) includes *Amnicola porata* Gould as a synonym.

Amnicola limosa occurs from Newfoundland to Saskatchewan, south to Texas and South Carolina (Baker 1928a, Richards 1934, Rehder 1949, Tudorancea *et al.* 1979).

This species is one of the most abundant freshwater snails in New York State. It was found at 103 sites during this survey: Delaware River watershed (457, 458, 464, 466, 468); Housatonic River watershed (294); Hudson River watershed (212, 265, 269, 271, 273, 276, 277, 284, 286, 287, 291, 292, 297, 299, 301, 303, 305, 317, 318, 319, 320, 321, 367, 381, 384, 386, 453, 599, 601, 604, 607, 610, 612, 613, 616); Mississippi-Ohio River watershed (427b, 430A, 430B, 431); St. Lawrence River watershed (141D, 259A, 262, 263, 278, 308, 311, 312, 336, 338, 340, 341, 345, 352, 353, 354, 357, 358, 360, 361, 363, 374, 377, 390, 408, 440, 448A, 448B, 449, 493, 495, 497, 498, 499, 500, 501, 502A, 502B, 505, 515, 517, 518, 520, 521, 524, 527, 529, 534, 535, 562, 563); and Susquehanna River watershed (400, 542, 571, 573, 582, 586, 592).

There are numerous publications referring to the presence of *A. limosa* in New York State. It has been found in the Erie Canal, Herkimer and Monroe Counties (Lewis 1860, 1872; Marshall 1894); the Finger Lakes (De Kay 1843, Lewis 1874, Beauchamp 1886b, Harman & Berg 1971); Chautauqua Lake and others in Chautauqua and surrounding counties (Maury 1898, 1916; Townes 1937); Niagara and Erie Counties (Walton 1891, Letson 1909); Livingston County (Walton 1891, 1898; Wade & Vasey 1976; Wade 1987); Oneida Lake, Oswego and Onondaga Counties (Baker 1916a, b, 1918a, b; Pratt 1923); Lake Ontario (Baker 1900b, Burdick 1939); the Hudson River drainage, Rockland County (Bretet & Carswell 1952); Albany and Troy, Albany and Rensselaer Counties (Marshall 1895); the Shawangunk Kill and Wallkill River, Ulster County (Strayer 1987); Lake Champlain (Lewis 1894, Harman 1973, MacNamara & Harman 1975); and the Adirondack region (Jacobson 1945, Buckley 1977).

Habitats of *A. limosa* include lakes, permanent ponds, and slowly flowing rivers and streams. The snails prefer decaying aquatic and terrestrial plants, logs, branches, rocks, bottles, and empty clam shells as substrata. They are frequently associated with aquatic vegetation, such as *Chara, Potamogeton, Vallisneria,* and *Elodea* spp., upon which they graze for algae, such as epiphytic diatoms (Berry 1943, Harman & Berg 1971, Harman 1972, Kesler 1981, Jokinen 1983, Smith 1987, Strayer 1987). During this survey in New York State, populations were found in 25 river and stream sites, 52 lake sites, 15 permanent ponds, five marshes, five canals, and a swamp.

This species has an annual life cycle. Oviposition begins in shallow water from late May to June, when the water warms to 22-23°C. Single eggs are laid on various substrata. Juveniles appear from late June to early August. A few mature snails continue to grow after reproduction, but most die as the juveniles grow. In autumn, the new generation migrates into deeper water, aggregates, and spends the winter in a dormant state. In early spring, when the water is approximately 10°C, the young migrate back to shallow water and grow rapidly prior to ovipositing (Pinel-Alloul & Magnin 1973, Horst & Costa 1975, Tudorancea *et al.* 1979, Kesler 1980, Jokinen 1985). *A. limosa* populations can dominate the benthos, and this species can be a major contributor to the energy budget (Tudorancea *et al.* 1979).

Ninety-six survey sites had the following water chemistry data: pH: 5.8-9.2 (7.2 ± 0.1); conductivity: 28-2320 μmhos/cm (258 ± 28); Ca^{++}: 1-89 ppm (17 ± 2); and Na$^+$: 1-291 ppm (19 ± 4). For North Dakota, Cvancara (1983) reported the following water chemistry values: pH: 8.5-9.2; conductivity: 485-760 μmhos/cm; and Ca^{++}: 110-130 ppm. *A. limosa* also was abundant in Connecticut's soft water: pH: 5.8-7.8; conductivity: 43-386 μmhos/cm; Ca^{++}: 2-35 ppm; and Na$^+$: 1-29 ppm (Jokinen 1983). This species appears to have a wide range of tolerance for pH and cations, and it is able to live in soft to hard waters. However, it is probably most successful in medium and medium-soft waters (McKillop & Harrison 1972). This survey and

Baily's (1929) study show the snail also has a high sodium tolerance and can be found in tidal areas of coastal waters.

Amnicola (Lyogyrus) walkeri Pilsbry, 1898
Canadian duskysnail
Fig. 10b

Shell conical, thin, 2.5 mm high, almost as wide as high, translucent, yellowish, corneous; umbilicus wide, deep; spire broadly conical; apex obtuse; nuclear whorl elevated above second whorl; whorls 4.0, convex, shouldered, increasing regularly and rapidly in size; sutures deeply impressed; aperture almost circular, slightly angled above; peristome continuous, contacting body whorl for short distance; operculum paucispiral; verge bifid, penis and secondary lobe arising together, with accessory duct; penis never coiling around secondary lobe (Baker 1928a, Berry 1943).

This species occurs from central New York State west to Wisconsin and south to the upper Mississippi River basin (Baker 1928a, Berry 1943, Harman & Berg 1971, Clarke 1981). It possibly reaches to the District of Columbia (Richards 1934).

No specimens of *L. walkeri* were taken during this survey. Harman & Berg (1971) found three populations, two from the western Otsego drainage and one from the Genesee River watershed.

Older records from scattered areas in the State document the presence of *A. walkeri*, then known as *Amnicola lustrica* Say. The earliest record is from De Kay (1843), who reported populations from Cayuga Lake, Cayuga, Seneca and Tompkins Counties, and from streams entering Lake Champlain, Clinton County. Lewis (1860, 1872) noted this species living in the Erie Canal; Mohawk River; Little Lakes and Smith's Pond, Herkimer County; and in Schuyler Lake, Otsego County. Additional early records are from Chautauqua Lake, Chautauqua County (Maury 1898, Baker 1928b); Onondaga County (Beauchamp 1886b); Niagara River, Niagara County (Letson 1909); Upper Cassadaga Lake, Canandaigua County (Townes 1936); Sodus Bay, Wayne County; and Little Sodus Bay, Cayuga County; Lake Ontario; and South Pond, Oswego County (Burdick 1939). The Museum of Comparative Zoology has a lot collected by E. Letson from Lime Lake, Cattaraugus County (MCZ 183481).

No living snails were found during this survey.

This species lives in sluggish streams and quiet ponds where dead aquatic plants have accumulated (Berry 1943, Clarke 1981). Populations occur in a range of lentic habitats, including oligotrophic lakes and marl ponds (Harman & Berg 1971).

Amnicola (Lyogyrus) pupoidea (Gould, 1841)
Pupa duskysnail
Figs. 10c, 11

Shell narrowly conical, 3 mm high; whorls attenuated; adult peristome continuous, not attached to or barely touching body whorl; operculum multispiral in center, paucispiral peripherally; verge bifid, lobes at acute angles to main trunk of verge; secondary lobe with accessory duct (Berry 1943, Thompson 1968, Jokinen 1983).

This species is generally distributed along the Atlantic coast from Massachusetts, Connecticut, and New York south to the District of Columbia, Louisiana, and Arkansas (Richards 1934, Jokinen 1983, Smith 1987). The precise distribution is unknown.

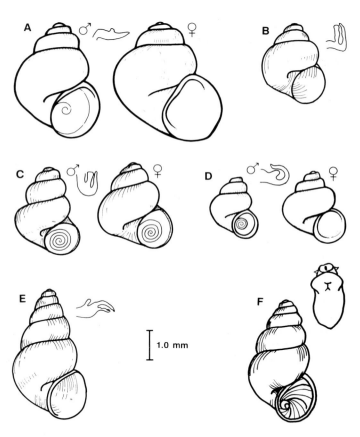

Fig. 10. a-e, Family Hydrobiidae, shells and penial structures: a, *Amnicola limosa*, male and female; b, *A. walkeri*, c, *A. (Lyogyrus) pupoidea*, male and female, operculum with multispiral center and paucispiral periphery; d, *A. (Lyogyrus) grana*, male and female; e, *Fontigens nickliniana*; f, Family Pomatiopsidae, shell and ventral view of foot showing mid-lateral indentations: *Pomatiopsis lapidaria*. Penial structures from Berry (1943) and Thompson (1968).

Sixteen colonies of *A. pupoidea* were located during this survey, all in eastern New York State: Delaware River watershed (457, 475); Hudson River drainage (286, 300, 301, 305, 317, 318, 320, 612); St. Lawrence River watershed (313, 336); Susquehanna River basin (568, 571, 573); and the Hackensack River system (606).

Bretet and Carswell (1952) found *A. pupoidea* in Upper Ferdun Pond, Rockland County. Harman & Berg (1971) found no colonies in central New York. Strayer (1987) located two populations in the Hudson River, Dutchess County, just below high tide mark.

During this survey it was found that *A. pupoidea* lives in small to large ponds and large rivers on organic debris and aquatic plants, confirming the work of Jokinen (1983) and Smith (1987).

The life cycle is annual, and there appears to be sexual dimorphism, with males being relatively longer and more slender than females (Jokinen, unpublished data).

Water chemistry data for 16 sites were: pH: 6.1-9.5 (7.4 ± 0.2); conductivity: 68-335 μmhos/cm (173 ± 20); Ca^{++}: 1-37 ppm (15 ± 3); and Na^+: 1-35 ppm (9 ± 2). For Connecticut, the values for 14 sites were similar: pH: 5.5-7.8; conductivity: 53-275 μmhos; Ca^{++}: 2-27 ppm; and Na^+: 5-31 ppm (Jokinen 1983). *A. pupoidea* has high tolerance for acidic, low calcium habitats. However, it does not appear to be tolerant of high sodium.

Amnicola (Lyogyrus) grana (Say, 1822)
Squat duskysnail
Figs. 10d, 11

Shell broadly conical, 3 mm high; umbilicus small; apex dome shaped; sutures deep; peristome adhering to body whorl; aperture orbicular; operculum multispiral in center, paucispiral at periphery; verge bifid; penis looped over secondary lobe (Thompson 1968, Jokinen 1983).

This species occurs on the east coast of North America east of the Appalachians and Alleghenies from New England south to North Carolina (Richards 1934, Jokinen 1983, Smith 1987).

In New York State, *A. grana* occurs in the Hudson River watershed (287, 304, 459, 602, 604, 610); Mississippi-Ohio River watershed (430A, 431); and St. Lawrence River watershed (259A, 339, 408).

In the 19th century, *A. grana* was reported from the Seneca River, Onondaga County (Beauchamp 1886b); Monroe County (Walton 1891); and Chautauqua Lake, Chautauqua County (Maury 1898). More recent publications do not report this species from New York State.

Individuals live on organic debris and vegetation in the standing water of larger ponds, lakes, and oxbows of major rivers (Clarke 1981, Jokinen 1983, Smith 1987).

Nine sites had water chemistry values of: pH: 6.6-8.2 (7.3 ± 0.2); conductivity: 189-452 μmhos/cm (287 ± 29); Ca^{++}: 3-49 ppm (21 ± 5); and Na^+: 1-39 ppm (15 ± 4). Connecticut values for 14 sites (Jokinen 1983) were more acidic: pH: 5.4-7.8;

conductivity: 39-241 μmhos/cm; Ca^{++}: 1-27 ppm; and Na^+: 2-19 ppm. This species has a high tolerance for acidic, low calcium habitats but limited tolerance to sodium.

Fontigens nickliniana (Lea, 1838)
Watercress snail
Fig. 10e

Shell elongate oval, 4.5 mm high, turreted, twice as high as wide, greenish-tan or white under a black organic coating; umbilicus subimperforate or absent; apex blunt; nuclear whorl partly concealed by second whorl; whorls 5.3, highly convex; sutures deep; aperture roundly ovate; peristome continuous, appressed to parietal wall for a considerable distance; operculum paucispiral; verge trifid, with 2 secondary lobes and 2 accessory ducts present; penis to right of lobes (Baker 1928a, Berry 1943).

This species was once considered a member of the genus *Hydrobia*.

Populations of *F. nickliniana* occur from Niagara Falls, New York, west to Wisconsin and south to Alabama (Baker 1928a, Berry 1943).

Populations of this species were not found in New York State during this survey, and Harman and Berg (1971) did not report finding the species in central New York. If present in the State, it might be limited to the western region.

Lewis (1872) reported the species as present in the Erie Canal at Mohawk, Herkimer County. Maury (1898) reported living populations to be present, but rare, in Chautauqua Lake, Chautauqua County. The Museum of Comparative Zoology has specimens from Niagara Falls, Niagara County (MCZ 186762).

This species resides in cool, shallow, slowly flowing springs where watercress (*Nasturtium officinale* R. Br.) grows in a thick mat (Goodrich 1932, Berry 1943).

Family Pomatiopsidae

Shell elongate, turreted, thin to thick, smooth, umbilicate; aperture expanded; peristome continuous, thin or slightly reflected; operculum corneous, subspiral with spiral sculpture; foot broad, truncated anteriorly, rounded posteriorly, with transverse sulcus between front and middle third of foot; species dioecious; verge simple, large (Baker 1928a).

Pomatiopsis lapidaria (Say, 1817)
Slender walker
Fig. 10f, 13

Shell up to 7 mm long, dark brown to chestnut; spire acute, 3 times as long as aperture, nuclear whorl partly embraced by second whorl; umbilicus well-marked; whorls 7.0, rounded, slowly and regularly increasing in diameter; sutures well-impressed; aperture elongate oval, narrowed and angled above, rounded below, somewhat purple within; peristome simple or thickened within, upper termi-

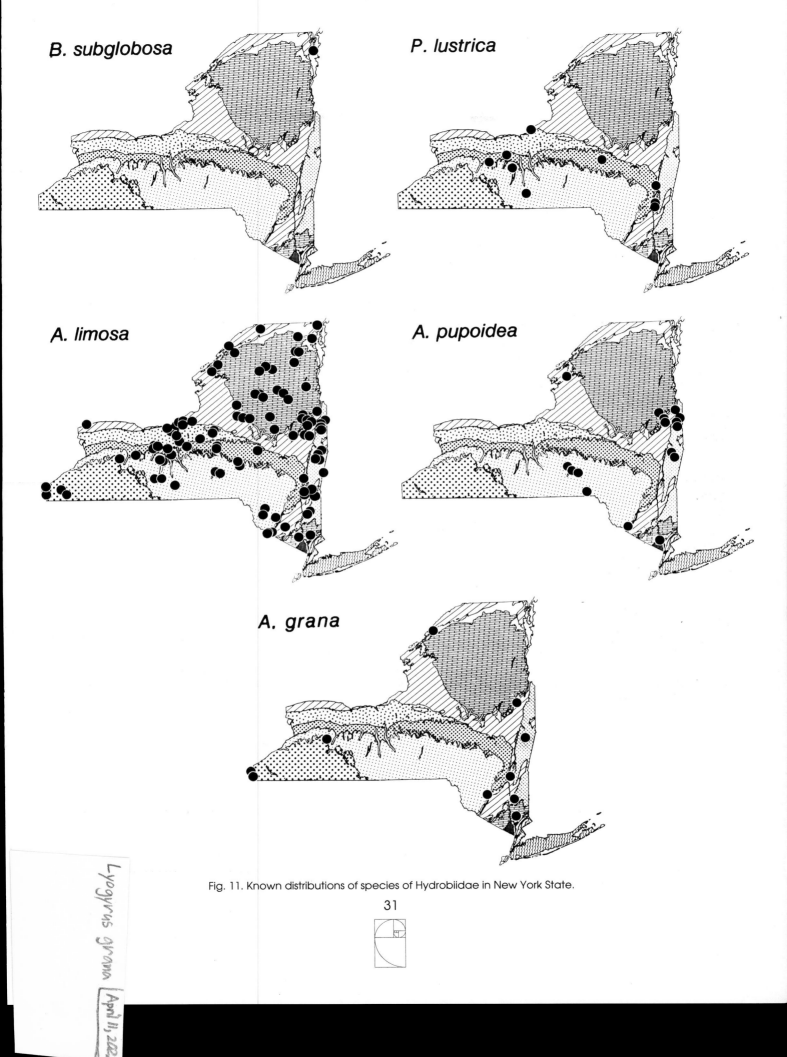

Fig. 11. Known distributions of species of Hydrobiidae in New York State.

31

nation connected on parietal wall by callus; tentacles short, tapering; verge large, sickle-shaped, posterior to right tentacle at right side of neck, not exposed beyond shell edge (Baker 1928a); populations dimorphic, males with higher whorl count and more slender shell than females (Dundee 1957).

Detailed anatomical descriptions can be found in works by Dundee (1957) and Davis (1967).

This species is widespread in eastern North America. It occurs from Minnesota to southern Ontario, south to Florida and Texas (Baker 1928a; Richards 1934; Berry 1943; Abbott 1948; Dundee 1957; Leonard 1959; Hubricht 1960; Clarke 1981; Thompson 1984a; Smith 1986, 1987; Branson et al. 1987; Burch 1989; Jokinen, unpublished data). It is rare in southern New England, and it is considered endangered in Massachusetts (Smith 1987; Jokinen, unpublished data).

Only one living population of P. lapidaria was found during this survey. It was located at Saw Kill stream and millpond (site 287), Annandale-on-Hudson, Hudson River watershed, Dutchess County. In addition, one shell was retrieved from marl from the Cayuga and Seneca Canal (site 534), Tyre, St. Lawrence River watershed, Seneca County, but no live population was found. Neither Strayer (1987) nor Harman & Berg (1971) located populations.

Several museum records indicate the existence of other populations of P. lapidaria, but even these are not abundant: Niagara Falls, Niagara County (1926, MCZ 282047; 1935, MCZ uncatalogued; 1951, MCZ 186760); Upper Red Hook, Dutchess County (1889, Teator Collection, MCZ 156830); South Bay at Saw Kill mouth, under rock in upper intertidal, Dutchess Co. (1971, Bard College collection); Hudson River, Greenbush, Rensselaer County (Beecher Collection, NYSM 31113).

Literature reports on P. lapidaria in New York also are sparse. The species has been reported from Monroe County (Walton 1891, 1898); the Erie Canal at Mohawk, Herkimer County (Marshall 1894); Niagara Falls, Niagara County (Letson 1909); the Normans Kill, Albany County; Troy and Greenbush, Rensselaer County (Marshall 1895); and the Hudson River at Hudson, Columbia County (Townes 1936). A distribution map in Dundee (1957) indicates several sites on the lower Hudson and Niagara Rivers.

This species is more amphibious than aquatic and is able to exist 150 m from a body of water (Berry 1943). Populations usually live on the moist soils of river banks, on marsh detritus, and on the lower stems of river bulrush (Scirpus fluviatilis (Torr.) Gray), often close to sensitive fern (Onoclea sensibilis L.) (Smith 1987, Thompson 1984a, Dundee 1957.)

In Michigan, P. lapidaria has a life span of three years, and populations have over two females for every male. The species has two major reproductive periods per year, the first from March to early July and a second from late August to early October. Eggs are laid singly on soil, and they are coated with a husk of soil and fecal pellets. At 15.6-18.3°C, incubation takes five to seven weeks. Newly hatched young, 0.5 mm in shell length and with 2.5 whorls, grow approximately 0.2 mm per week (Dundee 1957).

In Michigan, this species has two dormant periods, one in winter and one during summer drought. The snails, with their apertures closed by opercula, remain inactive under fallen vegetation or other objects, or in crevices (Dundee 1957).

Hubricht (1960) reports P. lapidaria to be calciphilic. The New York population in the Saw Kill (site 287) lived associated with hard water, pH: 7.6, conductivity: 335 μmhos/cm, Ca^{++}: 49 ppm, and Na$^+$: 10 ppm.

Family Pleuroceridae

Shell elongate to globose, thick, solid, without umbilicus; operculum corneous, subspiral; tentacles elongate; genital duct of 2 laminae forming closed canal; oviparous, lacking external verge (Baker 1928a).

Key to the Pleuroceridae
(based on adult characters)

1a. Aperture and spire approximately same length, shell conic ....Leptoxis carinata

1b. Spire considerably longer than aperture 2

2a. Whorls rounded, sometimes with spiral ridges ....
....Goniobasis virginica

2b. Whorls flattened, without spiral ridges 4

3a. Body whorl with distinct angulation ....
....Pleurocera acuta

3b. Body whorl without distinct angulation ....
....Goniobasis livescens

Pleurocera acuta Rafinesque, 1831

Sharp hornsnail
Figs. 12a, 13

Shell elongate, over 30 mm long, acute, turreted, of variable thickness; apex usually eroded; pale brown to chestnut to black, sometimes with yellow band encircling whorls just below suture; nuclear whorls wine colored; whorls up to 15.0, flat sided, regularly increasing in diameter; upper 7-11 whorls double-carinate just above suture; body whorl distinctly angulate with sharply defined carina, sometimes 1-2 small carinae encircling; aperture narrowed above, white, pale blue or purple within, produced and canaliculate below, near columella; peristome acute, smooth, thick; columella pale blue, twisted; terminations of peristome and columella joined by thick, somewhat spreading callus; operculum paucispiral, chitinous, thin, red-brown (Baker 1928a, Dazo 1965).

A detailed account of the anatomy of this species can be found in Dazo (1965).

Pleurocera acuta occurs from Quebec, Vermont, and northeastern New York, west to Kansas, Nebraska, and Minnesota, and south to Louisiana and the Mississippi drainage basin (Goodrich 1939a, b; Leonard 1959; Dazo 1965).

During this survey, populations were located at five New York sites, one in the Mississippi-Ohio River watershed (431) and four in the St. Lawrence River watershed (141C, 340, 531, 562).

The first report of this species occurring in New York was De Kay's (1843). The specimens came from Lake Erie. Lewis (1856b, 1860, 1874) reported *P. acuta* in Herkimer and Otsego Counties; from the Niagara River, Niagara County; and Mohawk, Herkimer County. In the late 19th and early 20th centuries, populations existed in the Erie Canal, Onondaga County (Beauchamp 1886b); Erie Canal (Walton 1891, 1898); Lake Ontario, (Marshall 1894); Irondequoit Bay in Lake Ontario; and the Erie Canal "Wide Waters", Rochester, Monroe County (Baker 1900b). Other sites include the Niagara River, Niagara County (Letson 1909), and Cayuga Lake, Cayuga and Seneca Counties (Maury 1916).

In the 1930s and 1940s additional populations were reported existing in Sodus Bay, Lake Ontario, Wayne County (Burdick 1939); the Hudson River, Hudson, Columbia County (Townes 1936); and in the vicinity of Mohawk,

Herkimer County (Goodrich 1942). More recently, specimens of this species have been found in Conesus Lake, Livingston County (Wade & Vasey 1976, Wade 1987), the Mohawk River at Cohoes, Albany County; and the Hudson River at Troy, Rensselaer County (Smith 1983). It is believed that *P. acuta* reached the Hudson basin via the Erie Canal (Goodrich 1942, Smith 1983, Strayer 1987).

This species can be found in a variety of habitats. In lakes, the snails live on boulders on exposed shores or in mud and sand. In rivers, they are usually on stones in a rapid current (Baker 1928a, Goodrich 1932). The snails tend to remain in shallow water up to 1 m deep, where they burrow under the sand and layers of decaying leaves and other organic matter (Dazo 1965). The five sites located during this survey included two rivers, two lakes, and a canal.

Research on the natural history of *P. acuta* was conducted in Michigan by Dazo (1965). The snails oviposit in April, as soon as they become active. The reproductive period peaks in April and May, and it does not extend into June. Eggs, deposited in masses of 1-19, are encased in clear, spherical compartments and are surrounded by a transparent, gelatinous matrix. Parent snails coat the upper sides of the masses with fine sand. Individuals lay 15 eggs/day. Females oviposit for the first time at two years of age, when their average shell length is 17 mm, the average number of eggs/mass being 2.8. At three years, the number of eggs/mass increases to 6.6. The young begin to hatch after two weeks. In both laboratory and field populations, females are more abundant than males. The female to male ratio was 2.1:1.0 in the laboratory and 3.0:1.0 in the field. Densities vary from 12-42 snails/m². Individuals slowly plow through sandy substrata with rostrum fully extended. In the laboratory, they migrated to aquarium bottoms at night and remained buried in sand until morning. Stomach contents indicate the diet of *P. acuta* to be primarily green and red algae, diatoms, and desmids. They also ingest decaying vegetation and fine sand grains.

Four New York sites had the following water chemistry values: pH: 6.9-8.4 (7.5 ± 0.4), conductivity: 162-600 μmhos/cm (352 ± 92), Ca^{++}: 7-26 ppm (18 ± 5), and Na^+: 7-92 ppm (35 ± 19). Field sites in Michigan had pH values of 7.5-8.6 and high oxygen concentrations (Dazo 1965). It appears that this species prefers moderate to hard waters and has a high sodium tolerance.

Goniobasis livescens (Menke, 1830)

Liver elimia
Fig. 12b, 13

Shell to 20 mm long, highly variable, elongate to ovate-acuminate, pale blue or tan to green and brown, often with 2 dark bands; frequently turreted on upper whorls; apex brown or wine colored; whorls 12.0, somewhat rounded, carina encircling center of spire whorls, obsolete

33

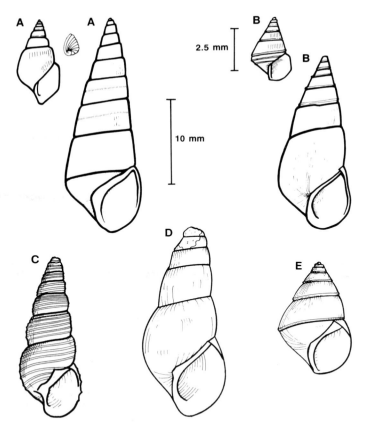

Fig. 12. Family Pleuroceridae, shells: a, *Pleurocera acuta*, with immature individual shown to the upper left; b, *Goniobasis livescens*, with immature individual shown to the upper left; c, *G. virginica*, ridged form; d, *G. virginica*, smooth form; e, *Leptoxis carinata*. All illustrations of adults are drawn to the same scale.

on last 2 whorls; sutures well-impressed; spire sharply coni-cal, last whorl somewhat bulbous; aperture large, purple within; peristome sharp, edge thin, thickened by callosity within outer lip; columella thick, solid, tinged blue or pur-ple, reflected over columellar region and lip (Baker 1928a, Goodrich 1932, 1939b).

Burch (1989) places this species in the genus *Elimia*. Anatomical details can be found in Dazo (1965).

The distribution of this species ranges from Quebec and Lake Champlain west to the Great Lakes region (except Lake Superior), and south to the Mississippi drainage in Iowa, Illinois, Indiana, and Ohio. The species moved into the Hud-son River drainage via the Erie Canal (Baker 1928a, Berry 1943, Goodrich 1945, Dazo 1965, Clarke 1981).

All New York State sites located during this survey are in the St. Lawrence River watershed (344, 404, 437, 494, 499, 504, 505, 513, 514, 515, 518A, 518B, 521, 527, 529, 530, 535).

Goniobasis livescens was first reported in New York State in the 1870s from the Niagara River, Niagara County; and

the Erie Canal and Mohawk River, Herkimer County (Lewis 1872, 1874). Soon after, the snails were found in the Mohawk River, Cohoes, Albany County; the Albany/Troy region in Albany and Rensselaer Counties (Marshall 1895); Onondaga County (Beauchamp 1886b); and the Erie Canal, Monroe County (Walton 1891). At the turn of the century, populations were reported from the Genesee River, Monroe County (Baker 1901); and Eighteen Mile Creek and the Niagara River, Niagara County (Letson 1909). By the 1910s, snail populations inhabited Oneida Lake, Oswego and Onondaga Counties (Baker, 1916a, b, 1918a, b; Pratt 1923). However, by 1968 Harman (1968a) could not find this species in that lake. Additional popula-tions were noted in the Erie Canal "Widewaters," Rochester, and the Genesee River, both in Monroe Coun-ty (Baker 1900b). Townes (1936) reported the species from the Hudson River from North Germantown, Columbia County, to Rhinecliff, Dutchess County. Burdick (1939) col-lected *G. livescens* from Lake Ontario at Sodus Bay and Port Bay, Wayne County, and from Little Sodus Bay, Cayu-ga County. More recently, this species has been found in Green Lake in the Oswego River watershed, Onondaga County (Harman 1970); Owasco Lake and Cayuga Lake, Cayuga County; Seneca Lake, Seneca and Yates Coun-ties; Keuka Lake, Steuben County; DeRuyter Lake, Madi-son County (Harman & Berg 1971); Conesus Lake, Livingston County (Wade & Vasey 1976); Mohawk River at Cohoes, Albany County; and in the Hudson River at Troy, Rensselaer County (Smith 1983).

G. livescens grazes in shallow water on stones and grav-el in lakes and clear, rapid streams (Baker 1928a). On rocky substrata in rivers, the snails cling to sides of algae-covered stones, whereas in lake situations they burrow into sand or move among aquatic plants. Densities vary from 11-892 snails/m^2 (Dazo 1965). During winter, with their apertures tightly closed, they survive under the ice, hidden under stones or layers of decaying matter (Goodrich 1945, Dazo 1965). The New York sites located during this survey include five river and stream sites, eight lake sites, two per-manent ponds, and two canals.

Individuals mate in autumn, hold sperm through the winter, and begin to oviposit in April as soon as they become active. Egg-laying peaks in April and May and continues until August (Dazo 1965). Eggs, uncovered except for a shell membrane, appear singly or in rows. Unlike *Pleurocera acuta*, *G. livescens* eggs lack a sand cover, but they do have a thin coating of soil which blends in with the substratum (Dazo 1965).

In the laboratory, young adults lay an average of 2.8 eggs/clutch, but in the field they lay 4.7 eggs/clutch. Older snails deposit 6.6 eggs/clutch in the laboratory and 9 eggs/clutch in the field. Over a period of 20 days, females can deposit an average of 3,264 eggs. The young begin to hatch two to three weeks after oviposition and live for approximately three years. Females outnumber males 6.5:1.0 in the field and 2.4:1.0 in the laboratory (Dazo 1965).

Individuals of *G. livescens* move over rocks and stones, scraping off green and red algae, diatoms, desmids, and bacteria for food (Dazo 1965). It has been hypothesized that the radula is best suited for obtaining large food particles, such as detritus, from sand. Compared to the pulmonates, this species is an inefficient alga grazer (Barnese & Lowe 1990).

At night in the laboratory, the snails, with their heads withdrawn, remain on the bottom of the aquarium on sand and gravel. In the morning, they crawl up the sides of the aquarium (Dazo 1965).

Water chemistry values for 16 of the collecting sites for *G. livescens* in New York are: pH: 7.3-8.5 (7.7 ± 0.1), conductivity: 178-820 µmhos/cm (342 ± 46), Ca^{++}: 9-40 ppm (23 ± 2), and Na^+: 6-125 ppm (26 ± 8). Harman & Berg (1971) documented pH values of 7.3-8.5 (mean = 7.9). Dazo (1965) noted that under experimental conditions, snails survived only at pH values 8.0-8.4 (Dazo 1965).

Goniobasis virginica (Say, 1817)
Piedmont elimia
Figs. 12c, d; 13

Shell elevated, thickened, yellow to yellow-green to fawn to chestnut, with two chestnut spiral stripes in medial and basal positions; nuclear whorls blue, chestnut, or white; whorls up to 12.0, usually 6-9, body and penultimate whorls shouldered, often with spiral carinae, turreted; sutures deep; aperture weakly angulate, lacrimate; peristome sharp, outer lip sinuous; columella smooth, imperforate, with suffusion of white callus at base (Harman & Berg 1971).

Burch (1989) places this species in the genus *Elimia*.

C. virginica is limited to the eastern Atlantic coastal states from Virginia to Connecticut (Richards 1934, Goodrich 1942, Jokinen 1983, Gerberich 1981, Smith 1987), including New York (Harman & Berg 1971, Strayer 1987).

Six populations of *G. virginica* were found during this study. The sites were in the Hudson River watershed (96A, 96B), Mississippi-Ohio River watershed (431), and the St. Lawrence River watershed (404, 531, 534).

Records of this species from Mud Creek, Onondaga County, can be traced back to De Kay (1843). Sometime between 1856 and 1869 the species was introduced into the Erie Canal, Mohawk, Herkimer County (Lewis 1860, 1868, 1872). Lewis (1872) reported that *G. virginica* also inhabited streams near Buffalo, Erie County. Other populations occurred in the Erie Canal and Seneca River, Onondaga County (Beauchamp 1886b); the Erie Canal between Ilion, Herkimer County and Utica, Oneida County (Bailey 1891); Irondequoit Bay, Lake Ontario, Monroe Country (Walton 1891, 1898; Baker 1900b); the Hudson River at Albany, Albany County; Normans Kill, Albany County; and the Erie Canal, Monroe County (Marshall 1894). By 1916, populations were found in Cayuga Lake,

Seneca and Cayuga Counties; and in Conesus Lake, Livingston County (Maury 1916). By the 1940s, however, Conesus Lake apparently no longer harbored the snail (Robertson & Blakeslee 1948). Townes (1936) reported the species in the Hudson River from Hudson, Columbia County, to Rhinecliff, Dutchess County, and Burdick (1939) described a population at the mouth of the Salmon River at Lake Ontario, Oswego County. Harman & Berg (1971) found only shells in the Oswego River watershed, but they located live populations in the Susquehanna drainage.

Individuals live on stones in the shallows of large rivers (Townes 1936, Jokinen 1983, Smith 1980). In deep water, they are found on all substrata, including vegetation. Populations living in lakes are found on silt-covered substrata of cobbles, gravel, sand, and clay (Harman & Berg 1971). Populations located during this survey were at four river and two canal sites.

In Maryland, *G. virginica* lays its eggs in June. They are spirally arranged in masses of 2-15 or more. They have a tough, outer, membranous covering, and septa divide the mass into compartments. Foreign matter is attached to the egg masses (Winsor 1933). It appears that little else is known about the natural history of this species.

At the three sites where data were taken, water chemistry values were: pH: 7.8, 8.0, 8.4, conductivity: 401, 600, 602 µmhos/cm, Ca^{++}: 26, 26, 32 ppm, and Na^+: 20, 88, 92 ppm. Harman & Berg (1971) reported pH values of 7.9-8.3 for four sites in the Susquehanna River watershed. The species tolerates up to 50% salinity (Baily 1929).

Leptoxis carinata (Bruguière, 1792)
Crested mudalia
Figs. 12e, 13

Shell up to 20 mm, globose to elevated, turreted or carinate, amber or olive to chestnut, sometimes with 2-3 chestnut spiral stripes on body and penultimate whorls; umbilicus imperforate; whorls 6.0-7.0, strong carina on center of whorls, sometimes disappearing on body whorl; sutures shallow; aperture thickened, not reflected, broadly lacrimate; outer lip of peristome straight, with wine or light blue callus; columella straight, smooth, wine or chestnut; operculum paucispiral, chitinous, fragile (Harman & Berg 1971).

Leptoxis carinata occurs on the Atlantic Coastal Plain, from New York south to North Carolina (Richards 1934, Goodrich 1942).

No specimens were collected during this survey. Harman and Berg (1971) found the species in tributaries of the Susquehanna River watershed. The New York State Museum has 11 lots collected between 1955 and 1966 in Broome, Chenango, Cortland, Otsego, Steuben, and Tioga Counties (NYSM 2235-2245).

Early literature records indicate that this snail inhabited Lake Champlain, Clinton County (De Kay 1843); Homer,

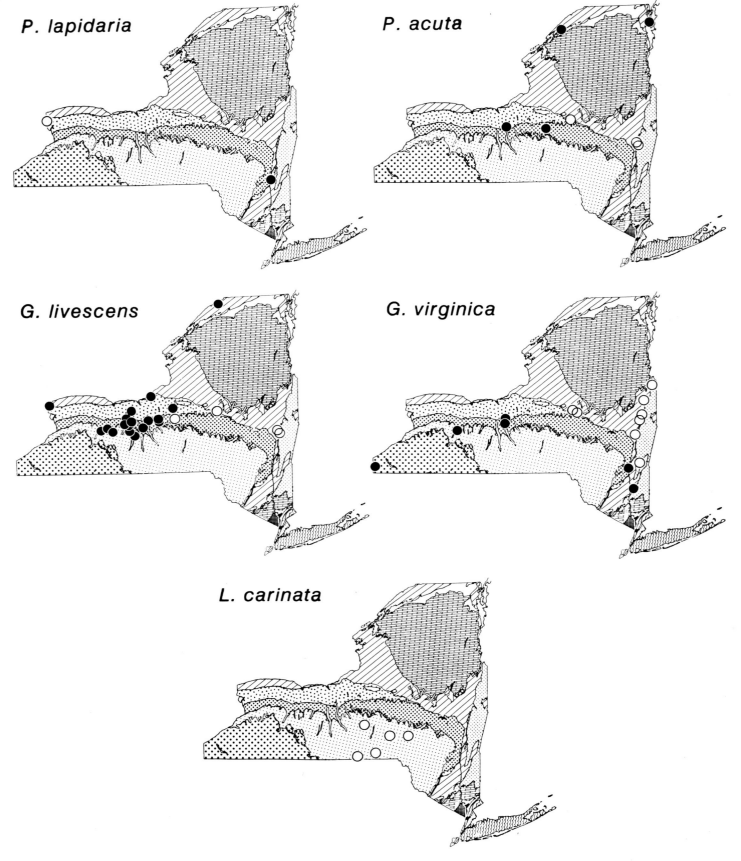

Fig. 13. Known distributions of *Pomatiopsis lapidaria* and species of Pleuroceridae in New York State. Closed circles indicate records from the present survey, and open circles indicate records from museum specimens.

Cortland County; Oneonta, Otsego County (Lewis 1874); and the Susquehanna and Chemung Rivers, Cortland County (Marshall 1894). More recent reports give sites that include Otsego Lake, Otsego County (Harman 1971, McNamara & Harman 1975); the Tioughnioga River, Broome County; the Susquehanna River, Otsego County; and the Unadilla River, Chenango, Otsego County (Aldridge 1982). Except for De Kay's (1843) possibly erroneous account, this species in New York is restricted to the Susquehanna River watershed.

It appears that *L. carinata* is restricted to riffle areas in larger rivers (Harman & Berg 1971), where it grazes on *Aufwuchs* (Aldridge 1982).

The snails live for two years and breed only once, in their second summer. In April, copulation occurs between 20-month-old snails. Oviposition begins when the water temperature rises to 18°C in late May or June. Afterward, all adult snails die. Egg deposition peaks in early June, and females produce an average of 13 eggs/m^2. Eggs are laid singly or in small masses up to an average of 296-381 eggs/female, but less than 10% of the eggs survive (Aldrich 1982). A population in Wood Creek, Pennsylvania, showed similar characteristics but oviposition began in late March (Hendrix 1986).

After an incubation period of 18-25 days, actively growing, young snails appear from August through October. A second season of growth occurs from May through August. At four sites in the Susquehanna River basin, mature colonies of snails have female to male ratios of 1.0:1.0 to 5.2:1.0 During the breeding period, female to male ratios are 1.4:1.0 to 6.6:1.0, and adult snail densities are 41-77 snails/m^2 (Aldrich 1982).

Subclass Pulmonata

Shell present or absent, spiral or saucer shaped; operculum absent. Primary gills absent; mantle cavity a functional lung, pseudobranch present or absent; species hermaphroditic and freshwater, terrestrial or, rarely, marine.

Order Basommatophora

Shell present, covered by corneous periostracum; single pair of tentacles present, flattened, triangular to subcylindrical, non-retractile; eyes sessile at tentacle base; species freshwater, amphibious, or rarely marine (Baker 1928a).

Egg capsule types for the basommatophoran families are illustrated in Bondeson (1950).

Family Lymnaeidae

Shell usually dextral, ovately-oblong or elongate; spire more or less attenuated; outer lip thin, sharp; columella axis thickened by shelly deposit; one large superior and two smaller, narrow, lateral jaws present; radula usually of 80-100 rows of overlapping teeth (Fig. 5b) (Baker 1928a).

Lymnaeid taxonomic relationships are discussed in Baker (1911), Hubendick (1951), Walter (1969), and Burch (1982).

Key to the Lymnaeidae

1a. Aperture markedly longer than spire 2

1b. Aperture same length or shorter than spire 4

2a. Aperture lacrimate; shell tapered; body whorl with spiral lines ....*Pseudosuccinea columella*

2b. Shell not as above 3

3a. Aperture very large, flared, ear-shaped ....
....*Radix auricularia*

3b. Aperture not flared ....*Stagnicola emarginata*

4a. Shell very narrow, needle-like ....*Acella haldemani*

4b. Shell not as above 5

5a. Shell with distinct spiral lines caused by folds in periostracum..*Stagnicola caperata*

5b. Shell without distinct spiral lines......................................6

6a. Shell thin, pale, large, greater than 30 mm long; spire acute ....*Lymnaea stagnalis*

6b. Shell not as above 7

7a. Shell sturdy, dark brown, large, greater than 30 mm long...*Bulimnea megasoma*

7b. Shell not as above 8

8a. Periostraum distinctly crenulated (Fig. 14a) ....*Stagnicola* spp., 9

8b. Periostracum not or only indistinctly crenulated (Fig. 14b) ....*Fossaria* spp., 10

9a. Spire elongate, usually longer than aperture ....*Stagnicola elodes*

9b. Spire short, same length or shorter than aperture ....*Stagnicola catascopium*

10a. Whorls shouldered...11
10b. Whorls rounded 12

11a. Whorls flattened; spire acute; shell elongate with whorls as high as wide; sutures deeply impressed......... ....*Fossaria exigua*

11b. Whorls below shoulder rounded; spire conic; whorls wider than high ....*Fossaria obrussa*

12a. Shell with five whorls less than 7 mm long; aperture ovate ....*Fossaria parva*

12b. Shell with five whorls greater than 8 mm long; aperture elongate..13

13a. Spire acute, usually longer than aperture, turreted; sutures very deeply impressed ....*Fossaria rustica*

13b. Spire broadly conic, usually as long as aperture; sutures not deeply impressed ....*Fossaria modicella*

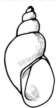

Lymnaea stagnalis (Linnaeus, 1758)

Swamp lymnaea

Figs. 15a, 17

Shell elongate, thin, somewhat fusiform, yellow to brown, large, 50-60 mm high; umbilicus closed or a small chink; spire long, acutely pointed, flat-sided, approximately one-half length of aperture; whorls 7.0, early ones not rapidly increasing in diameter; body whorl rapidly expanding, rounded; sutures distinct, sometimes impressed; aperture ovate, somewhat dilated above, rounded below; outer lip thin, acute; parietal wall with thin callus appressed to umbilical region; columella pillar gyrate, forming heavy, oblique, ascending plait (Baker 1911, 1928a).

Information on internal anatomy can be found in Carriker (1946) and McDonald (1969).

The range of this species is circumboreal. In North America it exists south of the Canadian treeline from the St. Lawrence River in Quebec to the Mackenzie and Yukon River watersheds south to Colorado and the Mississippi River system in North Dakota, Ohio, and Illinois (Clarke 1973, 1981; Cvancara 1983). Populations also occur in the northern branches of the Susquehanna River system in central New York (Harman & Berg 1971). This species apparently does not occur in southern New England (Jokinen 1983).

During this survey, *L. stagnalis* was found associated only with the mouths of Lake Champlain tributaries, St. Lawrence River watershed (259A, 259B, 262, 263). However, Harman & Berg (1971) reported populations in the Oswego River system of the St. Lawrence River watershed: Seneca Lake, Ontario County; Cayuga Lake, Cayuga County; Little Sodus Bay, Lake Ontario, Oswego County; and Big Lake, Onondaga County. Additional sites reported by Harman & Berg (1971) were in the northeast region of the West Branch of the Tioughnioga River in the Susquehanna River drainage basin. Localities from museum collections are indicated on Fig. 17.

The literature on *L. stagnalis* includes mention of it as an inhabitant of Lake Champlain, Clinton County (De Kay 1843); Canandaigua Lake, Ontario and Yates Counties (De Kay 1843, Mitchell 1899, Maury 1916); Cayuga Lake, Seneca and Cayuga Counties (De Kay 1843); Conesus Lake, Livingston County (Wade & Vasey 1976); Oneida Lake, Oswego and Onondaga Counties (Beauchamp 1886b; Baker 1916a, b, 1918a, b; Pratt 1923); Erie Canal "Wide Waters," Monroe County (Baker 1900b); Niagara River (Letson 1909); Buffalo, Erie County (Lewis 1874); Genesee County (Marshall 1894); and Conesus Lake, Livingston County (Wade & Vasey 1976).

This species is primarily an inhabitant of quiet, shallow lakes, river embayments, and lake inlets and outlets (Dawley 1947), but a subspecies (*L. stagnalis lillinae* Baker 1910) is typical of sandy shores with heavy wave action (Goodrich 1932). Observations in Michigan (Goodrich 1932) indicate that *L. stagnalis* was much more abundant before lumbering, pollution and wetland drainage occurred. This species is a carnivore and a detritivore (Baker 1918a).

The longevity of these snails can be as short as one year (McDonald 1969), or it can be as long as seven years for

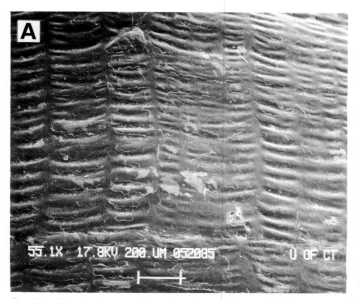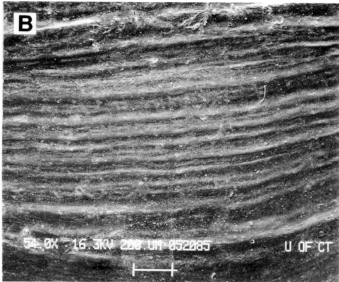

Fig. 14. Family Lymnaeidae, structure of the periostracum: a, *Stagnicola* sp., with numerous distinct crenulations between growth lines; b, *Fossaria* sp., with weak crenulations between growth lines or crenulations absent.

northern populations where ponds are ice-free for only five months of the year (Boag & Pearlstone 1979). Egg masses are deposited on species of *Nymphaea, Castalia,* dead *Typha,* and the floating leaves of *Potamogeton natans* L. (McDonald 1969). In northern populations, egg deposition occurs from mid May to late August, with a peak in May and June. Only snails with shells longer than 30 mm, in the second half of their third summer, are mature enough to deposit eggs. By their fourth summer, all snails are fecund, and egg production occurs for the remainder of life, making the reproductive pattern iteroparous. The average number of eggs/mass varies from 61-80 (Boag & Pearlstone 1979).

Under laboratory conditions, much of the mortality of newly hatched snails is caused by accidental ingestion by mature snails, especially at the air-water interface (Boag *et al.* 1984). The diet includes rooted vegetation, detritus at surface films where the snails hang upside down, and *Aufwuchs* covering submerged rocks, logs, etc. This species has been observed attacking small fish and feeding on fish eggs (McDonald 1969).

Lymnaea stagnalis has been shown experimentally to prefer substrata mimicking prostrate aquatic macrophytes, rocks, logs, debris, and dissected-leaved macrophytes (Kershner & Lodge 1990). In winter, as water temperatures decrease below 9°C, snails migrate into deeper water. At 2°C they are immobile and cling to any hard substratum until temperatures increase (Boag & Bentz 1980).

This species requires 20 ppm of calcium for growth (MacDonald 1969) and is best adapted to hard water. Water chemistry parameters for two of the sites located during this survey are: pH: 6.6 and 7.2, conductivity: 87 and 371 µmhos/cm, Ca^{++}: 9 and 44 ppm, and Na$^+$: 4 and 10 ppm. In Minnesota, this species occurs in soft as well as hard water (Dawley 1947).

Stagnicola elodes (Say, 1821)
Marsh pondsnail
Figs. 15b, 17

Shell elongate to elongate ovate, 35 mm long, thin, malleated, pale brown to black; umbilicus closed or narrowly open; spire sharp, pointed, 0.5-0.6 shell length; whorls 7.0, rounded; body whorl usually obese; sutures well-impressed; aperture roundly ovate to elongate ovate; outer lip thin, brown-purple varix within; columella axis twisted, forming heavy ascending columellar plait; callus heavy, formed by inner lip (Baker 1928a).

Synonyms are *Stagnicola palustris* (Müller) and *Lymnaea palustris.*

This species is distributed from New England to Manitoba and the Yukon, south to New Mexico and Kentucky (Baker 1928a, Clarke 1973, Goodrich & van der Schalie 1939, Branson & Batch 1983, Jokinen 1983).

Stagnicola elodes is widespread in New York except for the Delaware River watershed and the low calcium waters of the Adirondacks Mountains. The 48 sites where it was found are in the Hudson River watershed (212, 268, 269, 270, 271, 275, 318, 368, 451, 587); Ohio-Mississippi River watershed (417, 426); St. Lawrence River watershed (141A, 141B, 141D, 263, 307, 308, 337, 340, 390, 394, 396, 438, 441, 445A, 493, 494, 507, 508, 509, 521, 522, 526, 531, 532, 535, 559, 561, 566); and the Susquehanna River watershed (536, 537, 538, 541, 574, 590, 593).

This species has been known to be abundant in New York State since the middle of the 19th century (De Kay 1843). Lewis (1856b, 1860, 1872, 1874)) documents the snails in stagnant waters such as the Erie Canal and pools and ditches of Herkimer and Otsego Counties. Within a few years, populations were described from marshes at the foot of Owasco Lake, Cayuga County (Baker 1899); Onondaga County (Beauchamp 1886b); Erie Canal, Monroe County (Walton 1891); Jefferson, Rochester, and Niagara Counties (Marshall 1894); tidal creeks and brackish marshes of the Hudson River, Ulster and Orange Counties (Mearns 1898); New York City (Prime 1880); Canandaigua Lake, Ontario and Yates Counties (Mitchell 1899); Genesee River, Irondequoit Bay of Lake Ontario, and the Erie Canal at "Widewaters," Rochester, Monroe County (Baker 1900b, 1901); Cazenovia Lake, Madison County; Williamsville, Erie County; Goat Island, Niagara County (Letson 1909); in swales and swamps of Wyoming County (Baker 1913); Oneida Lake, Oswego County (Baker 1916a, b; Pratt 1923); Farm Creek, Ithaca, Tompkins County; and Cayuga Lake, Cayuga and Seneca Counties (Maury 1916).

More recently, *S. elodes* has been reported from the Salmon River, Wayne County; Oak Orchard Creek tributaries, Orleans County; and Little Sodus Bay in Lake Ontario, Cayuga County (Burdick 1939); Upper Ferdun Pond, between Piermont and Sparkill, Rockland County (Bretet & Carswell 1952); Brooklyn Botanic Gardens stream, Kings County (Freas 1950a); Crystal Brook, Mount Sinai, Suffolk County, Long Island, (Jacobson 1969); Oneida Lake and the Finger Lakes in Onondaga, Cayuga, Seneca, Steuben, and Ontario Counties (Harman & Berg 1971); Otsego Lake, Otsego County (Harman 1971; MacNamara & Harman 1975); the Hudson River basin, where the species is abundant but not in the main channel (Strayer 1975); and the lowlands surrounding the Adirondack Mountains (Jokinen 1991). The American Museum of Natural History has lots from a pond in Glen Cove, Long Island (AMNH 143436); Alley Pond, Hollis, Queens, Queens County (AMNH 143513); Bulls Head Pond, Staten Island, Richmond County (AMNH 143514); and Frerdon Pond, Sparkill, Rockland County (AMNH 143477).

This species is found in vernal and permanent ponds, marshes, edges of lakes and rivers, and ditches (Dawley 1947). It is frequently associated with cattails (*Typha* spp.). Of the 43 sites found during this study, 15 were edges of rivers and streams, seven were lake littoral zones, nine were small permanent and vernal pools, seven were ditches, two were marshes, two were canals, and one was a swamp. Temporary ponds were under-collected during this survey, and it is probable that *S. elodes* is more abundant than noted here.

In most habitats, the snails live to approximately 14 months. Adults lay eggs in spring on any stiff surface, such as terrestrial leaf and branch litter, stones, and shells of other individuals. In temporary pools and ditches, older snails migrate to deeper areas as the water level drops, and they become stranded as the water disappears. Young snails, however, do not follow the water level. They climb up terrestrial vegetation, even as high as 2 m up trees, and they attach themselves with the mucus that they use to close their apertures as they withdraw deeper into the shell to aestivate. The adults are open to predation and parasitism from sciomyzid fly larvae and other organisms (Jokinen 1978a, Barnes 1990), and usually they do not survive the summer. Before a pond refills, the aestivating snails move about during rains, but they do not appear to feed. When the autumn rains arrive and the pond begins to fill, the young migrate down to under the newly-fallen leaf litter and hibernate until ice melt in spring. They actively feed and grow to mature size before oviposition (Jokinen 1978a, McGraw 1970).

Stagnicola elodes appears to have a relatively high phenotypic plasticity which allows the individuals to survive at various levels of nutrition (Rollo & Hawryluk 1988). Populations exist in habitats with both low and high gastropod species diversity (Jokinen 1987). Physiological studies have been done by Hunter (1975a, b).

This species prefers submerged terrestrial leaf litter as its substratum, and individuals feed on the algae and bacteria covering it. Life history patterns and fecundity appear to be determined by the food quality and habitat trophic status (Eisenberg 1966, 1970; Hunter 1975b). In permanent habitats, *S. elodes* can have two generations each year (Hunter 1975b).

Forty-three collecting sites sampled during this survey had the following water chemistry parameters: pH: 6.0-8.4 (7.3 ± 0.1), conductivity: 84-2320 µmhos/cm (509 ± 67), Ca^{++}: 4-94 ppm (27 ± 3), and Na^+: 1-291 ppm (39 ± 8). In Connecticut, *S. elodes* was not abundant (12 sites) and tended to dwell in the harder waters of the Connecticut Valley. Connecticut water chemistry parameters were: pH: 6.2-7.9, conductivity: 63-387 µmhos/cm, Ca^{++}: 3-26 ppm, Na^+: 4-41 ppm (Jokinen 1983). In New York, this species is rare in the acidic, low calcium waters of the Adirondack Mountains (Jokinen 1991).

Stagnicola emarginata (Say, 1821)

St. Lawrence pondsnail
Figs. 15c, 17

Shell ovate to globose, inflated, up to 30 mm high, thin, malleated, nearly three-quarters as wide as high, translucent, white to dark brown; umbilicus a small chink to wide perforation, margined by inner lip; spire broadly, acutely pyramidal to depressed globose or flattened, often eroded; nuclear whorls 1.5, chestnut, wide, low, flattened; whorls 5.0-6.0, convex to subglobose, shouldered; body whorl large, convex, expanded, flared; sutures deeply impressed, sometimes bordered by white line; aperture ovate, large, 0.5-0.7 times shell length; outer lip thin, with thin white-brown varix; inner lip white, broadly reflected; columella smooth to plicated; parietal callus thick, raised to make aperture continuous (Baker 1928a, Goodrich 1932).

Information on anatomy can be found in Baker (1900a).

There has been an off-and-on synonymy of *S. catascopium* with *S. emarginata* dating back to Binney (1865). Strayer (1987) considers them to be a single species. For purposes of the present work, they are considered separate species.

S. emarginata occurs from Maine to western Ontario, south to Michigan, Pennsylvania, and New York State (Baker 1911, 1928a).

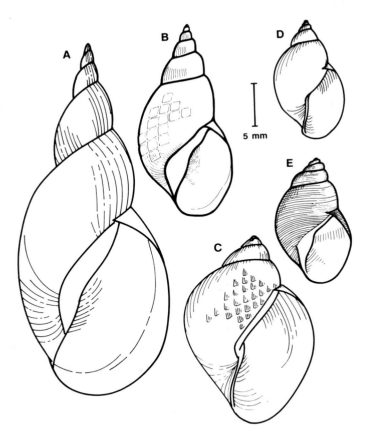

Fig. 15. Family Lymnaeidae, shells: a, *Lymnaea stagnalis*; b, *S. elodes*; c, *S. emarginata*; d, *S. catascopium*; e, *S. caperata*. All illustrations are drawn to the same scale.

41

This species was not found to be abundant in New York State. Sites were in the Hudson River watershed (460) and the St. Lawrence River watershed (398, 524A, 525, 531).

S. emarginata has been reported from the Mohawk River (De Kay 1843); Owasco Lake and Owasco River, Cayuga County (Lewis 1874, Baker 1899); Onondaga County (Beauchamp 1886b); Chautauqua Lake, Chautauqua County (Maury 1898, 1916; Townes 1937); Canandaigua Lake, Ontario and Yates Counties (Mitchell 1899); Cazenovia Lake, Madison Country (Henderson 1907); Oneida Lake, Oswego and Onondaga Counties (Baker 1916a, b; Pratt 1923; Harman & Berg 1971); Skaneateles Lake, Onondaga County, and Keuka Lake (shells only), Steuben County (Harman & Berg 1971); and Otsego Lake (shells only), Otsego County (Harman 1971, MacNamara & Harman 1975). Most localities are in central and western New York.

The habitats found during this survey included one lake, one ditch draining into a lake, and two canals. In Minnesota, the snails are especially adapted to large, hard water lakes (Dawley 1947). Studies at a Michigan lake revealed densities of up to 5 snails/m^2 on variable substrata (Clampitt 1973). In Skaneateles Lake, a population lived in water 3-15 m deep on sand or silt (Harman & Berg 1971).

Little has been documented on the life history of *S. emarginata*. During the summer in Michigan, the snails are in deep water (4 m), but they migrate to shallow water in the autumn and half bury themselves in sand (Goodrich 1932). In Oneida Lake, New York, they occur on bouldered shores (Baker 1918a).

Water chemistry values for four sites in New York are: pH: 7.6-8.4 (7.9 ± 0.2), conductivity: 240-1240 µmhos/cm (721 ± 209), Ca^{++}: 26-58 ppm (36 ± 8), and Na$^+$: 1-144 ppm (86 ± 30).

Stagnicola catascopium (Say, 1817)

Woodland pondsnail
Figs. 15d, 17

Shell short-ovate to elongate fusiform, 25 mm high, thin to thick, pale brown to dark chestnut; umbilicus closed or a small, narrow chink; apex acute; nuclear whorls small, well-rounded, white to wine colored; spire short, depressed, dome-shaped to turreted, acutely conical or pyramidal; whorls 5.0-6.0; body whorl large, moderately convex; sutures impressed, almost channeled; aperture ovate or elongate ovate, as long as or longer than spire; outer lip thickened by varix edged with narrow chestnut band; inner lip reflected, appressed to columellar region; columella with heavy oblique plait; axis twisted; callus thickened (Binney 1865, Baker 1928a).

This species occurs from Nova Scotia west to the Pacific coast and south to about 40°N. It is present, but rare, in western New England and common in all the Great Lakes except Lake Superior (Baker 1928a, Goodrich & van der Schalie 1939, Clarke 1981, Jokinen 1983, Cvancara 1983).

Stagnicola catascopium was found at 19 sites in the Hudson River watershed (961, 287, 370, 588, 589); Mississippi-Ohio River watershed (431, 432); St. Lawrence River watershed (141D, 259B, 260, 261, 339, 341, 352, 450, 524B); and the Susquehanna River watershed (567, 572, 591).

De Kay (1843) reported that *S. catascopium* was common in western New York. In the 19th century, populations were found in the Erie Canal, Herkimer County (Lewis 1860, Baily 1891); Onondaga County (Beauchamp 1886b); the Hudson River from Albany, Albany County, and Troy, Rensselaer County, the Normanskill, and the Mohawk River (Marshall 1895); Hudson River marshes, Orange and Ulster Counties (Mearns 1898); Chautauqua Lake, Chautauqua County (Maury 1898, 1916; Townes 1937); and Rochester, Monroe County (Walton 1891). Later, the snails were reported from Oneida Lake, Oswego and Onondaga Counties (Baker 1916a, b, 1918a, b; Pratt 1923); the Erie Canal "Wide Waters" in Rochester and the Genesee River, Monroe County (Baker 1900b, 1901, 1909); Niagara Falls, Niagara County; Lake Erie at Rose Hill, Erie Canal, and Frenchman's Creek (Letson 1909); Canandaigua Lake, Ontario and Yates Counties (Mitchell 1899). Later reports note this species from Lake Ontario near Oswego, Oswego County (Burdick 1939); the Hudson River from Hudson, Columbia County, to Verplanck, Westchester County (Townes 1936); Seneca Lake, Seneca and Yates Counties; Oneida Lake, Onondaga County; and Cross Lake, Onondaga and Cayuga Counties (Harman & Berg 1971). The American Museum of Natural History has lots from Niagara Falls, Niagara County (AMNH 143456); and the Hudson River, Highland Falls, Orange County (AMNH 143437).

Habitats include lakes, rivers, and streams. Young snails usually are found on mud, clay, and sand in deep water, whereas adults are more likely to live on boulders in shallow water, often in areas of heavy wave action (Binney 1865, Baker 1928a, Goodrich 1932, Goodrich & van der Schalie 1939). They actively migrate inshore (Boss *et al.* 1984). In Oneida Lake, *S. catascopium* is associated with filamentous algae (*Oedogonium, Cladophora*, and *Spirogyra* spp.) (Baker 1918a).

These snails consume organic detritus and algae, especially diatoms (Pinel-Alloul & Magnin 1979). The young snails are prey of the common sucker (*Catostomus commersoni* (Lacepède)) and the pumpkinseed (*Lepomis gibbosus* (L.)) (Baker 1918a, 1928a).

Stagnicola catascopium serves as an intermediate host for the swimmers' itch trematode, *Schistosomatium douthitti* Cort. Effects of infection on snail life cycle characteristics are described by Loker (1979).

Water chemistry values for 14 of the New York State sites were: pH: 6.4-7.8 (7.1 ± 0.1); conductivity: 47-760 µmhos/cm (275 ± 47); Ca^{++}: 3-49 ppm (16 ± 4); and Na$^+$: 1-122 ppm (19 ± 8). This species is able to tolerate the salinity of tidal rivers (Binney 1865; Jokinen 1983).

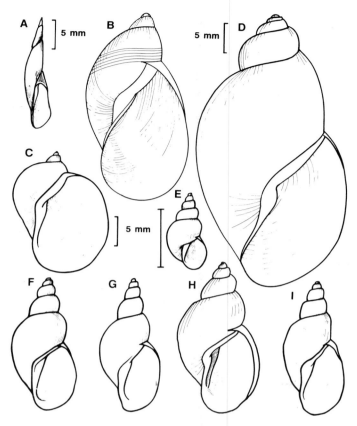

Fig. 16. Family Lymnaeidae, shells: a, *Acella haldemani*; b, *Pseudosuccinea columella*; c, *Radix auricularia*; d, *Bulimnea megasoma*; e, *Fossaria parva*; f, *F. modicella*; g, *F. rustica*; h, *F. obrussa*; i, *F. exigua*. Figs. a, c, and d are drawn to the same scale and Figs. b, e, f, g, h, and i are drawn to the same scale, twice that of a, c, and d.

Stagnicola caperata (Say, 1829)

Wrinkled pondsnail
Figs. 15e, 17

Shell ovately elongate, 17 mm high, turreted, solid, encircled by numerous, equidistant, heavily impressed, spiral lines, yellowish-tan to black; umbilicus narrow, deep; spire acutely conical, longer than aperture; nuclear whorl deep wine or brown; whorls 6.0-6.5, convex; sutures impressed; aperture ovate, reddish or purple within; inner lip reflected over umbilicus to form wide, smooth, triangular expansion; columella not twisted; callus thin (Binney 1865, Baker 1928a).

Comparative anatomical information can be found in Taylor *et al.* (1963).

This species occurs from southern Manitoba to southern Alberta, south to Nevada, North Dakota, Utah, Indiana, and the District of Columbia (Binney 1865, Baker 1911, Richards 1934, Taylor *et al.* 1963, Clarke 1981, Cvancara 1983).

Literature records for *S. caperata* are few. De Kay (1843) noted populations in the Mohawk River and Sandy Pond near Lake Ontario, Oswego County. Other sites listed in 19th and early 20th century records are Onondaga County (Beauchamp 1886b); Pittsford, Monroe County (Walton 1891); Litchfield, Herkimer County (Marshall 1894); Albany/Troy area, Albany and Rensselaer Counties (Marshall 1895); New York City (Prime 1880); and the Genesee River, Monroe County (Baker 1901). More recently, Buckley (1977) found two populations in ditches in Lewis County. No individuals of this species were located by Harman & Berg (1971) in central New York, by Strayer (1987) in the lower Hudson watershed, or during this survey. The American Museum of Natural History has a lot from Monroe County (AMNH 143455).

Stagnicola caperata is a common inhabitant of temporary ponds in wooded areas, ditches, sloughs, and shallow ponds (Baker 1911, Goodrich 1932, Dawley 1947, Taylor *et al.* 1963). Life history information seems to be unavailable. Temporary habitats were undersampled in New York State, so it is possible that this species is more common than presently known.

Acella haldemani (W.G. Binney 1867)

Spindle lymnaea
Figs. 16a, 17

Shell slender, 26 mm high, five times higher than wide, thin, fragile, yellowish white to brown; umbilicus a small chink; spire slender, acute, much longer than aperture; nuclear whorl elongate oval, resembling end of bullet; whorls 5.5, oblique, flat sided; sutures heavily impressed, bordered by narrow band; aperture elongate oval, narrow, 40% shell length, continuous, twisted to left; outer lip thin, acute; inner lip sometimes elevated; columella straight, not plaited (Baker 1928a, Clarke 1981).

This species occurs in the Great Lakes-St. Lawrence River drainage from southeastern Ontario, southern Quebec, and northern Vermont west to northern Minnesota and south to northern Illinois (Baker 1928a, Clarke 1981).

No colonies of *A. haldemani* were found during this survey or that of Strayer (1987). Harman & Berg (1971) located one colony in Oneida Lake, Oswego County.

Historically, this species (previously known as *Lymnaea gracilis* Jay) has been recorded from Lake Champlain, Clinton County (De Kay 1843); Schuyler Lake, Otsego County (Whittemore 1859; Lewis 1860, 1872); the Niagara River, Niagara County (Lewis 1874, Letson 1909); and Oneida Lake, Oswego and Onondaga Counties (Baker 1916a, b; 1918a, b; Pratt 1923; Harman & Berg 1971). The American Museum of Natural History has specimens from Strawberry Island, Niagara River, Niagara County (AMNH 70426 and part of 70464); Schuyler Lake, Otsego County (part of AMNH 70464, Crooke Collection, date: mid- to late 19th century); and Lake Champlain (part of AMNH 70464, Crooke Collection).

Acella haldemani has a scattered distribution in lakes, often found in only one location in the lake, and, therefore, it is easily overlooked (Dawley 1947). Substrata include submerged logs, silt, sand, and mud in water 0.3-2.0 m deep. The snails are usually attached to leaves and stems of pondweed (*Potamogeton interruptus* Kit., *P. natans* L.), bulrushes (*Scirpus smithii* Gray), flag (*Iris* spp.), floating cattails (*Typha* sp.), and water lilies (*Nymphaea odorata* Ait. and *Nuphar advena* (Ait.) Ait.). Young snails resemble leaves of submerged vegetation (Whittemore 1859; Baker 1918a, b; Morrison 1932; Herrington 1947; Harman & Berg 1971).

Individuals are usually found, spire down, firmly gripping reeds and rushes about 20 cm above the bottom (Goodrich 1932). They tend not to travel far from where they hatch, thus causing clumped populations. This species has an annual life cycle. One month after ice melts on the lake, eggs are laid in masses of 3-12 on rushes (*Juncus* sp.), dead and decaying pondweeds, burreed (*Sparganium* sp.), and small sticks and logs at the bottom. The young begin to hatch in about ten days. Juveniles grow rapidly, reaching full size by autumn. These individuals hibernate through winter, lay eggs in spring, and they die by midsummer (Morrison 1932).

Little is known about the chemical tolerances of this species. In Wisconsin, three populations studied by Morrison (1932) were in lakes with pH values of 7.4-7.7. Harman & Berg (1971) note that Oneida Lake, the one lake in which they located a population, had a pH of 8.1.

Pseudosuccinea columella (Say, 1817)
Mimic lymnaea
Figs. 16b, 17

Shell ovate, somewhat pointed, variable, 25 mm high, thin, fragile, translucent light green to yellow tan; umbilicus a narrow chink or closed; spire sharply conical, short; sculpture of impressed spiral lines; apex small, dark brown; whorls 4.0, well-rounded, rapidly enlarging; body whorl three times higher than spire; sutures lightly appressed; aperture ovate, dilated, expanded at lower part; outer lip thin, acute; inner lip closely appressed to body whorl, reflected over umbilicus; columella narrow (Baker 1928a).

In North America this species occurs from Nova Scotia south to Florida and west to Wisconsin, Arizona, central Texas and central and southern California (Baker 1928a, Richards 1934, Alexander 1947, Dawley 1947, Rehder 1949, Russell 1971, Taylor 1981, Jokinen 1983, Thompson 1984a). It extends into South America (Malek & Chrosciechowski 1964, Malek & Cogswell 1980, Gomez *et al.* 1986) and has been introduced into South Africa, South Mozambique, Rhodesia, Zambia, and Egypt (see references in Brown 1980). An introduction into New Zealand has resulted in

increased incidence of sheep liver fluke (Pullan *et al.* 1972; Harrison & Charleston 1976, 1977).

Pseudosuccinea columella is a common snail in New York State and was found at 71 sites in all major drainage basins: Delaware River watershed (457, 466, 468, 470, 474, 475); Hudson River watershed (276, 283, 285, 287, 290, 292, 293, 300, 301, 305, 317, 367, 383, 386, 455, 589, 599, 607, 611, 613); Ohio-Mississippi River watershed (420, 421); St. Lawrence River watershed (141D, 278, 298, 314, 316, 331, 332, 334, 338, 341, 349, 352, 353, 356, 358, 361, 366, 371, 377, 390, 396, 397, 409, 495, 496, 497); Susquehanna River watershed (540, 552, 553, 568, 569, 571, 572, 573, 574, 576, 577, 578, 580, 581, 582, 593); and Long Island coastal river system (322).

This species was first reported from the locks at Schenectady, Schenectady County, and from the western part of the State (De Kay 1843). Lewis (1856a, b; 1860; 1874) found *P. columella* populations in the lakes of Herkimer and Otsego Counties, but he believed the species was not abundant. Hubbard & Smith (1865) found it to be common on Staten Island, Richmond County, and Prime (1880) noted populations in New York City. Beauchamp (1886b) cited the Seneca River, Onondaga County, as having the species, and Walton (1891) noted sites in the Erie Canal, Monroe County. Marshall (1894) added records from Fort Hamilton, Long Island, Kings County; and Little Lakes, Herkimer County. Mearns (1898) found one specimen from Highland Falls, Orange County. Wheat (1907a) found *P. columella* living in all streams and ponds of Long Island, and Letson (1909) recorded populations in Park Lake, Buffalo, Erie County. The species has been found in Oneida Lake, Oswego and Onondaga Counties (Baker 1916a, b; 1918a, b; Pratt 1923; Harman & Berg 1971); Chautauqua Lake, Findley Lake, Bear Lake, Upper Cassadaga Lake, and Middle Cassadaga Lake, all in Chautauqua County (Maury 1898, Townes 1937); Otsego Lake, Otsego County (Harman 1971, MacNamara & Harman 1975); Cazenovia Lake, Madison County (Henderson 1907); Cayuga Lake, Seneca and Cayuga Counties; Conesus Lake, Livingston County; Cayuta Lake, Schuyler County (Maury 1916, Robertson & Blakeslee 1948); Lake Ontario (Burdick 1939); and the backwaters of Quaker Run in Allegany State Park, Cattaraugus County (Pinney & Coker 1934). The American Museum of Natural History has lots from Great Neck, Nassau County, Long Island (AMNH 143438); Princess Bay, Staten Island, Richmond County (AMNH 143444); Lake Allendale, Westchester County (AMNH 143478); and Center Moriches, Suffolk County, Long Island (AMNH 143488).

P. columella is primarily a still water species, frequently occurring in marshes, backwaters, lake littoral zones, ponds, and ditches. The snails glide on the underside of water lily leaves (*Nymphaea* sp.), on filamentous algae (e.g., *Oedogonium*), near cattails (*Typha* spp.) and other reeds, and on water hyacinths (*Eichhornia crassipes* (Mart.) Solms) (Baker 1918a, b; 1928a; Branson & Batch

1983; Jokinen 1983; Thompson 1984a). They are also common on decaying, submerged, terrestrial vegetation; rocks and occasionally sand, clay, and mud (Baker 1918a, Harman 1972, Jokinen 1983). These omnivorous snails prefer filamentous green algae over detritus as food (Kesler *et al.* 1986). Populations frequently exist in habitats with 3-10 other snail species. In habitats of even higher diversity the frequency of *P. columella* declines, indicating a possibly limited competitive ability (Jokinen 1987). However, colonization abilities appear to be good, and this species is found in high altitude habitats that have few other snail species (Jokinen 1991).

In temperate zones, *P. columella* can have two distinct breeding periods with complete replacement of the older generation by the younger one in spring. The early-hatching spring generation snails can become mature enough to lay eggs in late summer through autumn. The second generation snails continue to grow until December, hibernate inshore during winter, and begin to lay eggs when the water warms to 20°C in spring (Jokinen 1985). Experimental studies on a Florida population recorded life spans of 187-220 days and fecundity of 384 eggs/adult in each breeding season (McKillop & Harrison 1972). In other laboratory experiments, snails reached a mean age of 82-86 days before they oviposited, and both paired and isolated individuals produced viable eggs (Winsor & Winsor 1935). Some are as young as 40 days when they become reproductive (DeWitt & Sloan 1958). Snails living up to 139 days produce up to 725 eggs/snail with clutch sizes of 16-25 eggs (Baily 1931).

Mortality and shell size distribution in natural habitats can be greatly affected by predation by water bugs, *Belastoma* sp., (Hemiptera: Belostomatidae) (Kesler & Munns 1989).

Water chemistry parameters for 70 sites studied in New York State are: pH: 5.8-9.5 (7.0 ± 0.1), conductivity: 39-905 μmhos/cm (197 ± 19), Ca^{++}: 1-49 ppm (12 ± 2), and Na^+: 1-117 ppm (12 ± 2). Fifty-eight Connecticut sites also had wide ranges in chemical parameters: pH: 5.7-10.0, conductivity: 31-319 μmhos/cm, Ca^{++}: 1-23 ppm, and Na^+: 2-22 ppm (Jokinen 1983). This species is highly tolerant of low pH habitats with little calcium (Jokinen 1983, 1991).

Radix auricularia (Linnaeus, 1758)
Big-ear radix
Figs. 16c, 18

Shell inflated, 30 mm high, thin, fragile, tan to yellow; umbilicus a wide chink or covered; spire broadly concave; whorls 4.0-5.0; body whorl extremely inflated; sutures deeply impressed; aperture broadly lacrimate, earlike, sometimes same height as spire; outer lip thin, reflected in mature specimens; inner lip appressed to whorl above, reflected over plaited columella (Jacobson & Emerson 1961, Harman & Berg 1971).

This species is European and Asian (see Hubendick 1951) and has been introduced sporadically into North America. Populations have been found in the Canadian Interior Basin, in Bow River, Calgary, Alberta (Clarke 1973); Alaska; New Mexico; Colorado; Wyoming; California; Kentucky; and Vermont (Henderson 1918, Johnson 1945, Ingram & Kenyon 1947, Hubendick 1951, Beetle 1960, McCoy 1964, Branson & Batch 1969, Metcalf & Smart 1972). Eggs have been imported with plants from Belgium, and individuals probably arrived at the Great Lakes via the European-American lumber trade (Goodrich 1932, Wurtz 1956).

Only one population of *R. auricularia* was found during this survey: St. Lawrence River watershed, Niagara River (437). Jacobson & Emerson (1961) reported a population in Prospect Park, Brooklyn, Kings County, and at Cazenovia, Madison County. Harman & Berg (1971) found living animals at the Owasco Lake outlet, Onondaga County. The New York State Museum has recent specimens from Eldridge Swamp, Cambridge, Washington County (NYSM 2003, 2004).

There are only a few literature references to this species, and all are from Brooklyn. Call (1902) and Vanatta (1902) noted a population in a pond in Flatbush, Kings County. The snails might have been introduced on plants (Vanatta 1902). Another population was found in the lily ponds of Prospect Park, Brooklyn, Kings County (Wheat 1907a, b).

One population located by Harman & Berg (1971) lived in Owasco Lake outlet on boulders and vegetation both in and out of the direct current. A second population existed in a nearby anoxic strandpool of the outlet.

Water chemistry values for site 437 were: pH: 7.9, conductivity: 300 μmhos/cm, Ca^{++}: 27 ppm, and Na^+: 10 ppm.

Bulimnea megasoma (Say, 1824)
Mammoth lymnaea
Figs. 16d, 18

Shell ovate, inflated, large, 50 mm high, dark brown, green, or olive, often with longitudinal streaks of green, orange, or purple; umbilicus closed by callus; spire elongated to depressed, dome-shaped; apex with 1.3 nuclear whorls, yellow-tan to dark chestnut, outline of second whorl shouldered near suture of first whorl; whorls 5.0-5.5, rounded, somewhat flattened at previous suture; sutures impressed; aperture large, subovate, inflated, 0.5-0.7 shell length, acutely angled above, sharply rounded below, chestnut or dark purple within; peristome thin; columella plaited; callus thin, prominent, tightly appressed to body whorl (Baker 1928a).

This large lymnaeid is distributed throughout the St. Lawrence River drainage from northern Vermont (Lake Champlain and its tributaries) and Quebec, west to Manitoba and Minnesota, and south to upper tributaries of the Mississippi River watershed in Ohio, Wisconsin, Minnesota and Iowa (Baker 1928a, Goodrich 1932, Dawley 1947, Clarke 1973).

No populations of *B. megasoma* were found during this survey, and none were reported by Harman & Berg (1971) or Strayer (1987).

The New York and Vermont literature on this species is limited to a few 19th century reports from Lake Champlain (De Kay 1843, Lewis 1874, Marshall 1894). The American Museum of Natural History has specimens from Canton, St. Lawrence County (AMNH 1815, dated 1882); Burlington, Vermont (AMNH 130173, dated 1867); and Lake Champlain (AMNH 40564). Never abundant, this species might be extinct in New York.

Habitats of this species include ponds, large and small lakes, and shallow, quiet embayments of rivers where vegetation is sparse to thick. Substrata are of all kinds (Goodrich 1932, Dawley 1947, Clarke 1973, Jokinen, unpublished data). The life span has been estimated to be 14 months (Gilbertson *et al.* 1978), but it might be longer (Jokinen, unpublished data).

Bulimnea megasoma appears to have a tolerance to wide ranges of water chemistry parameters. In a series of lakes from northwestern Minnesota, pH was 5.5-9.3, and calcium concentration (except for a bog at pH 5.5) was 24-179 ppm (Gilbertson *et al.* 1978).

Fossaria parva (I. Lea, 1841)
Pygmy fossaria
Figs. 16e, 18

Shell small, 10 mm high, solid, turreted, translucent, light tan or yellow-white; umbilicus open; spire elevated, acute, generally longer than aperture; nucleus rounded, first whorl large; 5.0-5.5 whorls, convex, regularly increasing in size; sutures deeply impressed; aperture roundly and regularly elliptical, sometimes continuous; outer lip thin, with varix, inner lip broadly reflected over umbilicus; callus well-marked, thick (Baker 1928a, Goodrich 1932).

The range of this species includes southern New England west to California (north of 36°N), southeast to Arizona and New Mexico (Baker 1911, Johnson 1915, Clarke 1973, Taylor 1981, Jokinen 1983).

No New York populations were found during this survey.

Strayer (1987) noted the existence of scattered museum specimens of *F. parva* from New York, but he did not locate populations in the Hudson River watershed.

There is little information on *F. parva* in New York.

Buckley (1977) described several populations from the Black River system in and west of the Adirondack Mountains. There are no other references to this species in New York State, although its existence in Connecticut (Jokinen 1983) and states west of New York would indicate it is probably present but overlooked due to its habitat.

Habitats of *F. parva* include wet, marshy places. The snails can be amphibious, depending upon humidity and temperature (Hoff 1936, 1937). They are often out of water, on sticks, stones, or muddy flats of temporary ponds and intermittent streams (Jokinen 1983). In northern parts of its range, this species inhabits permanent bodies of water (Clarke 1973). It has an annual life cycle (Hoff 1936, 1937).

Fossaria parva in three Connecticut sites lived in acidic, low calcium habitats: pH: 4.9-6.8, conductivity 49-85 μmhos/cm, Ca^{++}: 2-5 ppm, Na^+: 2-3 ppm (Jokinen 1983).

Fossaria modicella (Say, 1825)
Rock fossaria
Figs. 16f, 18

Shell elongate-oval or fusiform, 15 mm high, light yellowish-tan; umbilicus small, narrow, distinct; apex with 1.3 nuclear whorls, first small, second large; whorls 5.0-5.5; body whorl large, flatly rounded; sutures well-impressed; aperture ovate or elongate ovate, narrowed above, 45-55% of shell height; outer lip thin; inner lip narrow, reflexed over umbilical region, rolled over, appressed at contact point with parietal wall (Baker 1928a, Clarke 1981, Jokinen 1983).

This species is widespread in North America south of the tree line in Canada and Alaska, south to southern California, Arizona, Texas, Alabama, and northern Florida (Baker 1928a, Clarke 1981, Thompson 1984a).

Except for the Adirondack Mountain region, *Fossaria modicella* is common in New York (61 sites): Delaware River watershed (458, 471); Hudson River watershed (288, 290, 367, 387, 453, 459, 460, 588); Ohio-Mississippi River watershed (426, 427A, 428, 429, 431); St. Lawrence River watershed (334, 335, 343, 344, 371, 373, 375, 401, 412, 436, 439, 442, 444, 445A, 495, 496, 497, 498, 500, 501, 503, 506, 511, 513, 516, 517, 520, 525); Susquehanna River watershed (389, 391, 400, 539, 546, 551, 554, 558, 572, 573, 575, 577, 582, 585, 586, 592, 594); and Housatonic River watershed (294).

This species was first reported (as *F. humilis* (Say)) in New York State from near the Susquehanna River at Owego, Tioga County (De Kay 1843). Additional sites included stagnant pools and the margins of streams and lakes in Herkimer County (Lewis 1860, 1872); Staten Island, Richmond County (Hubbard & Smith 1865); Onondaga County (Beauchamp 1886b); Cazenovia Lake, Madison County (Henderson 1907); Dweyers Pond, Ithaca, Tompkins County (Maury 1916); Oneida Lake, Oswego County; Tuttle Creek, a tributary of Chittenango Creek, Madison County (Baker 1918a, b); Chautauqua Lake, Chautauqua County (Baker 1928a); Stilsons Pond near Randolph, Cattaraugus County (Pinney & Coker 1934); Clymer Pond in the Allegheny River watershed, Chautauqua County (Townes 1936); Little Sodus Bay in Lake Ontario, Cayuga County; Red Creek Pond, Wayne County (Burdick 1939); and in Adirondack State Park, Warren County (Jacobson 1945). More recently, *F. modicella* has been found in Otsego Lake and New Pond, Otsego County (Harman 1971, MacNamara & Harman 1975); Canadarago Lake and Richfield Springs, Otsego County (Harman 1973).

The New York sites found during this survey were 31 river and stream sites, seven lake sites, 17 ponds, two ditches, and four canals. Habitats are often temporary ponds

(Goodrich 1932, Jokinen 1983). Baker (1918a) noted that, in Oneida Lake, the snails were common among floating filamentous algae (*Oedogonium* sp.), and on clay and mud substrata in water less than 15 cm deep. In a creek near Oneida Lake, they were in shallow water among *Oedogonium* sp. and *Cladophora* sp. (Baker 1918a). *F. modicella* also tends to live amphibiously in habitats such as vertical, sandstone cliffs and drying, flat, muddy beaches (van Cleave 1933, Dawley 1947). Individuals can produce two broods a year (van Cleave 1935).

Chemical parameters for 60 sites were: pH: 6.1-9.7 (7.4 ± 0.1), conductivity: 48-1240 μmhos/cm (353 ± 32), Ca^{++}: 2-70 ppm (24 ± 2), and Na^+: 1-144 ppm (22 ± 4). Connecticut data for 24 sites were: pH: 5.7-8.9, conductivity: 53-286 μmhos/cm, Ca^{++}: 2-35 ppm, and Na^+: 3-29 ppm (Jokinen 1983). This species is able to exist over a wide range of chemical values, including low calcium and high sodium.

Fossaria rustica (I. Lea, 1841)
Country fossaria
Figs. 16g, 18

Shell elongate, subfusiform, small, 11 mm high, light yellow to tan; umbilicus a narrow chink; spire long, acute, slightly longer than aperture; whorls 5.0-5.5, convex, slowly increasing in diameter; body whorl large; sutures impressed; aperture narrowly elliptical; outer lip thin, sometimes with a varix; inner lip narrow, reflected; lower part turned up; upper part at its junction with parietal wall impressed and flattened, forming a slight plait (Baker 1911).

This species was considered by Baker (1911, 1928a) to be a subspecies of *F. humilis* and later as a subspecies of *F. modicella*. However, the chromosome number differs from that of other *Fossaria* spp. (Burch 1960). It is being treated here as a species with the warning that the taxonomy of *Fossaria* needs revision (Burch 1982).

F. rustica occurs from Connecticut northwest to the Northwest Territories and south to Utah, Nebraska, and New Mexico (Baker 1928a, Clarke 1973).

Eleven sites in New York had populations of *F. rustica*: Delaware River watershed (463); Hudson River watershed (277, 290, 317); St. Lawrence River watershed (141A, 280, 309, 560, 563, 565); and the Susquehanna River watershed (583).

There appear to be no historical notes on this species for New York.

Three of the populations found during this survey were in rivers and streams, three in lakes, three in ponds, one in a ditch, and one in a canal. Habitats can include damp mud flats and bodies of water with fluctuations in water level (Baker 1911, Jokinen 1983).

Chemical parameters for the eleven sites were: pH: 6.4-8.3 (7.1 ± 0.2), conductivity: 75-863 μmhos/cm (265 ± 65), Ca^{++}: 5-35 ppm (13 ± 3), and Na^+: 1-43 ppm (12 ± 4). Connecticut data are limited and come from a mill pond that had great fluctuations in water levels. The pond had the following chemical values indicative of soft water: pH: 6.3, conductivity: 98 μmhos/cm, Ca^{++}: 3 ppm, and Na^+: 8 ppm (Jokinen 1983).

Fossaria obrussa (Say, 1825)
Golden fossaria
Fig. 16h, 18

Shell subconical, 13 mm high, pointed, oblong, thin, frequently inflated, light yellowish tan to black; umbilicus distinctly open to scarcely observable; spire acute, sharply conical; shell with sculpture of fine spiral lines, sometimes malleated; apex with 1.3 nuclear whorls; whorls 5-6, rounded, shouldered near suture; body whorl large, 0.5 times length of shell, usually compressed, sometimes obese; sutures deeply indented; aperture elongate-oval; outer lip thin, acute; inner lip reflected over umbilical chink to form a thin, narrow expansion appressed to umbilical region, giving axis a slight twist; callus thin (Baker 1928a).

This species occurs from the Atlantic to the Pacific Ocean, and from Canada south to Arizona and northern Mexico. It is present but rare in Upper Michigan (Baker 1928a, Richards 1934, Goodrich & van der Schalie 1939).

Twenty-one sites studied during this survey had populations of *F. obrussa*: Hudson River watershed (302, 368, 452, 589); Mississippi-Ohio River watershed (420, 422, 424); St. Lawrence River watershed (141B, 279, 308, 311, 332, 337, 345, 350, 371, 396, 405, 411, 440); and the Susquehanna River watershed (399).

Fossaria obrussa (called *Lymnaea decidiosa* Beck in some of the early literature) has been known to occur in New York State since De Kay (1843) reported it "from various parts of the state, in rivulets and small lakes." It also was reported from Herkimer and Otsego Counties (Lewis 1856b, 1860, 1872, 1874); Staten Island, Richmond County (Hubbard & Smith 1865); New York City (Prime 1880); Onondaga County (Beauchamp 1886b); Monroe County (Walton 1891); the Albany/Troy area, Albany and Rensselaer Counties, and Litchfield, Herkimer County (Marshall 1894, 1895); Erie Canal "Wide-waters" at Rochester, and from Irondequoit Bay, Lake Ontario, Monroe County (Baker 1900b); Cazenovia Lake, Madison County (Henderson 1907); Huntington, Suffolk County; Flushing, Queens County, Long Island (Wheat 1907a); Rose Hill, Squaw Island, Erie Canal, Lime Lake in Cattaraugus County, Muddy Creek in Buffalo, Erie County (Letson 1909); Wyoming County (Baker 1913); Sodus Bay in Lake Ontario, Wayne County (Burdick 1939); and in Adirondack State Park, Warren County (Jacobson 1945).

Harman & Berg (1971) followed the taxonomy of Hubendick (1951) and lumped all the *Fossaria* group into one species, *Lymnaea humilis* (Say, 1822). Burch (1982) distinguished the *Fossaria* as consisting of more than one species, and places *F. exigua, F. modicella, F. obrussa, F. peninsulae,* and *F. rustica* in a *F. obrussa* group.

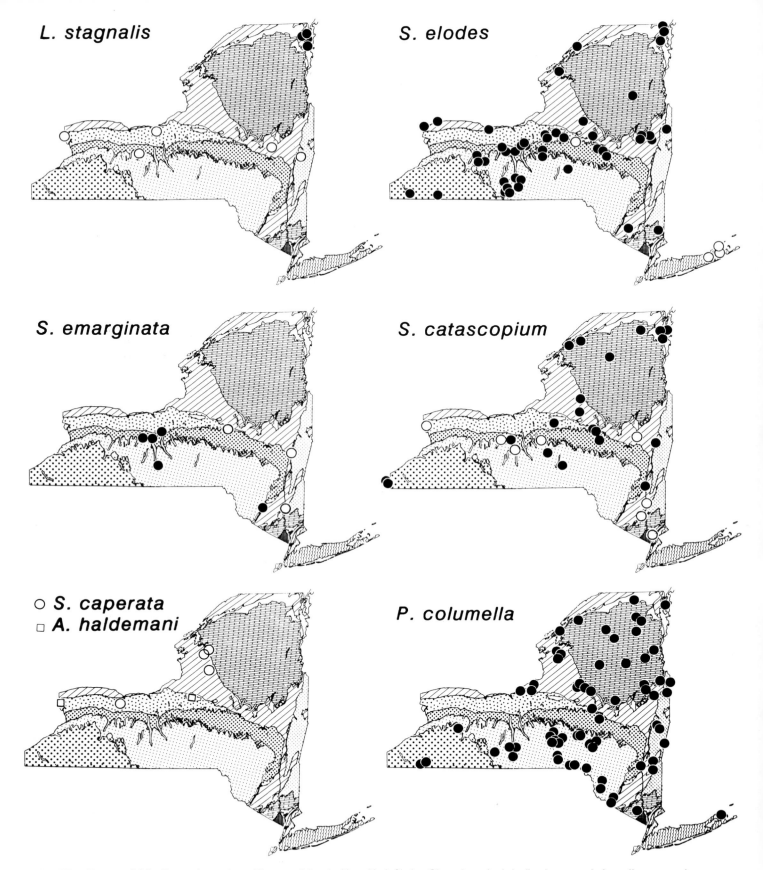

Fig. 17. Known distributions of species of Lymnaeidae in New York State. Closed symbols indicate records from the present survey, and open symbols indicate records from museum specimens.

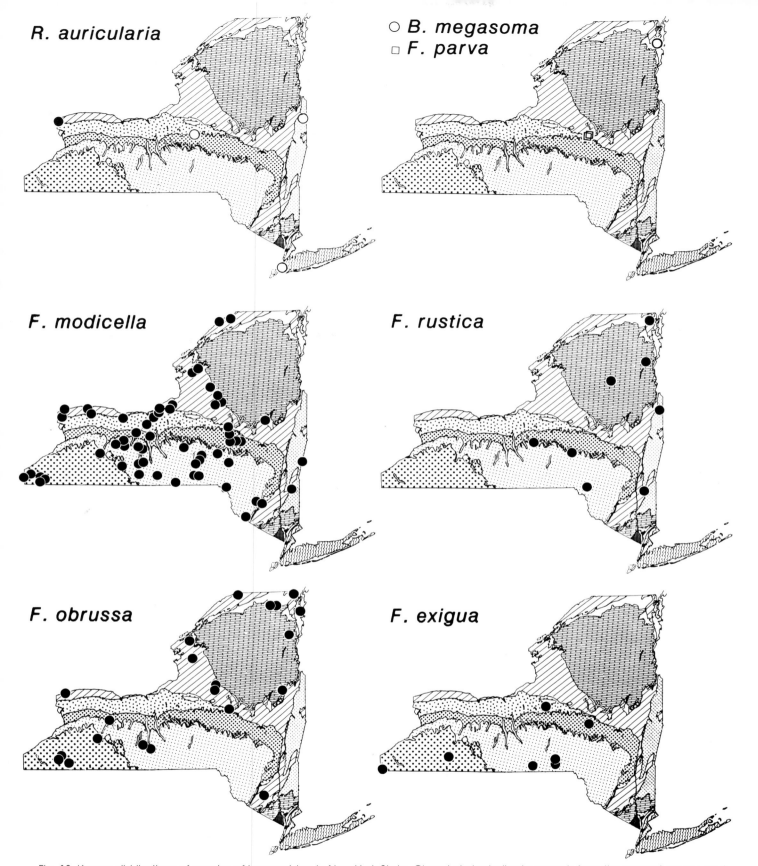

Fig. 18. Known distributions of species of Lymnaeidae in New York State. Closed circles indicate records from the present survey, and open circles indicate records from museum specimens.

During the present survey, *F. obrussa* was found in eight river and stream sites, four lakes, eight ponds, and one canal. In other areas of the country, this species lives in lakes; creeks; ponds; sloughs; bays; muddy, marshy areas along river banks; and intermittent small and large streams (Baker 1928a, Goodrich & van der Schalie 1939, Dawley 1947, Cvancara 1983). The snails are difficult to see in the field because of mud covering their shells (Goodrich 1932).

Chemical value for 20 sites were: pH: 6.5-7.8 (7.3 ± 0.1), conductivity: 64-1755 µmhos/cm (397 ± 84), Ca^{++}: 1-56 ppm (24 ± 4), and Na^+: 1-193 (26 ± 10).

Fossaria exigua (I. Lea, 1841)
Graceful fossaria
Figs. 16i, 18

Shell turreted, 9 mm high, subfusiform, generally narrow, brown; umbilicus small, narrow, or covered by inner lip; spire wide, elevated, turreted, slowly increasing in diameter, generally longer than aperture; whorls 5.0, well-rounded, slowly increasing in diameter; body whorl flattened, subcylindrical, 2/3 length of shell; sutures deeply impressed; aperture ovate, slightly flared at base; outer lip thin; inner lip slightly reflected with lower part nearly straight (Baker 1928a; Clarke 1973, 1981).

This species occurs from Maine west to Iowa and Minnesota, north to Hudson Bay, and south to Alabama (Baker 1928a, Nylander 1943, Clarke 1973).

Seven sites in New York yielded specimens of *F. exigua* during this survey: Mississippi-Ohio River watershed (415, 432); St. Lawrence River watershed (449); and Susquehanna River watershed (388, 552, 553, 591).

The only reference to *F. exigua* in New York is from the Black River drainage in Lewis and Oneida Counties (Buckley 1977).

New York habitats sampled during this survey included four river and stream sites, one lake, and one pond. This species is rare in New York State and Connecticut. In Connecticut, it was found in a cool inlet side of a small pond formed by road fill. Egg masses and immatures appeared in early June (Jokinen 1983). In Canada, *F. exigua* lives in lakes, subarctic muskeg, and slowly flowing sections of rivers (Clarke 1973). It can also inhabit bayous, small ponds, ditches and mud flats (Baker 1928a).

Chemical parameters for five of the New York sites are: pH: 6.8-7.7 (7.2 ± 0.2), conductivity: 191-284 µmhos/cm (237 ± 15); Ca^{++}: 4-25 ppm (12 ± 5), and Na^+: 1-12 ppm (7 ± 2). The single Connecticut population, living in a stream inlet near a pond, existed in water with chemistry parameters of pH: 6.4, Ca^{++}: 12 ppm, and Na^+: 10 ppm (Jokinen 1983).

Family Physidae

Shell sinistral, oval, elongate or globular, imperforate, thin to thick; spire short to elongate; sculpture smooth or with well-developed spiral lines; animal sinistral, with excretory and genital orifices on left; jaw single, arched; radula with teeth in oblique rows; lateral teeth comblike (Fig. 5c); form of penial complex diagnostic for genera and subgenera (De Kay 1843; Baker 1928a; Clampitt 1970; Te 1975).

Burch (1989) places most of the *Physa* species in the genus *Physella*.

Key to the Physidae

Physids are difficult to identify because of highly variable shell structure and general similarity among species. A major advance in identifying these species involves inspection of the shape of the penial apparatus, which is internal in a non-everted state.

To remove the male reproductive system in physids, first remove the snail from its shell (do not destroy the shell) and lay it on its right side in a small dish (Fig. 19a). The body should be covered with preservative. Carefully cut or rip the epidermis middorsally from the head to the beginning of the mantle. Pull back the skin. The male reproductive tract will be visible just behind the left tentacle (see Fig. 19b). Gently uncoil the vas deferens and pull the penial apparatus straight. It will be secured by tiny muscles that might have to be cut if they have not pulled apart. Figs. 19c and d illustrate the anatomy. If it appears that the normally obvious reproductive system is dwarfed or obliterated, the snail is probably infected with parasitic trematode larvae, which can cause castration. To measure the various regions of the penial apparatus accurately, the system will have to be removed from the snail at the male reproductive pore, placed on a slide, and examined with a microscope.

1a. Shell aperture approximately same length as spire.....2

1b. Shell aperture longer than spire....................................3

2a. Aperture base somewhat truncated; preputial gland present...*Physa vernalis*

2b. Aperture base rounded; preputial gland absent ....
....*Aplexa elongata*

3a. Penial sheath in two sections; shell sutures deep.........4

3b. Penial sheath in one section; shell sutures shallow.......5

4a. Outer lip of shell bordered by strong white varix, occasionally with a purple line on inner side; shell usually pale tan in color...*Physa integra*

4b. Outer lip of shell bordered by purple varix; shell usually dark in color ....*Physa heterostropha*

5a. Spire very short; outer whorl shouldered in adults ....
....*Physa ancillaria*

5b. Spire moderate in length; outer whorl not shouldered
....*Physa gyrina*

Aplexa elongata (Say, 1821)
Lance aplexa
Figs. 20a, 21

*Shell elongate, thin, transparent, polished, oily in appearance, light brown, up to 20 mm high; spire long, pointed, acute, 0.5 times shell length; apex large, flatly rounded, partly embraced by second whorl below which nucleus is sunken; whorls 6.0, rounded; body whorl long, narrow, compressed; sutures well-impressed, bordered below by narrow white zone; aperture 0.5 times shell length, narrowly elongate; outer lip thin; columella oblique, narrow, slightly twisted; callus a thin wash on pari-*etal wall. Mantle without digitations, not reflected over shell; penial gland absent (Baker 1928a, Te 1975).*

This species closely resembles the European *A. hypnorum* (L.), with which it has been confused in the past.

A. elongata occurs from the District of Columbia north to James Bay and arctic Alaska and south to Idaho (Goodrich & van der Schalie 1939; Dawley 1947; Clarke 1973, 1981; Cvancara 1983; Burch 1989).

Only two populations of *A. elongata* were found during this survey. They were in Dead Creek, Plattsburgh, St. Lawrence River drainage (259B) and an unnamed stream and vernal pond in Wallkill Township, Hudson River watershed (451). Strayer (1987) did not locate populations in the lower Hudson River watershed but notes that numerous museum records indicate its presence. This species' habitats were undersampled during this study.

There are numerous literature references to this species in New York. Early accounts are from Otsego and Herkimer Counties (Lewis 1856b, 1860, 1872); Onondaga County (Beauchamp 1886b); Pittsford, Monroe County (Walton 1891, Marshall 1894); Albany/Troy area, Albany and Rensselaer Counties (Marshall 1895); a marsh at the foot of Owasco Lake, Cayuga County (Baker 1899); Cazenovia Lake, Madison County (Henderson 1907); Huntington, Suffolk County, Long Island (Wheat 1907a); and Niagara and Erie Counties (Letson 1909). More recent accounts are from pools near Quaker Run, Allegany State Park, Cattaraugus County (Pinney & Coker 1934); Adirondack State Park, Warren County (Jacobson 1945); the Finger Lakes region of Oswego watershed (Harman & Berg 1971); Otsego County (MacNamara & Harman 1975); and Jefferson County (Buckley 1977). Specimen lots at the Museum of Comparative Zoology are from Baldswinsville, Onondaga County; Buffalo, Erie County; Mohawk and Frankfort, Herkimer County; and Cazenovia, Madison County. Specimens deposited in the American Museum of Natural History are from Wyoming County and Staten Island, Richmond County.

Aplexa elongata is an inhabitant of temporary pools, ditches, swampy meadows, bayous, marsh pools, swales, intermittent streams, and, less frequently, permanent ponds and lake shallows (Baker 1928a; Goodrich 1932; Dawley 1947; Harman & Berg 1971; Clarke 1973, 1981; Cvancara 1983). Sediments in these habitats range from mud to sand (Cvancara 1983), usually with decaying terrestrial plant litter (Archer 1939, Harman 1972). The snail is a detritivore (Brown 1982).

This species usually occurs in hard water. In North Dakota, Cvancara (1983) reported a habitat pH range of 7.8-8.9 and conductivity of 293-3900 µmhos/cm. Surveys in Southern Ontario showed the species reached its maximum shell size in hard water (McKillop & Harrison 1972). At 17 sites in central New York, pH values were 6.8-8.1 (Harman & Berg 1971). In this study, the two habitats of *A. elongata* had pH: 6.8, 8.1; conductivity: 212, 371 µmhos/cm; Ca^{++}: 13, 44 ppm; and Na^+: 10, 18 ppm.

51

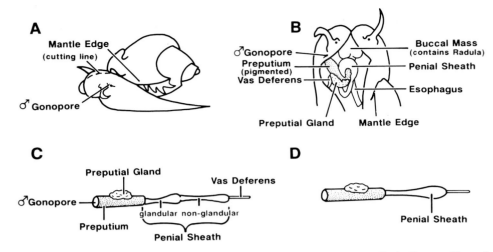

Fig. 19. Family Physidae, internal anatomy: a, body with shell removed, illustrating position of male gonopore; b, dissected head end in dorsal view, illustrating position of penial complex, dorsal view; c, penial complex with two-part sheath; d, penial complex with simple sheath (from Jokinen 1983).

Physa vernalis Taylor & Jokinen, 1984

Springtime physa
Figs. 20b, 21

Shell ovoid-fusiform, 11 mm high, thin, pale brown, silky to shiny; apex blunt; whorls 5.0-6.0, weakly convex; suture shallow, broadly attached; aperture elongate-oval, rounded anteriorly, acute posteriorly, widest at mid length; outer lip thin, sharp; columellar lip a rounded ridge forming a low plait as it enters whorl cavity; callus thin, white, closely appressed to parietal wall; male reproductive system with penial sac swollen proximally; mantle margin barely expanded over shell margin, with two groups of digitate projections (Taylor & Jokinen 1984).

The confirmed distribution includes Massachusetts, Connecticut, Rhode Island, New York, and probably Ohio, Michigan, and Canada (Taylor & Jokinen 1984). The shells of this species strongly resemble young of *Aplexa elongata*, and further examination of museum specimens might yield misidentified specimens of *P. vernalis*.

Two live populations of this species were found in New York. These were at Lake Conesus inlet, St. Lawrence River watershed (507) and a marshy tributary of Otselic Creek, Susquehanna River watershed (555). Strayer (1987) found one specimen in the Hudson River watershed, Dutchess County. One lot in the Museum of Comparative Zoology (MCZ 193794), originally identified as *Aplexa hypnorum*, is from Madison, Madison County.

Physa vernalis inhabits streams, ditches, temporary and permanent ponds, and shallows of lakes (Taylor & Jokinen 1984; this study). Although the snails graze diatoms in early spring and filamentous green algae in late spring and summer, their primary food source is detritus (Kesler *et al.*

1986). Field population numbers and differential survival of larger individuals are controlled in part by predation (Kesler & Munns 1989).

Little is known of the chemical parameters under which this species exists. In the region of eastern Connecticut where the first populations were described, the waters are soft. At twelve sites described in Taylor & Jokinen (1984), pH values were 5.9-7.1, conductivity: 31-283 μmhos/cm, Ca^{++}: 2-12 ppm, and Na^+: 3-30 ppm. A pond in Rhode Island had pH < 5.8 (Kesler *et al.* 1986). The two sites in New York had water chemistry values of pH: 6.5, 7.8; conductivity: 31, 283 μmhos/cm, Ca^{++}: 4, 28 ppm, and Na^+: 20, 24 ppm. It appears that *P. vernalis* can live in soft to hard waters.

Physa heterostropha (Say, 1817)

Pewter physa
Figs. 20c, 21

Shell cylindrical, sometimes inflated, 16 mm high, thin, translucent, surface smooth and shining, yellow-tan to chestnut; spire moderately long, acute, pointed; nucleus small, yellowish to slightly reddish, well-exerted above second whorl; whorls 5.0-6.0; body whorl large, compressed or flatly rounded; sutures impressed; aperture 2/3-4/5 shell length, tan with red-bordered varix; outer lip thin, flattened, slightly shouldered above, broadly rounded below; columella slightly oblique, thickened, not twisted; callus a thin wash on parietal wall (Baker 1928a); *male penial sheath of one section, approximately equal in length to preputium* (Fig. 20c) (Te 1975, Jokinen 1983).

This species occurs from the Atlantic provinces of Canada south to Ohio, Kentucky, Tennessee, Florida, and the

Bahama Islands (Clarke 1981; Jokinen 1983; Blair & Sickel 1986; Branson 1987; Burch 1989). The southern subspecies, *P. heterostropha pomilia* (Conrad), occurs throughout Florida.

P. heterostropha is common throughout New York, and it was found in the Delaware River watershed (455, 456, 468, 470); Hudson River watershed (96E, 96G, 96H, 265, 266, 268, 269, 274, 286, 287, 288, 289, 292, 293, 299, 320, 368, 379, 451, 452, 588, 589, 604, 613, 616); Ohio-Mississippi River watershed (420, 427A); St. Lawrence River watershed (262, 307, 312, 314, 315, 332, 334, 335, 336, 338, 339, 341, 342, 343, 344, 377, 390, 392, 393, 394, 395, 396, 397, 398, 401, 403, 405, 407, 408, 410, 433, 439, 440, 441, 445A, 445B, 445C, 448A, 448B, 493, 495, 496, 497, 507, 508, 509, 513, 519, 520, 521, 523, 525, 528, 533, 535, 559, 560, 561, 562, 565, 566); Susquehanna River watershed (388, 391, 399, 477, 537, 538, 540, 542, 544, 545, 547, 549, 550, 551, 553, 554, 558, 567, 570, 573, 577, 580, 593); Housatonic River watershed (294); Hackensack River watershed (605, 606); and Atlantic coastal streams and ponds (253, 322). Harman & Berg

(1971) found *P. heterostropha* to be common in central New York, and Strayer (1987) found it to be the most abundant physid in the lower Hudson River watershed.

There is extensive literature on this species in New York State. De Kay (1843) listed the species as "very common...in almost every pond and running stream." He specifically recorded it from Red Creek, Wayne County (as *P. cylindrica*); New York island (as *P. plicata De Kag*); and West Point, Orange County (as *P. aurea* Lea). Other 19th century authors recorded the species from Herkimer and Otsego Counties (Lewis 1856b, 1860, 1872); Staten Island, Richmond County (Hubbard & Smith 1865, Marshall 1894); Riverdale, Bronx County (Prime 1880); Onondaga County (Beauchamp 1886b); the Erie Canal (Baily 1891); Rochester, Monroe County (Walton 1891); Glen Cove, Nassau County, Long Island; Litchfield, Herkimer County; Pittsford, Monroe County (Marshall 1894); Albany/Troy area, Albany and Rensselaer Counties (Marshall 1895); Hudson River tide-creeks and marshes (Mearns 1898); Chautauqua Lake, Chautauqua County (Maury 1898); Canandaigua Lake, Ontario and Yates Counties (Mitchell 1899); Owasco River, Cayuga County (Baker 1899); and the Erie Canal "Widewaters" in Rochester, the Genesee River, and Irondequoit Bay in Lake Ontario, all in Monroe County (Baker 1900b, 1901).

Early 20th century reports record *P. heterostropha* from Cazenovia Lake, Madison County (Henderson 1907); Long Island (Wheat 1907a); Erie and Niagara Counties (Letson 1909); and the Oneida Lake region (Baker 1918a). Later reports are from Allegany State Park, Cattaraugus County (Pinney & Coker 1934); Bronx River at the south end of Bronx Park, Bronx County; stream in Brooklyn Botanic Gardens, Kings County; Forest Park Pond, Queens County (Freas 1950a); Upper Ferdun Pond, Rockland County (Bretet & Carswell 1952); Oakland Lake, Queens County, Long Island (Jacobson 1965); Crystal Brook, Mount Sinai, Suffolk County, Long Island (Jacobson 1969); Green Lake, Onondaga County (Harman 1970); Cayuga Lake, Seneca and Cayuga Counties; Oneida Lake, Oswego and Madison Counties; Green and Round Lakes, Onondaga County; Panther Lake, Oswego County; DeRuyter Lake, Madison County (Harman & Berg 1971); and Otsego Lake, Moe Pond, and New Pond, Otsego County (MacNamara & Harman 1975).

Physa heterostropha is abundant and ubiquitous in its habitats. The 121 sites found during this survey include 49 rivers and streams, 30 lakes, 24 permanent ponds, two temporary ponds, seven ditches, three marshes, and six canals. The breadth of potential habitats is similar in Connecticut (Jokinen 1983), Kentucky (Blair & Sickel 1986, Branson *et al.* 1987), and eastern Canada (Clarke 1981). The snails are most often found on silt and detrital substrata (Harman 1972). The species has a good dispersal rate, good colonization ability, and broad habitat tolerance (Jokinen 1987). However, it cannot colonize high altitude habitats (Jokinen 1991).

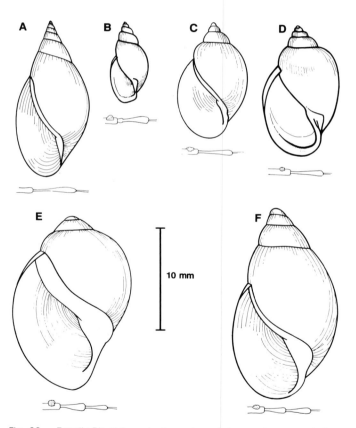

Fig. 20. Family Physidae, shells and penial complexes: a, *Aplexa elongata*, with penial complex lacking preputial gland; b, *Physa vernalis*, with penial sheath simple; c, *P. heterostropha*, with penial sheath simple; d, *P. integra*, with penial sheath simple; e, *P. ancillaria*, with penial sheath in two parts; f, *P. gyrina*, with penial sheath in two parts. All shell illustrations are drawn to the same scale.

This species also demonstrates a wide range of chemical tolerance. Water chemistry data from 111 sites found during this study are: pH: 6.0-8.8 (7.3 ± 0.1), conductivity: 39-2320 μmhos/cm (382 ± 28), Ca^{++}: 1-89 ppm (23 ± 2), and Na^+: 1-291 ppm (29 ± 4). Chemical data from Connecticut sites were: pH: 6-10, conductivity: 24-387 μmhos/cm, Ca^{++}: 1-35, and Na^+: 1-22 ppm. At Harman & Berg's (1971) 79 central New York sites, pH values were 6.8-8.5 (mean = 7.7). Baily (1929) noted this species to exist at 50% salinity in the Gunpowder Estuary of Chesapeake Bay. The water chemistry values indicate wide tolerance to low calcium and high sodium concentrations.

Physa integra Haldeman, 1841

Ashy physa
Figs. 20d, 21

Shell elongate-ovate, 17 mm high, thick, solid, white to yellow to tan, usually dull; spire wide; nucleus small, rounded, light brown with one whorl; whorls 5.0, rounded; body whorl large, a little shouldered; sutures deeply impressed; aperture ear-shaped, angled above, well-rounded below, 60-70% of shell length; outer lip thickened, with heavy, white varix; varix often edged by brown streak; up to 7 white streaks representing former lip varices visible through shell; columella oblique, thick, inner lip folding over into umbilical region to form wide, flat expansion continuous with outer lip, sometimes with plait-like ridge; callus on parietal wall thin to thick; penial sheath simple, approximately same length as preputium (Baker1928a, Te 1975).

The anatomy of *P. integra* is discussed in Baker (1928a) and Clampitt (1970).

This species occurs from Quebec west to Manitoba, and south to the Dakotas, Iowa, Tennessee, Kentucky, and West Virginia (Goodrich 1932, Goodrich & van der Schalie 1939, Dawley 1947, Clarke 1981, Branson 1987, Blair and Sickle 1986, Burch 1989). It is absent from southern New England (Jokinen 1983).

Physa integra was found in all major New York watersheds except the Delaware River watershed. During this study, populations were found in the Hudson River watershed (453, 596, 600, 608, 609, 614); Ohio-Mississippi River watershed (416, 417, 423, 424, 426, 427B, 428, 429, 430A, 431); St. Lawrence River watershed (345, 390, 406, 409, 412, 436, 437, 438, 439, 442, 445A, 445B, 449, 450, 498, 499, 501, 502B, 503, 504, 505, 506, 511, 512, 515, 516, 517, 518A, 518B, 521, 522, 524B, 525, 526, 529, 530, 531, 563, 564); and Susquehanna River watershed (389, 400, 552, 578, 581, 586, 591, 592, 595). The majority of sites were in central and western New York. These observations agree with those of Harman & Berg (1971), who found the species to be the most common physid in central New York (Oswego-St. Lawrence River and Susquehanna River watersheds), and with those of Strayer (1987), who found no living populations in the lower Hudson River watershed.

Physa integra was first reported from New York, Herkimer, and Otsego Counties by De Kay (1843), who identified it tentatively. Later, Marshall (1894) recorded locations in Little Lakes, Herkimer County, and the Erie Canal. Additional sites were the Genesee River (Baker 1901); Cazenovia Lake, Madison County (Henderson 1907); Erie and Niagara Counties (Letson 1909); Oneida Lake, Oswego and Onondaga Counties (Baker 1916a, b; 1918a); Allegheny River, Riverside Junction, Allegany State Park, Cattaraugus County (Pinney & Coker 1934); Hudson River from Hudson, Columbia County, to Chelsea, Dutchess County (Townes 1936); Lake Ontario (Burdick 1939); and Conesus Lake, Livingston County (Wade & Vasey 1976).

This species lives in a variety of habitats, with streams and rivers being most common (Goodrich 1932, Dawley 1947, Cvancara 1983) except in southeastern Canada, where it is most common in lakes in either exposed or protected situations (Clarke 1981). During this survey, populations were found to occupy 30 river and stream sites, 16 lake sites, 11 permanent ponds, one temporary pond, five ditches, and three canals.

Substrata range from clay and mud to boulders (Baker 1928a, Clampitt 1970, Harman & Berg 1971, Clarke 1981, Cvancara 1983). Snails are also common on and in floating masses of algae and higher aquatic plants, such as *Ceratophyllum demersum* L., *Myriophyllum spicatum exalbescens* (Fern.) Jeps., *Ranunculus longirostris* Godr., and *Potamogeton* spp. (Clampitt 1970). Depths range from just beneath the inshore water surface to over 13 m, depending upon the depth limit of the rooted aquatic vegetation (Clampitt 1970, Harman & Berg 1971). In Douglas Lake, Michigan, populations overwintering in water greater than 2 m deep migrate toward the cobble shore in late April and early May, where they spawn and die. In September, the new generation migrates into deep water to overwinter (Clampitt 1974).

Several studies have been done on *P. integra*, and life history and ecological details differ with geographic location. Life cycles have been described as univoltine for a backwater in New York (Eckblad 1973), bivoltine in an Iowa lake (Clampitt 1970), and multivoltine in an Iowa intermittent stream (Brown 1979). The snails begin to lay eggs when their shells reach 5 mm in height, about two to three months after hatching. The number of eggs deposited varies from 200-540 eggs/snail/month. Clutches contain 18-31 eggs (Clampitt 1970, Brown 1979).

Food consists of detritus, diatoms, and filamentous green and blue-green algae with some animal parts and vascular plant tissue. Relative proportions of food types depend on season. Sand grains are present in the gut (Clampitt 1970, Eckblad 1973). Dispersion in the field was relatively even in a backwater (Eckblad 1973) but clumped in an intermittent stream (Brown 1979). The life history pattern of the latter population was relatively insensitive to temperature changes (Brown 1979). In a lake population, the snails could not survive high summer temperatures, and they stayed in deeper, cooler water offshore. In winter, the snails were abundant on *Ceratophyllum* sp. (Clampitt 1970). Shell growth occurred in summer with little or no shell deposition over winter months (Clampitt 1970, Eckblad 1973).

Clampitt (1970) and Brown (1979) regarded these differences as adaptive for lake and intermittent stream populations, respectively. Adaptations to ephemeral habitats included reproduction at an earlier age, a shorter life cycle, more generations per year, and insensitivity to temperature (Brown 1979). Adaptations for lake populations were slower growth rates and a longer period of reproduction (Clampitt 1970).

For 61 New York collection sites, the water chemistry values are: pH: 6.0-9.7 (7.4 ± 0.1), conductivity 64-1240 µmhos/cm (431 ± 33), Ca^{++}: 3-70 ppm (26 ± 2), and Na^+: 1-144 ppm (29 ± 4).

In North Dakota, Cvancara (1983) recorded values of pH: 7.9-9.3 (8.4), conductivity: 605-3600 µmhos/cm (1815), and Ca^{++}: 50-600 ppm (104). Sixteen Michigan sites (Hunter & Lull 1977) yielded values of conductivity: 105-2500 µmhos/cm, and Ca^{++}: 25-177 ppm.

Physa ancillaria Say, 1825
Pumpkin physa
Figs. 20e, 21

Shell cylindrical, 20 mm high, greenish to tan to brown or red, thin to solid, shining; spire short, broad, obtuse; whorls slanting at 45° angle; nuclear whorl small, reddish; whorls 4.5-5.0, somewhat compressed, flat sided; body whorl strongly shouldered, large; sutures scarcely impressed; aperture large, 70-80% of shell length, purplish or liver colored inside; outer lip compressed and flattened, distinctly shouldered; columella straight with distinct plait (Baker 1928a). *Penial sheath in 2 sections* (Fig. 20e); *nonglandular section narrower and/or shorter than glandular section* (Jokinen 1983).

This species occurs in New Brunswick, Ontario, New York, Pennsylvania, and New England (Burch 1982).

Physa ancillaria was found at the following sites during this survey: Delaware River watershed (456, 457, 458, 462, 470, 471); Hudson River watershed (96C, 96F, 270, 276, 297, 319, 384, 455, 459B, 461, 603, 604); St. Lawrence River watershed (141A, 141B, 259B, 306, 313, 332, 346, 361, 437); and the Susquehanna River watershed (569, 571, 572). Most sites are in the eastern part of the State, with a few toward the central portion and one western. Harman & Berg (1971) found only one living specimen in central New York. Strayer (1987) found *P. ancillaria* to be the most common physid along the margins of the lower Hudson River.

The literature on this species indicates that it occurs across New York State. Early citations include the Mohawk and Hoosic Rivers, Rensselaer County (as *P. obesa* DeKay), and Lake Champlain, Clinton County (De Kay 1843); rivers of Herkimer County (rare) (Lewis 1860); Owasco Lake, Cayuga County (Lewis 1874, Maury 1916); Skaneateles Lake, Onondaga County (Beauchamp 1886b); Rochester, Monroe County (Walton 1891); Greenbush Lake, Rensselaer County (Marshall 1894); Albany/Troy area, Albany and Rensselaer Counties (Marshall 1895); Hudson River brackish marshes (Mearns 1898); Chautauqua Lake, Chautauqua County (Maury 1898, 1916; Evermann & Goldsborough 1901); Canandaigua Lake, Ontario/Yates County (Mitchell 1899); a marsh at the foot of Owasco Lake (Baker 1899); and Oneida Lake, Oswego and Onondaga Counties (Baker 1916a, b; Pratt 1923). Scarcity of recent reports could be due to the resemblance of immature *P. ancillaria* to immature *P. gyrina*. The male reproductive systems of the two species are similar, and immature *P. ancillaria* have not yet acquired the large, shouldered body whorl typical of the species (Jokinen, unpublished data).

This species can be found on substrata of allochthonous organic material, rocks, and decaying aquatic vegetation (Jokinen 1983). During this survey of New York State, *P. ancillaria* was located in 15 river and stream sites, nine lake sites, four permanent ponds, a temporary pond, and three canals. In Connecticut, habitats include permanent ponds and lakes with surface areas of 10-100 hectares and the Connecticut River (Jokinen 1983). *P. ancillaria* is found in most species-rich habitats but rarely in species-poor habitats (Jokinen 1987). In New York, it is able to migrate into high altitude habitats (Jokinen 1991).

An annual study of this species in a Connecticut lake indicated that there was a pattern of continuous juvenile recruitment throughout the summer. The population overwintered as a mixture of newly hatched and larger individuals up to 18 mm long. The larger snails deposited egg masses in April when the water temperature rose to 8.5°C, and then they died. The eggs hatched from mid May through mid June. By mid June, the earliest spring hatchlings and the overwintered immatures from the previous fall were large enough to deposit another generation of eggs. Newly hatched young appeared in the population until late October (Jokinen 1985). It appears that *P. ancillaria* is bivoltine or, possibly, trivoltine.

Chemistry data for 28 New York sites are: pH: 5.8-9.2 (7.3 ± 0.1), conductivity: 46-400 µmhos/cm (172 ± 18), Ca^{++}: 1-44 ppm (12 ± 2), and Na^+: 1-62 ppm (10 ± 1). In Connecticut, the ranges were: pH: 5.8-8.9, conductivity: 39-286 µmhos/cm, Ca^{++}: 2-21 ppm, and Na^+: 2-29 ppm (Jokinen 1983). *P. ancillaria* has a wide range of chemical tolerance, occurring in habitats with wide ranges of pH and calcium concentration.

Physa gyrina (Say, 1821)

Tadpole physa

Figs. 20f, 21

Shell subcylindrical, moderately elongated, 24 mm high, thin to slightly thickened, pale yellow-brown to grey-brown; spire short to long, acute; nuclear whorl small, red to reddish-brown; whorls 5-6, gently rounded, each partly enveloping preceding whorl; body whorl large, well-rounded, compressed to slightly inflated; sutures impressed, bordered below by narrow pale band; aperture loop-shaped, acute above, rounded at base, 60-80% of shell length, bordered inside by red band; outer lip thin to slightly thickened; columella oblique, thin to thickened; parietal wall callus a thin to thick, extensive wash (Baker 1928a, Clarke 1973). *Elongated penial sheath of two somewhat equal sections separated by prominent constriction* (Clampitt 1970).

The morphology of this species is discussed by Clampitt (1970).

Physa gyrina occurs from the Gulf of Mexico north to James Bay and drainage basins, west to California (Clarke 1973, Taylor 1981).

This species occupies all the major drainage areas of New York: Delaware River watershed (469, 472, 475); Hudson River watershed (271, 290, 300, 302, 317, 367, 382, 460, 587); Ohio-Mississippi River watershed (415, 421, 422, 432); St. Lawrence River watershed (141A, 141D, 259A, 259B, 279, 308, 309, 311, 316, 331, 333, 337, 340, 347, 349, 350, 351, 360, 366, 371, 373, 374, 375, 376, 396, 438, 441, 443, 444, 445A, 448B, 450, 493, 494, 502A, 516, 524A, 524B, 526, 527, 529, 530, 532, 563, 566); Susquehanna River watershed (389, 539, 541, 546, 548, 574, 575, 576, 578, 582, 583, 590, 591); and coastal Atlantic (250). Strayer (1987) reports it to be very common in the upland lakes and streams of the lower Hudson River valley. The species, with its subspecies *P. g. sayii* Tappan and *P. g. elliptica* Lea, is widely distributed throughout central New York (Harman & Berg 1971).

The historical literature contains numerous references to *P. gyrina* and the subspecies *P. g. sayii, P. g. elliptica,* and *P. g. hilderanthiana* (Lea). De Kay (1843) and Lewis (1874) note that it exists in various parts of the State. Other early references are for Onondaga County (Beauchamp 1886b); Erie Canal, Monroe County (Walton 1891); Baldwinsville, Onondaga County (Marshall 1894); the Genesee River (Baker 1901); Cazenovia Lake, Madison County (Henderson 1907); a number of sites near Buffalo, Erie and Niagara Counties (Letson 1909); near Warsaw, Wyoming County (Baker 1913); the west end of Oneida Lake, Oswego County (Baker 1916a, b); and Fall Creek, Ithaca, Tompkins County (Maury 1916). More recent references include collection sites at Allegany State Park, Cattaraugus County (Pinney & Coker 1934); Salmon Creek, Wayne County; Little Sodus Bay, Lake Ontario, Cayuga County (Burdick 1939); Six Mile Creek, Ithaca, Tompkins County

(Ingram 1941); and Conesus Lake, Livingston County (Wade & Vasey 1976).

Habitats include intermittent and small, permanent streams, small rivers, temporary and permanent ponds, soft to hard water lakes, prairie lakes, river lakes, and large lakes (Dawley 1947, Clarke 1973, Cvancara 1983, Jokinen 1983). In New York, *P. gyrina* occupied the following habitats: 22 river and stream sites, 22 lake sites, 19 permanent ponds, a temporary pond, six ditches, seven canals, and a swamp. Silt and detritus are the most common substrata (Harman 1972).

The longevity of this species is approximately 260 days, and only 1-3% of individuals survive to reproductive maturity. In Minnesota, the snails are common prey for northern pike (*Esox lucius* (L.)), pumpkinseed sunfish (*Lepomis gibbosus* (L.)), bluegill sunfish (*L. macrochirus* (Rafinesque)), black crappie (*Pomoxis nigromaculatus* (Lesueur)), and yellow perch (*Perca flavescens* (Mitchill) (Sheldon 1987). If the snails survive predation, they follow a semelparous life history pattern, dying after having passed through only one reproductive period (Clampitt 1970, Brown 1979).

Physa gyrina consumes a general diet of detritus, periphyton, and carrion (Clampitt 1970, Brown 1982). The snails will crawl over macrophytes and graze vascular tissue as well as periphyton. The density of snail grazing can strongly influence the abundance and diversity of macrophytes. The snails tend to select for grazing the fast growing macrophytes such as *Potamogeton richardsonii* (Ar. Benn.) Rydb. and *P. zosteriformis* Fernald. Snails also can be found on *Ceratophyllum demersum* L. and *P. robbinsii* Oakes, but they do not cause extensive tissue damage (Sheldon 1987).

This species is bivoltine, producing two generations per year. Individuals of an overwintering population grow in early spring and deposit eggs in late spring. Unlike many other pulmonates, the egg-laying snails continue to grow for part of the summer and increase in fecundity as the shell lengthens. The young grow until late summer and deposit a second generation of eggs when their shells are about 7 mm long, at approximately five weeks old. The hatchlings of these eggs overwinter and begin to deposit eggs in the spring when they are approximately 37 weeks old (Clampitt 1970; Brown 1979, 1982). Fecundity ranges from 700-1617 eggs/snail or 50-135 eggs/week (Clampitt 1970, Brown 1979).

Physa gyrina can temporarily survive temperatures up to 40°C, and they can withstand relatively long periods of desiccation. These traits enable the snails to inhabit temporary ponds and the warm littoral edges of lakes (Clampitt 1970). When temperatures are increased from 21-26°C, the growth rate increases, and oviposition occurs earlier. In addition, total fecundity, shell length at death, and survival time beyond first oviposition increase. Shell size at first reproduction and clutch size remain the same (Brown 1979). Because of temperature differences, growth rates in ponds are greater than those in lakes (Clampitt 1970).

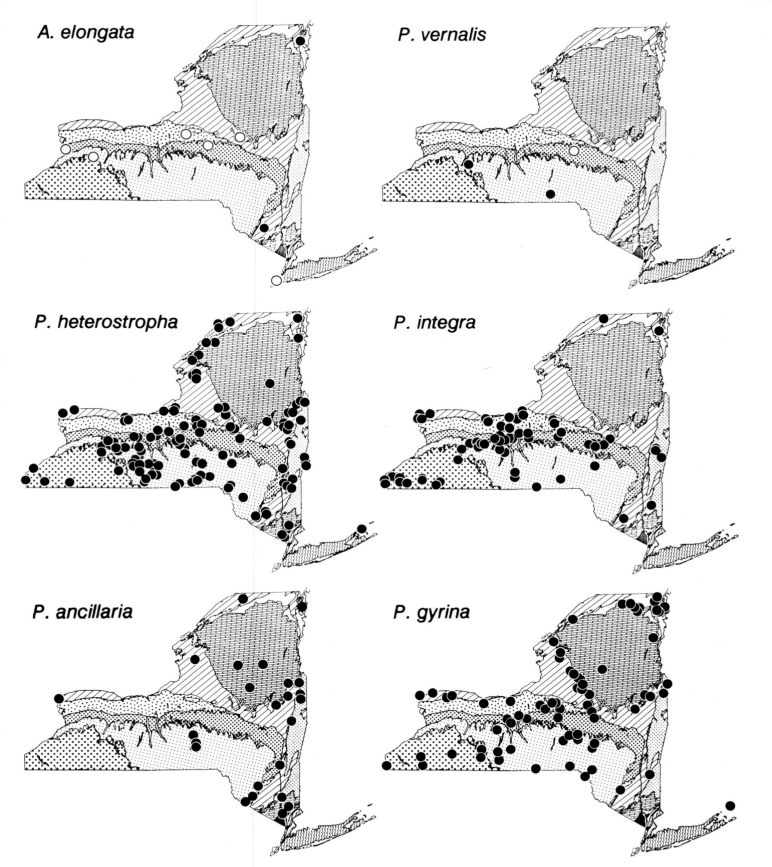

Fig. 21. Known distributions of species of Physidae in New York State. Closed circles indicate records from the present survey, and open circles indicate records from museum specimens.

Water chemistry values for 70 New York sites studied during this survey are: pH: 6.0-9.7 (7.3 ± 0.1), conductivity: 45-2320 μmhos/cm (364 ± 50), Ca^{++}: 1-94 ppm (21 ± 2), and Na^+: 1-291 ppm (24 ± 5). In Minnesota, *P. gyrina* tolerates a broad range of water hardness (Dawley 1947). In Connecticut, the snail was absent from highly organic and hard water habitats: pH: 5.7-7.2, conductivity: 40-148 μmhos/cm, Ca^{++}: 2-11 ppm, and Na^+: 2-11 ppm (Jokinen 1983). Cvancara's (1983) North Dakota values were: pH: 7.6-20.0 (8.6), conductivity: 300-8000 μmhos/cm (1480), and Ca^{++}: 30-360 ppm (159). In addition, North Dakota populations tolerated high total sulfates, total alkalinity, and total chlorides. *P. gyrina* populations show low variability in their calcium:tissue ratios over a range of environmental calcium values of 31-152 ppm and conductivities of 142-1350 μmhos/cm (Hunter & Lull 1977). This might account for the snails' ability to inhabit waters with a broad spectrum of hardness, pH, and calcium concentration.

Family Planorbidae

Animal sinistral but shell leaning to left, appearing dextral (ultradextral); upper side (right) umbilical; lower side (left) apical. Shell orbicular, wheel-shaped, disc-shaped, or, rarely, conical, thin to thick, 2-30 mm in diameter; aperture rounded, ovate, or half-moon shaped; genital and respiratory pores opening on left side; pseudobranch present; tentacles long, filiform; one superior and two lateral jaws present; hemoglobin present (Baker 1928a).

Key to the Planorbidae

1a. Shell diameter > 10 mm, or if < 10 mm (immatures), then height:diameter ratio > 0.5 2

1b. Shell diameter < 10 mm and height:diameter ratio < 0.5 4

2a. Whorls on apical side increasing only gradually in width so that center has appearance of a coiled rope (an Archimedes spiral); aperture flaring outward in mature specimens ....*Helisoma campanulatum*

2b. Whorls on apical side increasing rapidly in width (a geometric spiral)..3

3a. Whorls sharply angled on both sides...............................
....*Helisoma anceps*

3b. Whorls on one side rounded to only slightly angled ......
....*Helisoma trivolvis*

4a. Shell very flat and sharply angled at outer margin........
....*Promenetus exacuous*

4b. Shell not as above 5

5a. Teeth or lamellae present inside shell to a third of whorl behind aperture ....*Planorbula armigera*

5b. Teeth teeth and lamellae absent 6

6a. Shell with distinct raised ridges ....*Gyraulus crista*

6b. Shell without ridges 7

7a. Shell flattened on one side and rounded on the other, shoulder flattened ....*Micromenetus dilatatus*

7b. Shell rounded on both sides, not shouldered 8

8a. Shell with at least earliest whorls hirsute (appearing "hairy" when shell is dry) ....*Gyraulus deflectus*

8b. Shell not hirsute...9

9a. Both top and bottom of shell nearly identical; whorls increasing only gradually in width ....Gyraulus circumstriatus

9b. Top and bottom of shell clearly different; whorls increasing rapidly in width.................Gyraulus parvus

Gyraulus deflectus (Say, 1824)
Flexed gyro
Figs. 22a, 25

Shell depressed, planorboid, 8 mm in diameter, light tan to brown; spiral lines consisting of periostracal hair-like projections present; umbilicus wide, deep, showing all whorls; spire flat, all whorls in same plane except sunken apical whorl; whorls 4.5; base slightly concave, flattened, showing all volutions, sometimes acutely keeled peripherally; sutures impressed; aperture suboval, more or less deflected, higher than wide; interior brown; outer lip acute, thin; superior portion produced much beyond inferior portion; inside slightly thickened; callus thin, white (Baker 1928a, Clarke 1981).

Gyraulus deflectus occurs from mainland Canada north to the central Arctic coast and throughout Alaska, south to Nebraska, and east to Virginia (Baker 1928a; Clarke 1973, 1981; Jokinen 1983; Branson *et al.* 1987, Burch 1989).

Sites in New York where this species was found during this survey are: Delaware River watershed (455, 456); Hudson River watershed (212, 290, 291, 292, 300, 301, 304, 305, 384, 604); Mississippi-Ohio River watershed (427B); St. Lawrence River watershed (141A, 141D, 259A, 260, 262, 263, 264, 306, 313, 332, 336, 338, 339, 340, 349, 350, 352, 390, 401, 448A, 493, 497, 500, 502A); and Atlantic coastal drainage (253). Harman & Berg (1971) collected populations (determined as *G. hirsutus*) from lakes at the headwaters of the Tioughnioga River in the Susquehanna River watershed.

Gyraulus deflectus has been collected at numerous sites in New York State. Early reports include: Mohawk River; Newcomb's Pond, Pittstown, Rensselaer County (De Kay 1843); lakes in Herkimer and Otsego Counties (Lewis 1856b, 1860, 1872); Staten Island, Richmond County (Hubbard & Smith 1865); Onondaga County (Beauchamp 1886b); Brighton, Monroe County (Walton 1891); Albany/Troy region, Albany and Rensselaer Counties (Mar-shall 1895); Greenbush, Rensselaer County; Erie Canal, Monroe County; Little Lakes, Herkimer County; Seneca River (Marshall 1894); Chautauqua Lake, Chautauqua County (Maury 1898, 1916; Townes 1937); Irondequoit Bay, Lake Ontario, Monroe County (Baker 1900b); Cazenovia Lake, Madison County (Henderson 1907); Cayuga Lake, Seneca and Cayuga Counties (Maury 1916, Harman & Berg 1971); Fall Creek, Ithaca, Tompkins County; Cayuta Lake, Schuyler County; Hemlock Lake, Livingston and Ontario Counties (Maury 1916); and Oneida Lake, Oswego and Onondaga Counties (Baker 1916a, b; 1918a, b; Pratt 1923). More recent reports include Upper Cassadaga Lake, Chautauqua County (Townes 1937); Sodus Creek, Wayne County; Salmon River, Monroe County (Burdick 1939); Schroon River, Adirondack State Park, Warren County (Jacobson 1945); and Cross Lake, Cayuga and Onondaga Counties (Harman & Berg 1971).

This species lives in all types of permanent, quiet waters, including woods pools and dark streams issuing from swamps (Baker 1928a, Goodrich 1932, Dawley 1947, Jokinen 1983, Strayer 1987). It also lives in the tidal Hudson River (Strayer 1987). During this survey, populations were found living in ten river and stream sites, 16 lakes, five permanent ponds, two temporary ponds, three marshes, and two canals. Substrata can be of various types, including allochthonous organic matter with filamentous green algae (e.g., *Oedogonium* sp. and *Spirogyra* sp.) and rooted aquatic vegetation (Baker 1918a, Clarke 1981, Jokinen 1983). In Oneida Lake, individuals can be found to a depth of 9 m (Baker 1918a).

In a small, eutrophic lake in Connecticut, these snails have a bivoltine life cycle. Eggs first appear after the water temperature raises above 23°C from late June to early July. The hatchlings from this brood mature and produce a second batch of eggs from early September through early October. The autumn-hatched young overwinter and produce eggs the following spring (Jokinen 1985).

For 36 of this survey's New York sites, the water chemistry values are: pH: 6.4-8.5 (7.2 ± 0.1), conductivity: 47-2320 μmhos/cm (287 ± 63), Ca^{++}: 1-89 ppm (21 ± 3), and Na^+: 1-291 ppm (19 ± 8). In Connecticut, 29 sites had chemistry values of pH: 5.6-7.0, conductivity: 43-319 μmhos/cm, Ca^{++}: 1-4 ppm, and Na^+: 2-29 ppm (Jokinen 1983). Three sites in central New York had pH values of 7.1-8.3 (7.8) (Harman & Berg 1971). *G. deflectus* can live in waters with a broad range of calcium concentrations, pH, and salinity. In the Adirondack Mountains, it occurs at all altitudes and water chemistry values (Jokinen 1991).

Gyraulus parvus (Say, 1817)
Ash gyro
Figs. 22b, 25

Shell depressed, 5 mm in diameter, tan to black; umbilicus wide, shallow, exhibiting all volutions; spire flat, with

first two whorls sunken below body whorl; nucleus small, rounded; whorls 3.5, rapidly enlarging, rounded below periphery, flattened above; body whorl somewhat flattened above; sutures deeply impressed; aperture elongate-oval, usually nearly in same plane as body whorl; interior white to pale yellow; outer lip acute, thin; superior margin produced more than inferior margin; callus a thin wash on parietal wall (Baker 1928a).

The distribution of this species is broad, including all of Canada south of the tree line, and south to California, Florida, and Cuba (Taylor 1960, 1981; Clarke 1981).

G. parvus occupies all the major watersheds of New York: Delaware River watershed (455, 457, 470, 471, 472, 475); Hudson River watershed (212, 265, 268, 269, 270, 271, 275, 276, 277, 282, 283, 285, 286, 288, 289, 291, 292, 293, 300, 301, 303, 317, 319, 320, 367, 387, 459, 460, 461, 588, 600, 601, 602, 604, 608, 610, 616); Mississippi-Ohio River watershed (426, 430A, 430B, 431); St. Lawrence River watershed (141B, 141D, 259A, 259B, 261, 262, 263, 278, 279, 280, 298, 306, 307, 308, 309, 311, 313, 314, 332, 336, 337, 338, 339, 340, 341, 343, 349, 351, 360, 361, 371, 373, 375, 390, 392, 407, 408, 409, 410, 412, 439, 440, 441, 445A, 445C, 448A, 448B, 449, 450, 493, 495, 496, 498, 499, 500, 501, 502A, 502B, 505, 512, 515, 520, 523, 524A, 524B, 527, 529, 531, 534, 535, 562, 563); Susquehanna River watershed (400, 539, 540, 542, 543, 546, 558, 568, 569, 570, 571, 572, 573, 577, 579, 580, 582, 583, 586, 592, 593, 594); Atlantic coastal drainage (253, 322); Hackensack River watershed (606); and the Housatonic River watershed (294). Harman & Berg (1971) found a large number of localities from the Susquehanna and Otsego River basins in central New York. Strayer (1987) reported that *G. parvus* is abundant everywhere in the Hudson River basin.

In the past, *G. parvus* also was reported from many sites in New York State. Early citations include the Mohawk River (De Kay 1843); Herkimer and Otsego Counties (Lewis 1856b, 1860, 1872); Staten Island, Richmond County (Hubbard & Smith 1865); Tibbet's Brook, Riverdale, Bronx County (Prime 1880); Onondaga County (Beauchamp 1886b); Charlotte, Monroe County (Walton 1891); Albany/Troy region, Albany and Rensselaer Counties (Marshall 1895); Mohawk River, Cohoes, Albany County; Normans Kill, Albany, Albany County (Marshall 1894); Chautauqua Lake, Chautauqua County (Maury 1898, 1916; Townes 1937); Owasco River near Auburn, Cayuga County (Baker 1899); Irondequoit Bay, Lake Ontario, Monroe County (Baker 1900b); Cazenovia Lake, Madison County (Henderson 1907); Long Island (Wheat 1907a); Fort Erie trenches, Frenchmen's Creek; Lime Lake, Cattaraugus County (Letson 1909); Cayuga Lake, Seneca and Cayuga Counties (Maury 1916); Oneida Lake, Oswego County (Baker 1916a, b; 1918a, b; Pratt 1923). More recently, collections have been made at the Hudson River, Dutchess County (Townes 1936); Findley Lake, Bear Lake, Upper Cassadaga Lake, Lower Cassadaga Lake, and Clymer Pond, Chau-

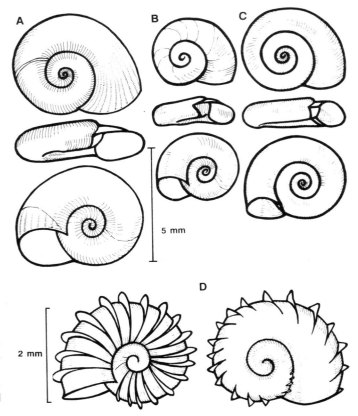

Fig. 22. Family Planorbidae, shells: a, *Gyraulus deflectus*; b, *G. parvus*, c, *G. circumstriatus*; d, *G. crista*. Figs. a-c are drawn to the same scale.

tauqua County (Townes 1937); Lake Ontario bays (Burdick 1939); Adirondack State Park, Warren County (Jacobson 1945); Lake Beechwood and Lake Mohegan, Peekskill, Westchester County; Hempstead State Park, Nassau County, Long Island; "Kensington Pond;" Valley Stream, Nassau County, Long Island (Jacobson & Emerson 1961); Green Lake, Onondaga County (Harman 1970); and Otsego Lake, New Pond, and Canandarago Lake, Otsego County (Harman 1971, 1973; MacNamara & Harman 1975).

G. parvus habitats include permanent and temporary ponds, small lakes, quiet embayments of large lakes, pools of permanent and intermittent streams, and marshes (Lewis 1856b; Goodrich 1932; Burdick 1939; Leonard 1959; Jacobson & Emerson 1961; Harman & Berg 1971; Clarke 1973, 1981; Cvancara 1983; Strayer 1987). These snails also occur in the tidal Hudson River (Strayer 1987). In Connecticut, they were found most commonly in ponds of one to nine hectares surface area (Jokinen 1983). During the current survey, populations were found in 42 river and stream sites, 44 lakes, 38 permanent ponds, two temporary ponds, three ditches, four marshes, six canals, and a swamp. This species is fairly ubiquitous in quieter waters.

Preferred microhabitats of *G. parvus* include allochthonous organic matter, tree branches, stones, and aquatic plants such as *Potamogeton, Myriophyllum, Vallisneria, Typha, Spirogyra* and *Chara* spp. (Baker 1927, Goodrich 1932, Leonard 1959, Jacobson & Emerson 1961, Eckblad 1973, Clarke 1981, Jokinen 1983). Substrata can be anything from mud to rock (Clarke 1981, Pace *et al.* 1979, Cvancara 1983). In Grand Traverse Bay, Lake Michigan, offshore densities of 2.4-28.4 snails/m² have been reported (Pace *et al.* 1979). In a pond habitat, distributions can be aggregated (Eckblad 1973).

Laboratory observations indicate that this species deposits capsules containing 1-7 eggs. They are laid at night on aquarium glass, stems and leaves of dead and living vegetation, and snail shells. Development takes 6-10 days (Krull 1931, Leonard 1959). The snails hatch with shells 0.5 mm in diameter. In 15-17 days they are half-grown, and in 4-5 weeks they are fully grown. At 6-7 weeks they are mature and ready to oviposit (Krull 1931). In field populations, eggs are present from June through September. The species appears to be multivoltine (Eckblad 1973). Food consists of dead terrestrial vegetation, from which the snails consume the leaf pulp, leaving the vascular bundles intact as skeletonized leaves (Krull 1931). They also consume periphyton on submerged aquatic vegetation (Eckblad 1973).

This survey's New York State water chemistry values for 134 *G. parvus* habitats are: pH: 5.8-9.6 (7.2 ± 0.1), conductivity: 42-2320 µmhos/cm (306 ± 25), Ca^{++}: 1-89 ppm (20 ± 1), and Na^+: 1-291 (20 ± 3). In Connecticut, chemistry values for 39 sites are: pH: 6.1-10.0, conductivity: 53-346 µmhos/cm, Ca^{++}: 3-42, and Na^+: 2-29 (Jokinen 1983). Values for North Dakota are: pH: 7.6-10 (mean = 8.6, 67 sites), conductivity: 300-5000 µmhos/cm (1465, 57 sites), and Ca^{++}: 50-360 ppm (146, 21 sites) (Cvancara 1983). For 79 central New York sites, Harman & Berg (1971) recorded pH values of 6.8-8.5 (7.6). In the Adirondack Mountains, this species is ubiquitous, occurring at all altitudes and in all water chemistry types (Jokinen 1991). Its tolerance to wide ranges of pH and calcium concentrations is reflected in its wide geographic and habitat distributions. Even though *G. parvus* lives in the tidal Hudson River (Strayer 1987), the data do not demonstrate a high sodium tolerance.

Gyraulus circumstriatus (Tryon, 1866)
Disc gyro
Figs. 22c, 25

Shell depressed, planospiral, 5 mm in diameter, semi-transparent; umbilicus wide, all whorls visible; spire whorls rounded, usually in same plane; whorls 4.5, slowly and regularly increasing in diameter; last whorl not greatly enlarged over previous, with several raised revolving lines on base; body whorl slightly rounded, slightly flattened above, obtusely subangulate below; sutures deeply impressed; aperture roundly ovate, not oblique; outer and inner lips often joined by parietal callus (Baker 1928a).

This species occurs from Prince Edward Island and New England west to northern British Columbia and south to California, New Mexico, and Kansas (Leonard 1959, Clarke 1981, Taylor 1981, Cvancara 1983, Jokinen 1983).

Populations were collected from eight sites in four watersheds during this survey: Hudson River watershed (290); St. Lawrence River watershed (306, 339, 402); Susquehanna River watershed (536, 537, 555); and the Atlantic coastal drainage (252). Strayer (1987) noted populations from the Hudson River basin. Harman & Berg (1971) did not list this species, and there is no mention of it in the older literature.

G. circumstriatus commonly lives in quiet waters of lakes and ponds and in intermittent ponds and streams. During this survey, populations were found in one river, two lakes, three permanent ponds, one temporary pond, and one ditch. Substrata range from mud to gravelly sand, and the snails are often associated with dead and living aquatic vegetation (e.g., *Chara* sp.) and allochthonous detritus (Leonard 1959, Clarke 1981, Cvancara 1983, Jokinen 1983). A population in Roseland Lake, Connecticut, exhibits continual recruitment of young from May through November. This probably reflects a bivoltine or multivoltine life cycle (Jokinen 1985).

Water chemistry values for seven sites studied during this survey are: pH: 6-9.8 (7.3 ± 0.5), conductivity: 110-312 µmhos/cm (247 ± 25), Ca^{++}: 4-34 ppm (16 ± 5), and Na^+: 6-47 ppm (16 ± 5). Connecticut values for three sites are: pH: 6.2-7.3, conductivity: 61-316 µmhos/cm, Ca^{++}: 3-20 ppm, and Na^+: 5-8 ppm (Jokinen 1983). Seven sites in North Dakota had values of: pH: 7.6-10.0 (8.7), conductivity: 293-4650 µmhos/cm (1500), and Ca^{++}: 110 ppm (single reading) (Cvancara 1983). Populations were not found in the acidic waters or high altitudes of the Adirondack Mountains (Jokinen 1991). The data available indicate that this species might be intolerant of waters with extremely low pH and calcium values.

Gyraulus crista (Linnaeus, 1758)
Star gyro
Figs. 22d, 25

Shell depressed, 2 mm in diameter, fragile, tan to brown, variably costate on periphery with folds of periostracum projecting conspicuously; umbilicus region broad, deep, exhibiting all whorls; spire flat; nucleus large, roundly ovate; 2.5 whorls, rapidly increasing in diameter, base well-rounded; sutures deeply impressed to channeled; aperture ovate, flattened above, rounded below, appressed to body wall a short distance, slightly expanded at parietal wall; outer lip thin, simple, touching or appressed to previous whorl (Baker 1928a).

At times, this species has been placed in the genus *Armiger*.

G. crista has a Holarctic distribution. In North America, it ranges from Ontario to the Northwest Territories and Alaska and south to California (Clarke 1973, 1981; Taylor 1981).

Three populations were found during this survey, all in the St. Lawrence River watershed (496, 523, 524A). Neither Strayer (1987) nor Harman & Berg (1971) found sites that harbored this species. The only historical note (Burdick 1939) appears to be on a population in Sodus Bay, Lake Ontario, Wayne County.

G. crista inhabits the slowly flowing water of lake shores, permanent and temporary ponds, and slow-moving streams. During this survey, it was found in one lake and two permanent ponds. The substrata can be mud or muddy sand, and the microhabitat consists of dense aquatic vegetation or water-logged wood and rotting terrestrial leaves (Goodrich 1932, Clarke 1981, Cvancara 1983). Snails remain in shallow water and will often burrow 10 cm into the substratum among the roots of aquatic vegetation (e.g., *Cladium* sp.) (Richardot-Coulet & Alfaro-Tijera 1985).

This species is trivoltine. Egg capsules with one to two eggs are first deposited when the water temperature exceeds 8°C in spring. After ovipositing, the adults die. The early spring hatchlings become reproductively mature by early summer, and they produce a second generation which hatches, matures, and oviposits in autumn. The summer and autumn generations overwinter. Longevities are four months for the spring generation, 10-12 months for the summer generation, and 6-8 months for the autumn generation. There appears to be no differential mortality as all age classes are affected equally throughout the year (Richardot-Coulet & Alfara-Tejera 1985).

Water chemistry values for the three New York State sites studied during this survey are: pH: 7.3, 7.4, 8.2; conductivity: 349, 680, 760 μmhos/cm; Ca^{++}: 29, 34, 36 ppm; and Na^+: 58, 83, 122 ppm. In North Dakota, values for three sites are: pH: 7.6-8.5 (8.1) and conductivity: 435-4650 μmhos/cm (1940) (Cvancara 1983). Values from both regions reflect high calcium, neutral environments.

Helisoma anceps (Menke, 1830)
Two-ridge rams-horn
Figs. 23a, 25

Shell ultradextral, discoidal, 19 mm in diameter, yellowish to dark tan, dark brown, or reddish; more or less angulate above and below, with periphery rounded or flattened; umbilicus deep, exhibiting all volutions; spire a funnel-like depression, exhibiting all volutions; nuclear whorl small; whorls 3.5; sutures impressed; aperture lunately-ovate, bluntly rounded or V-shaped above, usually V-shaped below body whorl, higher than wide in mature specimens; outer lip acute, thin, expanded, thickened within by bluish-white varix lined with reddish-brown; callus thin (Baker 1928a).

Synonyms include *Planorbis bicarinatum* Say 1817 and *Helisoma antrosum* Conrad 1834.

This species occurs throughout most of Canada south of the tree line, south to Florida and northwest Mexico. It has been introduced into Italy (Clarke 1981, Cvancara 1983, Thompson 1984a).

H. anceps is widespread across New York in all the major watersheds: Delaware River watershed (466, 471, 473, 474, 475); Hudson River watershed (141D, 212, 271, 274, 275, 277, 285, 292, 293, 295, 302, 303, 304, 305, 320, 321, 381, 383, 384, 385, 386, 452, 459, 599, 600, 604, 607, 616); Mississippi-Ohio River watershed (415, 420, 421, 430B); St. Lawrence River watershed (141D, 260, 261, 263, 309, 316, 331, 336, 338, 340, 347, 351, 354, 356, 357, 360, 361, 363, 374, 377, 392, 394, 411, 493, 494, 517, 518B, 530, 531, 534, 535, 562, 563); Susquehanna River watershed (478, 539, 546, 553, 555, 568, 581, 583, 584, 591, 592); and Housatonic River watershed (294). Harman & Berg (1971) found it to be common throughout central New York State. It also is abundant in the lower Hudson River watershed (Strayer 1987).

Historical literature citing localities for *H. anceps* is abundant. Populations have been reported from the State in general (De Kay 1843); Herkimer and Otsego Counties (Lewis 1856b, 1860; Marshall 1894); Riverdale, Bronx County (Prime 1880); Onondaga County (Beauchamp 1886b); Rochester, Monroe County (Walton 1891); Albany/Troy region, Albany and Rensselaer Counties (Marshall 1894, 1895); Chautauqua Lake, Chautauqua County (Maury 1898, Evermann & Goldsborough 1902, Maury 1916; Townes 1937); Highland Lake, Orange County (Mearns 1898); Owasco Lake, Cayuga County (Baker 1899); Canandaigua Lake, Ontario and Yates County (Mitchell 1899; Maury 1916); Irondequoit Bay, Lake Ontario, Monroe County (Baker 1900b); Cazenovia Lake, Madison County (Henderson 1907); Long Island (Wheat 1907a); Erie and Niagara Counties (Letson 1909); Cayuga Lake, Cayuga and Seneca Counties; Cayuta Lake, Schuyler County; Fall Creek, Ithaca, Tompkins County (Maury 1916); Allegany State Park, Cattaraugus County (Pinney & Coker 1934); Oneida Lake, Otsego and Onondaga Counties (Baker 1916a, b; 1918a, b; Pratt 1923); Hudson River from North Germantown, Columbia County, to Rhinecliff, Dutchess County (Townes 1936); Findley Lake, Bear Lake, Upper Cassadaga Lake, and Clymer Pond, Chautauqua County (Townes 1937); Lake Ontario watershed (Burdick 1939); and Schroon River, Adirondack State Park, Warren County (Jacobson 1945). More recent reports include Upper Ferdun Pond, Rockland County (Bretet & Carswell 1952); Oakland Lake, Queens County, Long Island (Jacobson 1965); Green Lake, Onondaga County (Harman 1970); Otsego Lake, Otsego County (Harman 1971, MacNamara & Harman 1975); Wilber Reservoir, Moe Pond, and Susquehanna River, Oneonta, Otsego County; and Delaware River, Walton, Delaware County (Katsigianis & Harman 1973; MacNamara & Harman 1975).

Helisoma anceps exists in a wide range of habitats, including lakes, ponds, rivers, streams, and occasionally temporary ponds or intermittent streams. During this survey, it was found in 17 river and stream sites, 33 lakes, 25 permanent ponds, three temporary ponds, one ditch, two marshes, and three canals. Its substrata include allochthonous organic matter, rocks, living and dead aquatic vegetation, sand, and mud (Baker 1928a, Goodrich 1932, Franzen & Leonard 1942, Dawley 1947, Clarke 1981, Taylor 1981, Jokinen 1983, Cvancara 1983, Strayer 1987, Pip 1987). The abundance of this species indicates that it has good dispersal and colonization rates (Jokinen 1987). Food consists of diatoms and other algae (Goodrich 1932).

Apparently the longevity of this species is variable. In Connecticut, the snails live one year. They reach maturity in early spring, oviposit, then die. Hatchlings appear from mid May, when the water temperature exceeds 20°C, through July (Jokinen 1983). Under other circumstances, *H. anceps* appears to live two years, not reproducing until its second summer when the shell diameter exceeds 8 mm (Boerger 1975, Hermann & Harman 1975). Egg deposition occurs when the water temperature exceeds 10°C. The egg laying period is long, up to 18 weeks, and during the first eight weeks, the snails deposit an average of 300 eggs each. They continue to grow during oviposition and produce more eggs/snail as their shell diameters increase (Boerger 1975).

Water chemistry values for the 83 survey sites in New York State are: pH: 5.8-9.5 (7.1 ± 0.1), conductivity: 28-2320 μmhos/cm (238 ± 31), Ca^{++}: 1-89 ppm (14 ± 2), and Na^+: 1-291 ppm (18 ± 4). In Connecticut, the data for 54 sites are: pH: 5.8-8.9, conductivity: 40-387 μmhos/cm, Ca^{++}: 2-35 ppm, and Na^+: 2-29 ppm (Jokinen 1983). In central New York, Harman & Berg (1971) found *H. anceps* in a pH range of 7.1-8.4 (7.7). Values from North Dakota are: pH: 8.1-9.2 (8.7, 15 sites), conductivity: 461-1870 μmhos/cm (765, 8 sites), and Ca^{++}: 50-170 ppm (111, 7 sites) (Cvancara 1983). In Canada, the species has a relatively high tolerance to a wide range of chemical parameters (Pip 1987). In the Adirondack Mountains and surrounding lowlands, it is ubiquitous, occurring at all altitudes and in waters with a wide range of chemical parameters (Jokinen 1991). *H. anceps* appears to have few chemical restrictions, a likely factor in its widespread continental and local distribution.

Helisoma campanulatum (Say, 1821)
Bellmouth rams-horn
Figs. 23b, 25

Shell discoidal, rounded below, subcarinate above, base exhibiting 2.5 volutions, 16 mm in diameter, brown to reddish; umbilicus deep; spire flat, exhibiting all volutions, closely coiled; nuclear whorl small; whorls 4.5; last half of body whorl often elevated above general plane of spire; sutures deeply impressed; aperture lunate, dilated in mature specimens, forming bell-shaped lip, slightly wider than high; outer lip thin, sharp, heavily ridged within where aperture begins to expand; parietal callus thin (Baker 1928a).

Burch (1989) places this species in the genus *Planorbella*.

H. campanulatum occurs from Vermont west to Saskatchewan and south to Minnesota, Ohio, and Illinois. Only a fossil has been found in North Dakota (Baker 1928a, Clarke 1973, Cvancara 1983).

During this survey of New York State, this species was located at 41 sites and in all major watersheds: Delaware River watershed (457, 466); Hudson River watershed (212, 276, 283, 293, 297, 300, 317, 318, 320, 384, 604, 616); Mississippi-Ohio River watershed (430B); St. Lawrence River watershed (141D, 259A, 260, 263, 278, 298, 306, 307, 309, 336, 337, 338, 339, 340, 341, 344, 350, 352, 353, 493, 531, 562); Susquehanna River watershed (568, 582, 592); and Housatonic River watershed (294). Strayer (1987) found it in the lower Hudson River basin, and postglacial fossil evidence indicates that this species might have been more abundant previously. In central New York, Harman & Berg (1971) noted colonies in both the Susquehanna and Otsego River basins.

Helisoma campanulatum was first noticed in "most of the lakes in the western end of the state" (De Kay 1843). Following that record, colonies were noted from Herkimer and Otsego Counties (Lewis 1856b, 1860); Onondaga County (Beauchamp 1886b); Pittsford, Monroe County (Walton 1891, Marshall 1894); Cedar Lake, Herkimer County (Marshall 1894); Chautauqua Lake, Chautauqua County (Maury 1898, Evermann & Goldsborough 1902, Maury 1916, Townes 1937); Canandaigua Lake, Ontario and Yates Counties (Mitchell 1899); Owasco River near Auburn and the inlet of Lake Owasco at Cascade, Cayuga County (Baker 1899); Irondequoit Bay, Lake Ontario, Monroe County (Baker 1900b); Cazenovia Lake, Madison County (Henderson 1907); Lime Lake, Cattaraugus County, and the Niagara River (Letson 1909); Oneida Lake, Oswego County (Baker 1916a, b; 1918a, b; Pratt 1923); Cayuta Lake, Schuyler County; and Conesus Lake, Livingston County (Maury 1916). More recent records include Findley Lake, Bear Lake, Upper Cassadaga Lake, and Lower Cassadaga Lake, Chautauqua County (Townes 1937); Little Sodus Bay, Lake Ontario, Cayuga County; Glenwood Lake, Orleans County (Burdick 1939); Brant Lake, Adirondack State Park, Warren County (Jacobson 1945); Otsego Lake, Otsego County (Harman 1971, MacNamara & Harman 1975); and Conesus Lake, Livingston County (Wade & Vasey 1976).

This species is found primarily in ponds and lakes. During this survey, it was found in five river and stream sites, 19 lakes, 12 permanent ponds, one temporary pond, two marshes, and two canals. It is associated with a variety of substrata, such as rock, sand, mud, allochthonous detritus, and occasionally rooted aquatic vegetation (Baker 1918a, 1928a; Jokinen 1983, Pip 1987). In Oneida Lake, Baker (1918a) found the species on all types of substrata, 0.5-3.0 m deep, associated with the filamentous algae *Oedogonium*, *Spirogyra*, and *Cladophora* spp. Harman & Berg (1971) located individuals in Oneida Lake, where they were most common at 5-9 m.

This species has an annual life cycle. It has a distinct reproductive peak in the spring, from the end of May through July, after which the adult snails die. The hatchlings grow rapidly and obtain a shell diameter of over 10 mm by summer's end. The snails overwinter as adults (Boerger 1975; Jokinen 1985). *H. campanulatum* is present in most species-rich habitats, and it is less frequent in species-poor habitats. It is generally absent from ponds with fewer than three species (Jokinen 1987).

Water chemistry values for the 41 New York sites of the present survey are: pH: 6.1-9.2 (7.3 ± 0.1), conductivity: 42-2320 μmhos/cm (272 ± 55), Ca^{++}: 1-89 ppm (18 ± 3), and Na$^+$: 1-291 ppm (18 ± 7). In Connecticut, water chemistry values for 16 sites are: pH: 5.8-7.6, conductivity: 38-319 μmhos/cm, Ca^{++}: 1-27 ppm, and Na$^+$: 2-8 ppm (Jokinen 1983). Harman & Berg (1971) found the species at 16 sites with a pH range of 7.1-8.3 (7.8). In the acidic Adirondack Mountain waters and surrounding hard-water areas, this species is ubiquitous. Distribution does not seem to be limited by low water chemistry values or high altitude (Jokinen 1991). However, the species seems to succeed best in lakes and larger ponds, as described by Pip (1987) for Canadian populations.

Helisoma trivolvis (Say, 1817)
Marsh rams-horn
Figs. 23c, 25

Shell discoidal, flat, carinate above, subcarinate below, 32 mm in diameter, yellowish to brownish to chestnut; umbilicus narrow, deep, funnel-shaped; spire perfectly flat in young, sunken below last whorl in adults, exhibiting all volutions; nuclear whorl small; whorls 4.0, rounded on periphery; base indented, showing 2-3 volutions; sutures deep, V-shaped; aperture broadly lunate, somewhat expanded below, with V-shaped angle above, exactly the height of body whorl, bluish-white or tan, bordered within by wide brown or yellow band; outer lip thin, acute, rounded outward; callus thin (Baker 1928a).

Burch (1989) places this species in the genus *Planorbella*.

This species occurs throughout the Canadian boreal forest and New England, south to the Mississippi River drainage, Florida, and the Dominican Republic (Baker 1928a, Branson 1963, Beetle 1973, Clarke 1973, Thompson 1984a, Gomez *et al.* 1986).

Helisoma trivolvis is abundant and found in all of New York's major watersheds: Delaware River watershed (455, 458, 474); Hudson River watershed (96B, 96D, 96F, 96G, 269, 271, 274, 282, 286, 288, 289, 290, 291, 317, 367, 453, 608, 609); Mississippi-Ohio River watershed (415, 420, 426, 427A, 428, 430B, 431); St. Lawrence River watershed (141A, 259B, 260, 261, 263, 307, 308, 309, 312, 314, 316, 331, 332, 337, 338,

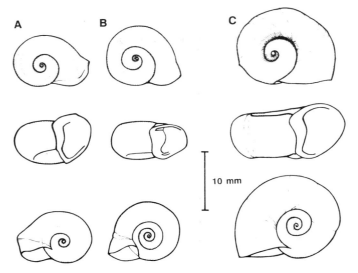

Fig. 23. Family Planorbidae, shells: a, *Helisoma anceps*; b, <u>H.</u> *campanulatum*; c, *H. trivolvis*. All illustrations are drawn to the same scale.

339, 343, 376, 390, 392, 396, 405, 408, 409, 439, 440, 441, 443, 444, 445B, 448A, 448B, 449, 450, 493, 494, 497, 500, 502A, 502B, 503, 507, 512, 518B, 524A, 524B, 527, 533, 534, 562, 563); and Susquehanna River watershed (537, 546, 552, 553, 569, 571, 572, 573, 591, 592, 594). Harman & Berg (1971) and Strayer (1987) found it to be abundant in central New York and the Hudson River basin, respectively.

There are also numerous earlier reports of *H. trivolvis* occurring in New York State. Sites include: New York State in general (De Kay 1843); Herkimer and Otsego Counties (Lewis 1856b, 1860, 1872); Riverdale, Bronx County; Van Cortland Lake, Bronx County (Prime 1880); Onondaga County (Beauchamp 1886b); Erie Canal between Ilion and Utica, Herkimer County (Baily 1891); Charlotte, Monroe County (Walton 1891); Albany/Troy area, Albany and Rensselaer Counties (Marshall 1895); Normans Kill, Albany,

Albany County; Cortland, Cortland County; Greenbush, Rensselaer County; Onondaga Lake, Onondaga County (Marshall 1984b); ponds and the Hudson River, Orange and Ulster Counties (Mearns 1898); Canandaigua Lake, Ontario and Yates Counties (Mitchell 1899; Maury 1916); Owasco Lake, Cayuga County (Baker 1899); Genesee River, above and below falls, Irondequoit Bay, Lake Ontario, Monroe County; and Erie Canal "Wide-Waters," Monroe County (Baker 1900b, 1901); Chautauqua Lake, Chautauqua County (Evermann & Goldsborough 1902; Maury 1898, 1916; Townes 1937); Cazenovia Lake, Madison County (Henderson 1907); Long Island (Wheat 1907a, Jacobson 1951); Prospect Park Lake, Brooklyn, Kings County (Wheat 1907b; Freas 1950a); Erie and Niagara Counties (Letson 1909); Conesus Lake, Livingston County (Maury 1916, Wade & Vasey 1976); and Oneida Lake, Oswego County (Baker 1916a, b; 1918a; Pratt 1923). More recent reports are from: lake at school, Allegany State Park, Cattaraugus County (Pinney & Coker 1934); Hudson River from Coxsackie, Greene County to Camelot, Dutchess County (Townes 1936); Clymer Pond, Chautauqua, Chautauqua County (Townes 1937); ponds and creeks of Lake Ontario watershed (Burdick 1939); Brooklyn Botanic Gardens stream, Kings County (Freas 1950a; Jacobson & Emerson 1961); near Valley Stream, Nassau County, Long Island (Jacobson & Emerson 1961); Oakland Lake, Queens County, Long Island (Jacobson 1965); Otsego Lake, Otsego County (MacNamara & Harmann 1975).

Helisoma trivolvis inhabits a wide variety of aquatic habitats, from temporary ponds and streams to rivers and lakes. During this New York State survey, 29 river and stream sites, 18 lakes, 20 permanent ponds, two temporary ponds, three ditches, four marshes, eight canals, and a swamp were found to harbor it. This species lives on various substrata, from clay and mud to boulders, allochthonous organic material, algal species of *Chara* and *Spirogyra*, and rooted aquatic vegetation, such as *Myriophyllum, Ceratophyllum, Elodea, Lemna, Potamogeton, Typha,* and *Scirpus* spp. (Baker 1918a, 1928a; Leonard 1959; Branson & Batch 1983; Cvancara 1983; Jokinen 1983; Strayer 1987; Pip 1987). The immatures seem to prefer macrophytes, whereas the mature snails are most frequently found on inorganic substrata (Harman 1972).

Helisoma trivolvis has variable longevity and reproductive patterns. In a South Carolina impoundment where annual water temperatures range from 11-36°C, it has two periods of egg deposition, one from May through June and a second from late August to mid February. It appears that longevity is one year or less (Wood 1978). In cooler climates, the life span can be one to two years, dependent upon the temperature and trophic richness of the habitat. In richer and warmer habitats, snails reach maturity and oviposit at one year of age. In less rich and cooler habitats, they do not mature and oviposit until their second year (Eversole 1978, Morris & Boag 1982). Individuals are at least 18 mm in diameter before maturation. Egg

capsules contain 24-30 eggs and appear in June in Waterloo, Ontario (Boerger 1975), and as early as March in Kansas, where they continue to appear through November or later (Leonard 1959).

This species is a generalist, consuming similar amounts of periphyton, detritus, and carrion (Brown 1982). The size and thickness of its shell allows it to maintain viable populations in co-existence with predators, such as crayfish (Covich 1981). It has high dispersion rate and colonization success (Jokinen 1987, Pip 1987).

Water chemistry data from 78 sites studied during this survey are: pH: 5.8-8.6 (7.4 ± 0.1), conductivity: 48-2320 μmhos/cm (371 ± 35), Ca^{++}: 1-89 ppm (26 ± 2), and Na^+: 1-291 ppm (26 ± 5). For 20 sites in Connecticut, values are: pH: 6.3-10.0, conductivity: 89-316 μmhos/cm, Ca^{++}: 6-23 ppm, and Na^+: 5-12 ppm (Jokinen 1983). Sites in North Dakota yielded pH: 7.6-9.8 (mean = 8.5, 34 sites), conductivity: 293-5000 μmhos/cm (1185, 32 sites), and Ca^{++}: 60-130 (99, 7 sites) (Cvancara 1983). Values of pH for 52 sites in central New York were 7.0-8.4 (7.6) (Harman & Berg 1971). In the Adirondack Mountains and surrounding lowlands, *H. trivolvis* appears to be limited to sites with Ca^{++} values greater than 9 ppm (Jokinen 1991). Laboratory studies have demonstrated that adults can survive pH values as low as 4.9 and have normal fecundity. However, low pH values cause high percentages of embryonic abnormalities and juvenile mortality (Hunter 1988). However, Pip (1987) found *H. trivolvis* to have the widest tolerance ranges for water chemistry values as well as water body and substratum types.

Planorbula armigera (Say, 1821)
Thicklip rams-horn
Figs. 24a, 26

Shell depressed, subcarinate above and below periphery, 8 mm in diameter, yellow to brown to black; umbilicus round, deep, wide, funnel-shaped, exhibiting all volutions; spire concave, apical whorls depressed below general plane; whorls 4.5, regularly and slowly increasing in diameter, with base rounded; body whorl abruptly deflected near aperture; aperture subovate, slightly oblique, armed within by 6 lamellae, pearly white with reddish band just within aperture extending parallel to its edge; outer lip acute, slightly thickened inside; superior margin slightly produced (Baker 1928a).

This species occurs from New Brunswick and James Bay south to Georgia and west to Minnesota (and possibly North Dakota) (Baker 1928a, Goodrich 1932, Dawley 1947, Freed 1957, Beetle 1973, Clarke 1981, Cvancara 1983, Jokinen 1983, Branson *et al.* 1987).

Planorbula armigera was found at only three sites during this survey: the Delaware River watershed (462) and the St. Lawrence River watershed (259B, 450). Harman & Berg (1971) located populations in the St. Lawrence-

Oswego River watershed, and Strayer (1987) reported the existence of museum specimens from the Hudson River basin.

Historical records indicate that this species is possibly more abundant across the State than recent collections imply. De Kay (1843) found it to be common in all parts of the State. It was later reported to occur in Herkimer and Otsego Counties (Lewis 1856, 1860, 1872); Riverdale, Bronx County (Prime 1880); Onondaga County (Beauchamp 1886b); Brighton, Monroe County (Walton 1891); Albany/Troy area, Albany and Rensselaer Counties (Marshall 1895); Pittsford, Monroe County (Marshall 1894); Irondequoit Bay, Lake Ontario, Monroe County (Baker 1900b); Jamaica, Queens County, Long Island (Wheat 1907a); Niagara and Erie Counties (Letson 1909); Cayuga Lake, Cayuga and Seneca Counties (Maury 1916); Oneida Lake, Onondaga County (Baker 1918a, b); Side's Pond, Randolph, Allegany State Park, Cattaraugus County (Pinney & Coker 1934); and Upper Ferdun Pond, between Piermont and Sparkhill, Rockland County (Bretet & Carswell 1952).

P. armigera inhabits relatively stagnant bodies of water, such as ditches, swales, subarctic muskeg, edges of lakes, permanent and temporary ponds, marshes, swamps, and slow streams. Its typical substratum consists of decaying allochthonous vegetation, such as logs and leaves (Baker 1928a, Goodrich 1932, Dawley 1947, Clarke 1981, Harman & Berg 1971, Jokinen 1983). The three sites located during this survey are a slow, marshy stream, a ditch, and a canal.

In a lake habitat, this species is bivoltine. The young first appear in late May, after the water warms to 20°C. Individuals become reproductively mature by autumn and produce a second generation in early September (Jokinen 1985). In temporary pond habitats, the species probably reproduces only once each year and aestivates under logs and leaf litter when the pond dries in summer (Jokinen, unpublished data).

Water chemistry data are available for two of the New York sites (259B and 462): pH: 7.2 and 8.4, conductivity: 371 and 156 μmhos/cm, Ca^{++}: 44 and 23 ppm, and Na^+: 10 and 1 ppm. Sixteen sites in Connecticut had pH: 5.7-8.9, conductivity: 53-262 μmhos/cm, Ca^{++}: 2-17 ppm, and Na^+: 3 ppm (Jokinen 1983). Values of pH for nine sites in central New York are 6.9-8.4 (7.5) (Harman & Berg 1971).

Micromenetus dilatatus (Gould, 1841)
Bugle sprite
Figs. 24b, 26

Shell flat above, convex below, 3 mm in diameter, tan to brown; umbilicus open, deep; spire flattened; whorls 3.0, bluntly squared around periphery; body whorl with sharp margin on level with spire; sutures impressed; aperture large, expanded, trumpet-shaped (Binney 1865).

Burch (1989) places this species in the genus *Menetus*.

This species occurs on the Atlantic coast from Nova Scotia to Florida and west to the Mexican Plateau, Texas, Oklahoma, and central and northern California (Branson 1963, Beetle 1973, Taylor 1981, Davis 1983, Thompson 1983, Jokinen 1983). A subspecies, *M. d. avus* (Pilsbry), extends south through the Florida peninsula to Haiti, Jamaica, and Panama (Thompson 1983, 1984a).

M. dilatatus was found across New York State in all the major watersheds during this survey, but it was more common in the southeastern part of the State: Delaware River watershed (455, 457, 466, 467, 468, 470, 474, 475); Hudson River watershed (283, 289, 290, 292, 304, 317, 384, 385, 386, 387, 459, 599, 602, 608, 612); Mississippi-Ohio River watershed (420, 421, 430A, 431); St. Lawrence River watershed (338, 354, 396); Susquehanna River watershed (478, 540, 568, 571, 573, 577, 579, 581); Atlantic coastal watershed (251); and the Hackensack River watershed (606). Harman & Berg (1971) collected only one specimen. It was found in a creek in Oswego County, Oswego River watershed. This species is widely distributed in the Hudson River drainage basin in Dutchess, Orange, and Ulster Counties (Strayer 1987).

There are only a few historical records of this species in New York State, including that of Lewis (1874). Later records are from Southold, Suffolk County, Long Island (Wheat 1907a); Lime Lake, Cattaraugus County (Letson 1909); pool by Quaker Run, Allegany State Park, Cattaraugus County (Pinney & Coker 1934); and Coan Pond, Oswego County (Burdick 1939).

M. dilatatus inhabits springs, streams, lakes, ponds, and quiet sections of rivers. In New York State, habitats studied during this survey include five rivers and streams, 20 lakes, 13 permanent ponds, one temporary pond, and a canal. Snails can be found on submerged allochthonous litter and wood, aquatic vegetation, rocks, and gravel (Taylor 1981, Davis 1983, Jokinen 1983, Thompson 1984a, Strayer 1987).

It appears that this species is multivoltine. In Connecticut, young first appear in late May, when water temperatures reach 22°C. A second reproductive period occurs in early August. There is an additional oviposition period in mid September, which might be just an extension of the August period (Jokinen 1985). Egg masses contain one to two eggs, which incubate one to two weeks at room temperature and hatch when shells are 0.3 mm in diameter. Snails are reproductively viable when the shell diameter reaches 1.9 mm (Jokinen 1983, unpublished data). This species has high colonization and dispersal rates (Jokinen 1987).

Water chemistry values for 38 sites in New York State are: pH: 5.8-9.5 (7.1 ± 0.1), conductivity: 28-495 μmhos/cm (141 ± 17), Ca^{++}: 1-35 ppm (7 ± 1), and Na^+: 1-63 ppm (11 ± 3). In Connecticut, values for 58 sites are: pH: 5.6-7.5, conductivity: 31-319 μmhos/cm, Ca^{++}: 1-22 ppm, and Na^+: 1-22 ppm (Jokinen 1983). One site in central New

York had a pH value of 7.1 (Harman & Berg 1971). In the Adirondack Mountains and surrounding lowlands, *M. dilatatus* occurs at all altitudes and in all types of water. It has a wide chemical tolerance range and is able to survive acidic, low calcium waters, conditions that some other species cannot.

Promenetus exacuous (Say, 1821)

Sharp sprite
Figs. 24c, 26

Shell much depressed, with acute periphery, 9 mm in diameter, tan to brown to reddish; umbilicus narrow, deep, exhibiting all volutions; spire flat; all whorls in same plane or apical whorls slightly sunken; nuclear whorl small, rounded; whorls 4.0, rapidly increasing in diameter, sloping in a flatly-rounded curve to acutely keeled periphery; base of body whorl flatly convex; sutures well-impressed; aperture obliquely, obtusely triangular or ovate; outer lip thin, acute, with superior part much produced above inferior part and expanded near periphery; slight varix thickening lip; callus a thin wash (Baker 1928a).

This species occurs from the Arctic boreal zone in Canada south to California, New Mexico, Nevada, Texas, and east to New England (Baker 1928a, Goodrich 1932, Leonard 1959, Branson 1963, Clarke 1973, Taylor 1981, Cvancara 1983, Jokinen 1983, Pratt 1983).

P. exacuous was found in all major New York State watersheds during this survey: Delaware River watershed (470, 472); Hudson River watershed (212, 265, 269, 284, 285, 290, 304, 317, 384, 461, 599, 602, 604, 607, 615); Mississippi-Ohio River watershed (427B); St. Lawrence River watershed (141A, 141D, 259A, 259B, 306, 313, 314, 336, 338, 339, 340, 390, 441, 445A, 494, 495, 497, 500, 502A, 502B, 512, 524A); Susquehanna River watershed (400, 582, 591, 592, 593); and Hackensack River watershed (606). Harman & Berg (1971) located scattered populations in the Oswego River watershed in central New York. This species is common in the Hudson River watershed (Strayer 1987).

There are numerous references to *P. exacuous* populations in New York. Early references report sites from northern and western New York (De Kay 1843); Herkimer County (Lewis 1860); Onondaga County (Beauchamp 1886b); Albany/Troy area, Albany and Rensselaer Counties (Marshall 1895); Cedar Lake, Herkimer County (Marshall 1894); Chautauqua Lake, Chautauqua County (Maury 1898, 1916); Jamaica, Queens County, Long Island (Wheat 1907a); Cazenovia Lake, Madison County (Henderson 1907); Lime Lake, Cattaraugus County; Erie and Niagara Counties (Letson 1909); Oneida Lake, Onondaga County (Baker 1916a, b; 1918a, b); Cayuga Lake, Cayuga and Seneca Counties (Maury 1916); Red Salamander Hill, Allegany State Park, Cattaraugus County (Pinney & Coker 1934); Hudson River from North Germantown, Columbia County, to Hyde Park, Dutchess County (Townes 1936);

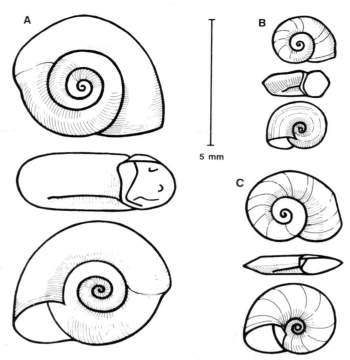

Fig. 24. Family Planorbidae, shells: a, *Planorbula armigera*; B. *Micromenetus dilatatus*; c, *Promenetus exacuous*. All illustrations are drawn to same scale.

Lake Ontario bays; and a backwater of Salmon River, Monroe County (Burdick 1939). More recent reports cite Upper Ferdun Pond, between Piedmont and Sparkhill, Rockland County (Bretet & Carswell 1952); Green Lake, Onondaga County (Harman 1970); Otsego Lake, Otsego County (Harman 1971, MacNamara & Harman 1975); and Conesus Lake, Livingston County (Wade & Vasey 1976).

This species lives in ponds, marshes, slow streams, lakes, sloughs, mountain stream mud flats, temporary ponds, intermittent streams, and swamps. It also inhabits the freshwater tidal Hudson River (Strayer 1987). During this survey, it was found in 14 river and stream sites, 16 lakes, 10 permanent ponds, two temporary ponds, and a marsh. The snails are usually on allochthonous decaying vegetation, like deciduous tree branches and decaying aquatic vegetation, such as floating *Typha* leaves. Other aquatic vegetation on which they can be found includes *Potamogeton*, *Spirodela*, *Riccia*, *Mimulus*, *Eleocharis*, *Scirpus*, and *Zinzania* spp.. Substrata can be mud, decaying organic matter, and shale (Baker 1927, 1928a; Goodrich 1932; Dawley 1947; Leonard 1959; Harman & Berg 1971; Pip & Paulishyn 1971; Harman 1972; Taylor 1981; Cvancara 1983; Jokinen 1983; Pratt 1983).

An isolated population in a temporary pond in Texas demonstrated a semelparous reproductive pattern with an early spring breeding period. January adult densities

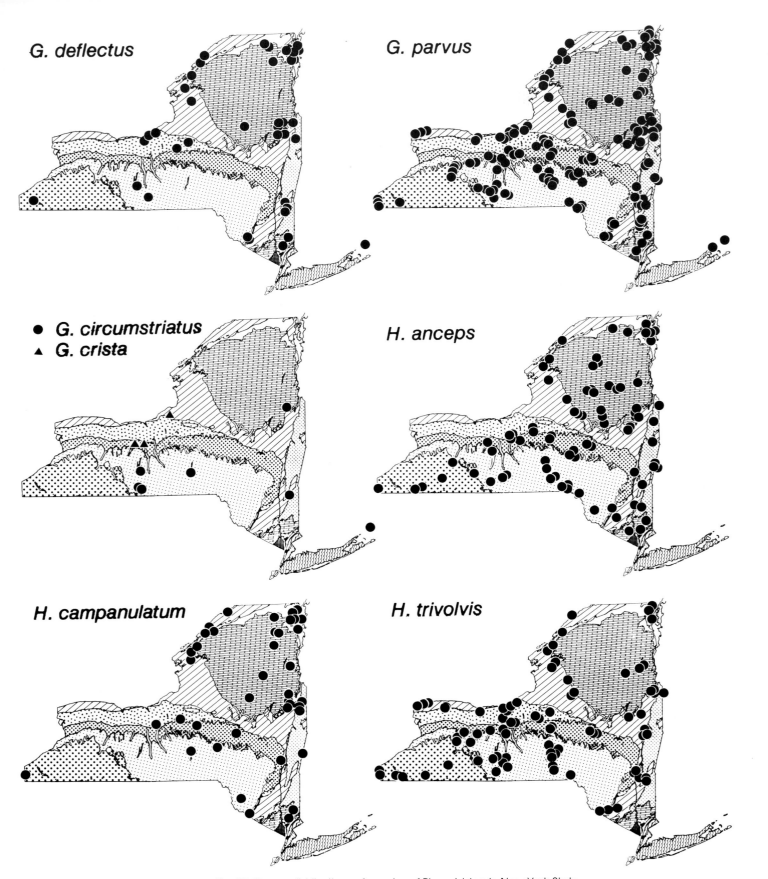

Fig. 25. Known distributions of species of Planorbidae in New York State.

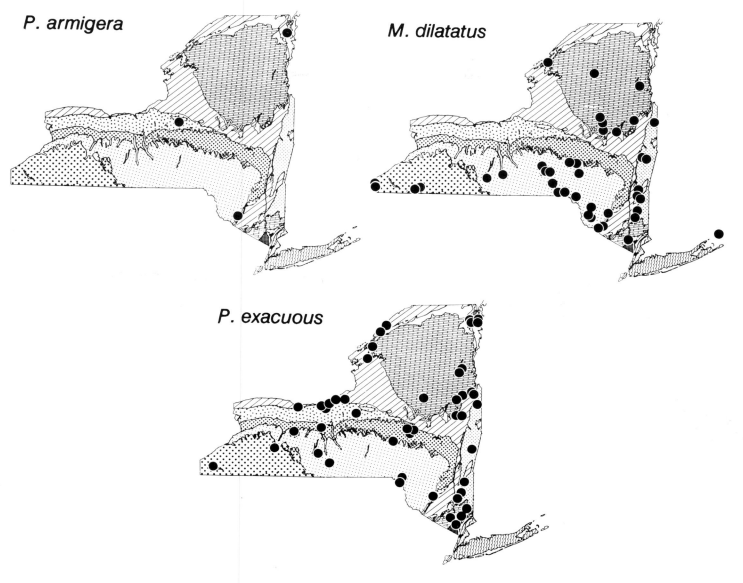

Fig. 26. Known distributions of species of Planorbidae in New York State.

were 13.5 snails/m^2. Postreproductive and juvenile densities in April were 139 snails/m^2 (Pratt 1983). In a Connecticut lake, this species was bivoltine. The first period of reproduction occurred from early July to mid August, when overwintered individuals 6 mm in diameter produced eggs. A second period occurred in early October when hatchlings from the earlier reproductive period reached shell diameters of 4 mm (Jokinen 1985).

Forty-three New York sites located during this survey had the following water chemistry values: pH: 6.3-9.6 (7.3 ± 0.1), conductivity: 62-1120 μmhos/cm (336 ± 35), Ca^{++}: 2-60 ppm (20 ± 2), and Na$^+$: 1-125 ppm (25 ± 5). Twenty-two Connecticut sites had values: pH: 5.7-8.9, conductivity: 24-319 μmhos/cm, Ca^{++}: 3-42 ppm, and Na$^+$: 1-2 ppm (Jokinen 1983). In North Dakota, water chemistry values were: pH:

7.6-8.9 (mean = 8.1, 8 sites), conductivity: 325-1500 μmhos/cm (880, 11 sites), and Ca^{++}: 95 ppm (one site) (Cvancara 1983). Sixteen sites in central New York had a pH range of 7.2-8.4 (8.4) (Harman & Berg 1971). In the Adirondack Mountains and surrounding lowlands, the distribution of *P. exacuous* is limited to sites with calcium greater than 9 ppm (Jokinen 1991). It appears that this species is only an occasional resident of acidic, low calcium habitats.

Family Ancylidae

Shell cap-shaped, up to 10 mm long, without coiling; aperture subovate to subelliptical; foot large, oval; tentacles short, blunt, cylindrical; eyes sessile at tentacle base; jaw in three parts; animal sinistral; genital and breathing pores on left side (Baker 1928a, Basch 1963).

Key to the Ancylidae

1a. Tentacle cores black ....*Laevapex fuscus*

1b. Tentacle cores white...2

2a. Sides of shell nearly parallel ....*Ferrissia parallela*

2b. Sides of shell not parallel..3

3a. Apex very off-center, almost to right edge of shell........
....*Ferrissia walkeri*

3b. Apex centered or only slightly off-center......................4

4a. Apex centered, shell sturdy; usually restricted to flow-
ing water ....*Ferrissia rivularis*

4b. Apex somewhat off-center, shell delicate; usually
found in quiet waters ....*Ferrissia californica*

Laevapex fuscus (C.B. Adams, 1840)

Dusky ancylid

Figs. 27a, 28

Shell depressed, 6 mm long, oval or slightly obovate, tan, translucent; anterior slope straight or slightly curved; posterior slope slightly convex; right lateral slope straight; left lateral slope straight or slightly convex; apex obtuse, smooth, not rising above general contour of, and placed behind middle of, shell, somewhat to right; animal with distinct black pigment in tentacle cores (Baker 1928a, Basch 1959).

The anatomy of this species is described in detail by Basch (1959).

L. fuscus has a disjunct distribution. One population occurs in northwestern Ontario. The other is distributed from southern Ontario and Quebec south to Florida, and west to Minnesota, Oklahoma, Iowa, Kansas and Texas

(Baker 1928a, Richards 1934, Dawley 1947, Basch 1963, McMahon & Aldridge 1976, Jokinen 1983, Thompson 1984a).

This species is only moderately common in New York. It occurs in the Hudson River watershed (212, 286, 292, 604), Mississippi-Ohio River watershed (431), St. Lawrence River watershed (259A, 263, 331, 332, 336, 337, 338, 339, 341, 409, 495, 497, 498, 500, 502A, 502B, 505, 524A, 531, 535), and the Susquehanna River watershed (400). It is absent from the Adirondack Mountains but common in the western lowlands (Jokinen 1991). Strayer (1987) noted a number of Hudson River basin sites, but Harman & Berg (1971) located only four sites in central New York.

Populations have been recorded from the lakes and waterfalls of the Mohawk River, Herkimer County (Lewis 1860); Schuyler's Lake, Otsego County (Lewis 1872); Tibbet's Brook, Riverdale, Bronx County (Prime 1880); Albany/Troy region, Albany and Rensselaer Counties, and the Normans Kill, Albany County (Marshall 1894, 1895); Flushing, Queens County, Long Island (Wheat 1907a); Oneida Lake, Oswego County (Baker 1916a, b; 1918a); Hudson River from Barrytown to Camelot, Dutchess County (Townes 1936); Sodus and Wolcott Creeks, Monroe County (Burdick 1939); Lake Mohegan, Peekskill, Westchester County; Flushing, Queens County, Long Island; Huntington, Suffolk County, Long Island (Jacobson & Emerson 1961); and Conesus Lake, Livingston County (Pinney & Coker 1934).

This species appears to be most common in still waters, such as impoundments, backwaters, ponds, and small lakes with a surface area of 10-100 hectares. On occasion it has been located in temporary habitats and rivers. Substrata are usually allochthonous organic matter, rocks, debris (such as bottles and cans), clam shells, and aquatic vegetation (water lilies, cattails, sedges, etc.) (Townes 1936, Dawley 1947, Basch 1963, Harman & Berg 1971, Jokinen 1983, Thompson 1984a, Strayer 1987). During this survey, populations were found at seven river and stream sites, 13 lake sites, three permanent ponds, two marshes, and a canal.

The snails feed on algal *Aufwuchs*, which vary in quality from habitat to habitat (McMahon *et al.* 1974). Temperate zone habitats with low productivity have snail populations with only one generation per year, slow maturation time, low fecundity (27 eggs/breeding season/adult), and long life span (over 400 days). In eutrophic, temperate zone habitats, there are two generations per year, the young grow rapidly, and egg production is high (70 eggs/adult). Longevity is 155 days for the spring generation and 320 days for the overwintering generation (McMahon 1975). A population in a small, eutrophic Connecticut lake had a generation that hatched in early July and, possibly, a second generation in autumn (Jokinen 1985). In warmer climates, such as occur in Texas, there can be as many as three generations per year (McMahon 1976). The snails are not simultaneous hermaphrodites as is common with most pulmonates. They are protandric, with the timing of the sex change caused by water temperatures and/or habitat trophic differences (Russell-Hunter & McMahon 1976).

Laevapex fuscus is absent from low diversity habitats, tends to have low colonization rates, competes well, and has high tolerance for poor resources (Jokinen 1987).

Twenty-four sites in New York State located during this survey had the following water chemistry values: pH: 6.9-8.4 (7.4 ± 0.1), conductivity: 93-905 µmhos/cm (375 ± 39), Ca^{++}: 4-44 ppm (27 ± 3), and Na^{+}: 1-122 ppm (28 ± 7). In Connecticut, 25 sites had these values: pH: 5.8-7.6, conductivity: 30-319 µmhos/cm, Ca^{++}: 2-22 ppm, and Na^{+}: 1-18 ppm (Jokinen 1983). In the region of the Adirondack Mountains, *L. fuscus* is limited to lowlands in habitats of Ca^{++} values greater than 9 ppm (Jokinen 1991). In general, it appears to be absent from mountainous regions throughout its range (Basch 1963).

Ferrissia rivularis (Say, 1817)
Creeping ancylid
Figs. 27b, 28

Shell ovate, 7 mm long, pale tan; margins regularly curving; ends rounded; anterior slope convex; posterior slope concave below apex, but more or less straight near peritreme; right lateral slope slightly convex or straight; left lateral slope straight; apex subacute, well-elevated, inclining somewhat toward right, situated half of distance from posterior end, radially striate; peritreme flat; shell widest in front of apex, narrowing posteriorly (Baker 1928a).

The anatomy of this species was described by Hoff (1940).

F. rivularis occurs from New Brunswick and Maine west to Saskatchewan and California and south to North Carolina (Baker 1928a, Goodrich 1932, Richards 1934, Taylor 1981, Cvancara 1983, Jokinen 1983).

Ferrissia rivularis is fairly common in New York and occurs in the Delaware River watershed (471), Hudson River watershed (286, 287, 369, 380, 453, 600, 601, 615), Mississippi-Ohio River watershed (421, 425), St. Lawrence River watershed (307, 335, 343, 372, 375, 516, 517, 527), and the Susquehanna River watershed (391, 538, 539, 550, 554, 556, 557, 567, 583). It is common in the Hudson River and its upland streams (Strayer 1987) and in the Oswego and Susquehanna watersheds (Harman & Berg 1971).

Reports of this species in New York State have been relatively common, a number of them being listed under the synonym *Ancylus tardus* Say (see Basch (1963) for synonymies). Early records cite the Mohawk River and lakes of Herkimer and Otsego Counties (Lewis 1856b, 1860, 1872); Onondaga County (Beauchamp 1886b); Genesee River and Irondequoit Bay, Lake Ontario, Monroe County (Walton 1891); Ontario County (Marshall 1894); Albany/Troy region, Albany and Rensselaer Counties (Marshall 1895); Chautauqua Lake, Chautauqua County (Maury 1898, 1916;

Townes 1937); Genesee River above first falls (Baker 1901); East Aurora, Erie County (Letson 1909); Cazenovia Lake, Madison County (Henderson 1907); Cayuga Lake, Cayuga and Seneca Counties (Maury 1916); Quaker Run, Allegany State Park, Cattaraugus County (Pinney & Coker 1934); and Findley Lake, Chautauqua County (Townes 1937).

This species almost always occurs in running water or river lakes (expansions of large rivers), although it does occur in lakes or ponds if the water is well-oxygenated. Preferred substrata are rocks, living and dead clam shells, submerged tree limbs, and debris such as bottles. Occasionally, snails are found on aquatic vegetation, such as cattails and lily pads (Goodrich 1932, Dawley 1947, Harman & Berg 1971, Taylor 1981, Cvancara 1983, Jokinen 1983, Strayer 1987). During this survey, *F. rivularis* was found at 23 river and stream sites, a lake, a river marsh, and three canals.

In temperate climates, the life history pattern of *F. rivularis* varies with the trophic richness of the habitat. In more eutrophic habitats, there are two generations per year. The spring generation lives for 11 months, and the summer generation lives for 3 months. Growth rates are high, and more eggs per limpet are laid. In the less eutrophic habitats, there is only one generation per year, longevity is 13 months, growth rates are slower, and each limpet produces fewer eggs (Burky 1971).

Water chemistry data for 27 sites surveyed in New York State are: pH: 6.1-8.2 (7.2 ± 0.1), conductivity: 56-530 µmhos/cm (268 ± 24); Ca^{++}: 1-50 ppm (18 ± 3), and Na^{+}: 1-45 ppm (14 ± 2). In Connecticut, ranges for 16 sites were: pH: 5.9-7.9, conductivity: 58-387 µmhos/cm, Ca^{++}: 2-26 ppm, and Na^{+}: 5-17 ppm (Jokinen 1983). North Dakota values were: pH: 7.9-9.3 (mean = 8.4, 52 sites), conductivity: 605-3150 µmhos/cm (1670, 25 sites), and Ca^{++}: 50-320 ppm (174, 33 sites) (Cvancara 1983). In the Adirondack region, *F. rivularis* inhabits waters in the western lowlands with high pH and calcium values (Jokinen 1991). In Connecticut and New York outside of the Adirondack Mountains, this species has a tolerance for low pH and low calcium, although it predominates in harder waters.

Ferrissia walkeri (Pilsbry & Ferriss 1907)
Cloche ancylid
Figs. 27c, 28

Shell moderately elevated, 5 mm long, thin, pale tan; anterior and lateral left slopes convex; posterior and lateral right slopes concave; apex depressed, radially striate, situated behind posterior third and much nearer right than left margin; peritreme oval (Pilsbry & Ferriss 1907).

The full distribution of this species is unknown. It occurs in Arkansas, Michigan, southern California, southern Oklahoma, Massachusetts, Vermont, and Connecticut (Basch 1963; Jokinen 1978b, 1983). It has not been reported from Canada (Clarke 1981).

F. walkeri was located at ten surveyed sites in the Delaware River watershed (466, 471), the Hudson River watershed (367, 588), the St. Lawrence River watershed (396, 445C, 493, 533), and the Susquehanna River watershed (546, 577). Neither Strayer (1987) nor Harman & Berg (1971) found this species in eastern or central New York.

There appears to be no historical literature on this species in New York State.

Individuals can be found on rocks, glass bottles, and allochthonous submerged twigs and leaves. In New England, where they are rare, they are found in exceptionally clear, soft water lakes that harbor no other snail species (Jokinen 1978b, 1983). In New York, *F. walkeri* has been found at three river and stream sites, four lakes, one permanent pond, one temporary pond, and one canal.

Little is known about the life history of this species.

Water chemistry values for the 10 sites in New York State are: pH: 6.4-8.2 (7.1 ± 0.2), conductivity: 60-2320 μmhos/cm (585 ± 219), Ca++: 1-89 ppm (24 ± 9), and Na+: 1-291 ppm (56 ± 28). In southern New England, *F. walkeri* was found only in lakes of acidic, exceptionally soft water (Jokinen 1978b, 1983).

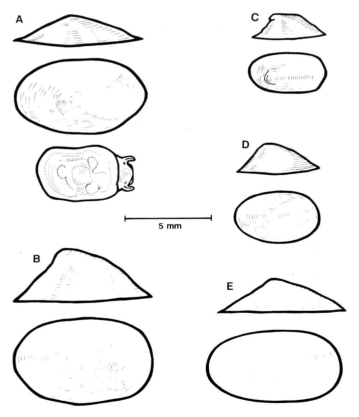

5 mm

Fig. 27. Family Ancylidae, shells: a, *Laevapex fuscus*, lateral and dorsal views of shell and dorsal view of body showing black tentacle cores; b, *Ferrissia rivularis*; c, *F. walkeri*; d, *F. californica*; e, *F. parallela*. All shell illustrations are drawn to same scale.

Ferrissia californica (Rowell, 1863)
Fragile ancylid
Figs. 27d, 28

Shell small, fragile, 3.5 mm long, sometimes septate; sides nearly parallel, but diverging anteriorly; anterior slope convex; posterior slope concave; apex elevated, acute, curved backwards in midline or slightly to right, approximately 2/3 of shell length from anterior end (Tryon 1863, Clarke 1981).

Synonyms for *F. californica* are *F. fragilis* (Tryon), *F. novangliae* (Walker), and *F. shimekii* (Pilsbry).

In Canada, this species has been recorded from southwest British Columbia, Quebec, and southern Ontario (Clarke 1981). Farther south, populations have been recorded from New England to Maryland and Kentucky, southwest to northern Mexico and California (Leonard 1959, McMahon & Aldridge 1976, Gerberich 1981, Taylor 1981, Jokinen 1983, Branson *et al.* 1987, Blinn *et al.* 1989). Although Basch (1963) referred to *F. hendersoni* Walker as a subspecies of *F. californica*, Thompson (1984a) separated the two into distinct species, with *F. californica* occurring north of North Carolina and *F. hendersoni* occurring from North Carolina to Florida. It is not known if Beetle's (1968) Ocracoke Island, North Carolina, location is for *F. californica* or *F. hendersoni*.

During this survey, this species was found scattered throughout New York State in the Hudson River watershed (269, 276, 277, 293, 317, 318, 383, 384, 459, 602), the St. Lawrence River watershed (279, 280, 332, 341, 354, 402, 409, 412, 436, 439, 502B, 524B), the Susquehanna River watershed (571), and the Atlantic coastal drainages (253). Harman & Berg (1971) did not report it from central New York, but Strayer (1987) located it in the Hudson River basin.

Marshall (1893) recorded *F. californica* from Canandaigua Lake, Ontario County.

This species prefers the quiet waters of lakes, ponds, and ditches, but it occasionally lives in slowly flowing streams. It is common on allochthonous organic material, aquatic plants, such as cattails and pond lilies, and occasionally rocks (Jokinen 1978b, 1983; Clarke 1981; Taylor 1981). During this survey, populations were found in three river and stream sites, 10 lakes, 10 ponds, and a marsh.

A study in Arizona showed that *F. californica* individuals are first active in early April, when they can be found on the undersides of lily pads (*Nuphar luteum polysepalum* (Engelm.) E.O. Beal). The snails exhibit negative phototaxis; when the lily pads are turned over, they migrate to the lower surfaces. Average densities were 112 snails/m². By early November the snails disappear from the lily pads and are found among the fibrous roots of *Carex senta* Boott. Diet consists primarily of closely adnate diatoms, including *Epithemia* spp. and *Cocconeis* spp. Ribbon-like chains of *Synedra* sp. and *Nitzchia* sp. are not ingested (Blinn *et al.* 1989).

In an eutrophic Connecticut lake, *F. californica* appears to have a bivoltine or trivoltine reproductive pattern with eggs produced during two or three periods: late May,

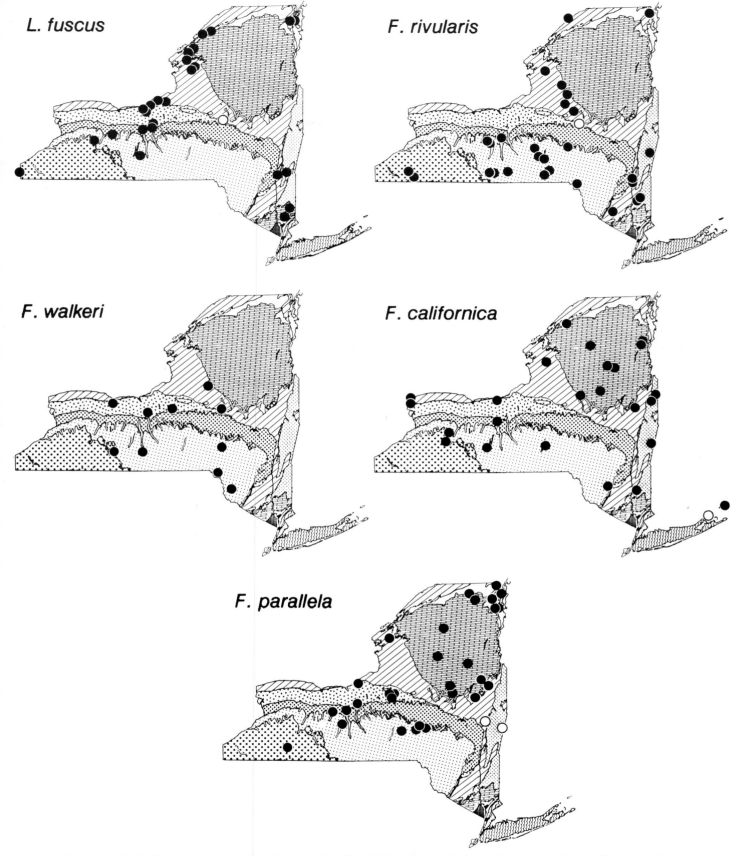

Fig. 28. Known distribution of species of Ancylidae in New York State. Closed circles indicate records from the present survey, and open circles indicate records from museum specimens.

early August, and mid September (Jokinen 1985). In the northeastern United States, *F. californica* is ubiquitous in habitats of low to high snail diversity, but it is less frequently found in those with high diversity (Jokinen 1987).

Water chemistry values for 23 New York State sites studied during this survey are: pH: 5.8-8.2 (7.2 ± 0.1), conductivity: 28-1755 μmhos/cm (340 ± 74), Ca^{++}: 2-74 ppm (23 ± 4), and Na^{+}: 1-122 ppm (17 ± 6). Values for 46 Connecticut sites are: pH: 5.1-7.5, conductivity: 38-346 μmhos/cm, Ca^{++}: 1-27 ppm, and Na^{+}: 1-40 ppm (Jokinen 1983). This species occurs at all altitudes and in all types of water in the region of the Adirondack Mountains and surrounding lowlands (Jokinen 1991).

Ferrissia parallela (Haldeman, 1841)
Oblong ancylid
Figs. 27e, 28

Shell narrow, elongate, 8 mm long, pale tan; lateral margins nearly straight; ends well-rounded; anterior slope long, slightly convex; posterior slope shorter than anterior, straight to slightly concave; right lateral slope nearly straight; left lateral slope slightly convex; shell radially striate; apex subacute, slightly turned toward right, slightly anterior of shell center (Baker 1928a).

In Canada, this species occurs from Newfoundland and Prince Edward Island west to southern Manitoba (Clarke 1981). In the United States, it ranges from New England west to Minnesota and, possibly, North Dakota; it appears to be limited to the northern tier of states (Baker 1928a, Dawley 1947, Basch 1963, Cvancara 1983, Jokinen 1983).

Ferrissia parallela is relatively common in New York State but appears to be limited to the northern sections of the watersheds: Hudson River watershed (270, 273, 300, 304, 385, 386); Mississippi-Ohio River watershed (415); St. Lawrence River watershed (141C, 260, 262, 263, 308, 336, 349, 351, 357, 361, 448B, 449, 450, 498, 515, 518B, 524A, 534); and Susquehanna River watershed (536, 574, 579, 581, 582). Strayer (1987) noted its presence in the Hudson River basin, and Harman & Berg (1971) found it scattered throughout central New York.

This species has been reported from Herkimer County (Lewis 1860); Schuyler's Lake, Otsego County (Lewis 1872); Riverdale, Bronx County (Prime 1880); Onondaga County (Beauchamp 1886b); Charlotte, Monroe County (Walton 1891); Little Lakes, Herkimer County, and the Normans Kill, Albany, Albany County (Marshall 1894); Albany/Troy region, Albany and Rensselaer Counties (Marshall 1895); "Chippawa" (Letson 1909); Fall Creek, Ithaca, Tompkins County, and Cayuga Lake, Cayuga and Seneca Counties (Maury 1916); Oneida Lake, Oswego and Onondaga Counties (Baker 1916a, b; 1918a; Pratt 1923; Harman & Berg 1970; Sodus Bay, Wayne County, and Little Sodus Bay, Cayuga County, Lake Ontario (Burdick 1939); woodland pond near Annsville, Westchester County (Jacobson & Emerson 1961); Canandarago Lake, Otsego County (Harman 1973); Moe Pond, Otsego County (MacNamara & Harman 1975); and Lewis, Oneida, and Jefferson Counties (Buckley 1977).

F. parallela usually is found in permanent, quiet waters, and it is associated with aquatic vegetation, including *Oedogonium, Cladophora, Nymphaea, Nuphar, Castalia, Typha, Scirpus, Vallisneria, Potamogeton, Zinzania,* and *Sparganium* spp. in water 0.5-11.0 m deep (Baker 1918a, 1928a; Dawley 1947; Basch 1963; Harman & Berg 1971; Harman 1972; Jokinen 1983). During this survey, this species was located in four river and stream sites, 12 lakes, seven permanent ponds, two ditches, three marshes, and two canals.

Little appears to be known about the life history of this species. *F. parallela* is ubiquitous in habitats of different diversities (Jokinen 1987).

Water chemistry values for 26 New York State sites studied during this survey are: pH: 6.0-8.0 (7.0 ± 0.1), conductivity: 33-760 μmhos/cm (204 ± 35), Ca^{++}: 2-44 ppm (15 ± 2), and Na^{+}: 1-122 ppm (16 ± 6). For 11 sites in Connecticut, values are: pH: 6.2-7.6; conductivity: 31-319 μmhos/cm, Ca^{++}: 2-35 ppm, and Na^{+}: 2-18 ppm (Jokinen 1983). In central New York (Harman & Berg 1971), pH values ranged from 7.3-8.1 (mean = 7.7). For the Adirondack Mountains and associated lowlands, *F. parallela* is ubiquitous relative to altitude and water chemistry (Jokinen 1991).

GLOSSARY

adnate - grown together.

aestivation - a period of dormancy in the summer when ponds or streams dry up.

allochthonous - having an external origin (e.g., allochthonous organic matter in a lake consists of terrestrial leaf litter and branches that have fallen into the lake).

AMNH - American Museum of Natural History, New York City.

aperture - opening, or mouth, of shell.

apex - tip of shell, pointed in most species.

Aufwuchs - see periphyton.

auriculate - ear-like in shape.

autochthonous - having an internal origin (e.g., autochthonous organic matter in a lake consists of aquatic vegetation and its remains).

Barge Canal - the reconstructed Erie Canal system, plus the Champlain Canal.

bifid - divided into two lobes.

bifurcate - divided into two branches.

biomass - the weight of living material within an area; the higher the biomass, the higher the productivity.

bivoltine - having two generations per year.

body whorl - last whorl of a spiral shell, containing the aperture.

Ca^{++} - calcium ion concentration in solution, usually measured as parts per million (ppm) or milligrams per liter (mg/l); soft water has less than 5 ppm dissolved calcium.

callus - deposit of shelly material that covers inner lip or columellar region of shell.

campanulate - shaped like a bell.

canaliculate - channeled or grooved.

carinate - keeled or ridged.

channeled - grooved or formed like a channel.

chink - a narrow opening; in shells, it refers to a slit-like umbilicus.

collabral - conforming to shape of the outer lip at an earlier growth stage as shown by growth lines.

columella - the centrally located pillar surrounding the axis of coiling of a spiral shell.

conductivity or specific conductance - the ability of a solution to conduct an electrical current, measured in micromhos per centimeter (μmhos/cm). High conductivity results from high dissolved ion concentration.

corneous - consisting of a horny substance.

decollated - "beheaded" or cut off, like the apex of some shells.

dentate - with points or nodules resembling teeth.

detritus - dead organic matter and its associated microbes.

dextral - coiled to the right (opposite of sinistral). When held with the apex up and the aperture facing the viewer, the aperture of a dextral shell is on the right side.

dioecious - having male reproductive organs in one individual and female in another.

discoidal - shaped like a flat disc.

distal - far from a point of origin or attachment (opposite from proximal).

emarginate - bluntly notched.

escarpment - land form consisting of a precipitous face of a ridge.

eutrophic - rich in nutrients, especially phosphorus.

expanded - spread out, as the lip of some shells.

filiform - thread-like.

fusiform - tapering from the middle toward each end.

gelatinous - jelly-like.

globose - inflated and approaching the shape of a sphere.

habitat - type of site where a species normally lives and grows.

hardness - quality of water that prevents soap from dissolving; primarily caused by high calcium and magnesium ion concentrations.

herbivorous - feeding on plants.

hermaphrodite - an individual having both male and female reproductive organs.

hirsute - appearing hairy.

imperforate - not perforated or umbilicated.

impressed - marked by a furrow.

inflated - swollen, enlarged.

iteroparous - having more than one reproductive season, as in viviparid snail species that can produce several broods in a lifetime.

keeled - with a more or less sharp projection at the periphery.

lacrimate - shaped like a tear drop.

lamellae - thin plates or blade-like ridges.

lentic habitats - standing waters, such as lakes and ponds.

limpet - a snail with a noncoiled shell variously peaked to flattened

lip - rim of aperture.

littoral - the shallow, near-shore region of a body of water, often defined as the band from zero depth to the edge of the rooted-plant zone.

lotic habitats - running waters, such as streams and rivers.

macrophytic vegetation - rooted aquatic plants.

malleated - appearing as if shaped by hammering.

mantle - fleshy tissue that secretes the molluscan shell and lies against its inner surface.

marl - earthy lake or river deposit consisting of clay and calcium carbonate.

monoecious - hermaphroditic, with the sexes united in one individual.

multispiral - consisting of many whorls.

multivoltine - pertaining to populations having more than three generations per year.

MCZ - Museum of Comparative Zoology, Harvard University.

Na$^+$ - sodium ion concentration in solution, usually measured in parts per million (ppm) or milligrams per liter (mg/l); most inland waters in New York State have low salinity, less than 5 ppm sodium.

notched - nicked or indented, like the anterior canal of some snails.

nucleus - the first whorl, or nuclear whorl, of a spiral shell.

NYSM - New York State Museum, Albany.

oblique - slanting, like the apertures of some shells that are not parallel to the longitudinal axis.

obovate - ovate with a narrow end at the base

obtuse - dull or blunt, like the apex of some shells, with the angle exceeding 90 degrees.

operculate - having an operculum.

operculum - horny or shelly, plate-like structure attached to the foot of most prosobranch snails. It seals the shell aperture when the animal is contracted within.

orbicular - circular, disc-like.

outer lip - the portion of the lip on the right side of the aperture of a dextral shell or the left side of the aperture of a sinistral shell.

ovately conic - shaped like an egg, but with a somewhat conical apex.

oviparous - bringing forth young in an egg that hatches after it is laid.

ovoviviparous - bringing forth young in an egg that hatches before it is laid.

parietal - the part of the aperture adjacent to the preceding whorl.

parthenogenic - capable of reproduction without fertilization of eggs.

patelliform - shaped like a flattened-out cone; obtusely conic.

paucispiral - consisting of few spirals or less than one complete spiral.

pellucid - transparent or clear.

penultimate whorl - the whorl preceding the last, or body, whorl.

periostracum - the organic outer layer of the shell.

periphyton - the biota attached to submerged surfaces; the community of sessile, or attached, organisms on lake and stream plants, rocks, etc.

peristome - lip.

peritreme - outer rim of a limpet shell.

pH - a measure of acidity or alkalinity of a solution (values 1-6 indicate decreasing acidity, 7 is neutral, and values 8-14 indicate increasing alkalinity).

phenotypic plasticity - the capacity of a species to respond to an environment physically or physiologically without genetic change.

plait - a spiral, flattened ridge on the columella.

planorboid - flat and orb-like, coiled approximately in a single-plane.

planospiral - coiled in a single plane.

prosobranchs - gill-breathing, operculate, and usually dioecious snails of the subclass Prosobranchia.

proximal - nearest end of an object (opposite from distal).

pseudobranch - a secondary gill formed from an extension of the mantle in some pulmonate snails.

pulmonates - "lung" breathing, nonoperculate, monoecious snails of the subclass Pulmonata.

radiating - extending from a common center.

reflected - bent back, like the lip of some snails.

retractile - capable of being drawn in.

rimate - provided with a small hole or crack, like the place where an umbilicus is very narrowly open.

semelparous - having only one reproductive period, usually with a large number of offspring, during a life span.

septate - with one or more internal, shelly partitions.

sessile - attached without a stem.

shouldered - shaped like a shoulder, with a flattened upper surface bounded by a definite angle.

sinistral - coiled to the left (opposite of dextral). When held with apex up and aperture toward the viewer, the aperture of a sinistral shell is on the left side.

spire - the upper portions of spiral shells from above body whorl to the apex.

spire angle - angle at the apex formed by the cone of the spire.

sp. - abbreviation for species (singular).

spp. - abbreviation for species (plural).

striae - impressed lines or narrow grooves.

striated - marked by lines or striae.

subangulated - moderately angled.

subcarinated - moderately carinated.

subconical - moderately conical.

subcylindrical - moderately cylindrical.

subglobose - moderately globose.

sulcated - grooved

suture - external juncture line between adjacent shell whorls.

trifid - separated into three lobes.

trivoltine - having three generations per year.

truncate - terminating abruptly, appearing as if cut squarely off.

turbinate - having the form of a top.

turreted - having whorls forming a high conical spiral.

ultradextral - anatomically sinistral; but appearing dextral because of the angle at which the shell is held.

umbilicated - with a wide umbilicus.

umbilicus - the opening at the base of a shell, opposite the spire; the hollow center, if present, of the axis of rotation of a shell.

univoltine - having one generation per year.

varix - a thickened mark on the surface of a shell at a former position of the aperture lip during a period of arrested growth.

vernal - occurring in the spring.

verge - in some snails, an organ of the male genital tract that bears the penis.

volution - a complete turn of a spiral shell; a whorl.

whorl - a single complete turn of a spiral shell, a volution.

REFERENCES CITED

Abbott, R.T. 1948. A potential snail host of oriental schistosomiasis in North America (*Pomatiopsis lapidaria*). Proceedings of the United States National Museum 98: 57-68.

Abbott, R.T. 1950. Snail invaders. Natural History 59: 80-85.

Abbott, R.T. 1980. Morris Karl Jacobson (1906-1980). The Nautilus 94: 129.

Abbott, R.T. & M.E. Young (eds.). 1973. American Malacologists. American Malacologists, Falls Church, Virginia. 494 pp.

Adams, C.B. 1840. Descriptions of thirteen new species of New England shells. Boston Journal of Natural History 3: 318-332.

Aldrich, T.H. 1869. Partial list of shells found near Troy, New York. Annual Report of The Regents of the University of the State of New York, on the Condition of the State Cabinet of Natural History and the Historical and Antiquarian Collection Annexed Thereto 22 (1868): 17-24.

Aldridge, D.W. 1982. Reproductive tactics in relation to life-cycle bioenergetics in three natural populations of the freshwater snail, *Leptoxis carinata*. Ecology 63: 196-208.

Alexander, R.C. 1947. Freshwater mollusks of Cape May, New Jersey. The Nautilus 61: 1-3.

Ancey, C.F. 1887. Description of North American shells. Conchologists' Exchange 2: 79-80.

Anonymous. 1873. List of Long Island Mollusca, presented to the State Museum. Annual Report on the New York State Museum of Natural History by The Regents of the University of the State of New York 25 (1872): 35-38.

Anonymous. 1875a. List of Gould types of Mollusca, in the collection of the State Museum. Annual Report on the New York State Museum of Natural History by The Regents of the University of the State of New York 27 (1873): 47-55.

Anonymous. 1875b. List of land and fresh-warter shells presented to State Museum by T.H. Aldrich. Annual Report on the New York State Museum of Natural History by The Regents of the University of the State of New York 27 (1873): 43-46.

Anonymous. 1882. List of shells presented to the State Museum by Dr. James Lewis, March 15, 1875. Annual Report on the New York State Museum of Natural History, by The Regents of the University of the State of New York 35 (1881): 112-117.

Anthony, J.G. 1840. Descriptions of three new species of shells. Boston Journal of Natural History 3: 278-279.

Archer, A.F. 1939. The ecology of the mollusca of the Edwin S. George Reserve, Livingston County, Michigan. Occasional Papers of the Museum of Zoology, University of Michigan 398: 1-24.

Baily, A. 1891. Shells of the Erie Canal. The Nautilus 5: 23.

Baily, J.L., Jr. 1929. Fresh water Mollusca in brackish water. The Nautilus 6: 36.

Baily, J.L., Jr. 1931. Some data on growth, longevity, and fecundity in *Lymnaea columella* Say. Biologia Generalis 7: 407-428.

Baker, F.C. 1898. The molluscan fauna of western New York. Transactions of the Academy of Science of Saint Louis 8: 71-94.

Baker, F.C. 1899. Notes on the Mollusca of Owasco Lake, N.Y. The Nautilus 13: 57-59.

Baker, F.C. 1900a. The gross anatomy of *Limnaea emarginata* Say, var. *Mighelsi*, Binney. Bulletin of the Chicago Academy of Sciences 2: 189-224.

Baker, F.C. 1900b. Shell collecting near Rochester, N.Y. The Nautilus 14: 69-71.

Baker, F.C. 1901. The molluscan fauna of the Genesee River. American Naturalist 35: 659-664.

Baker, F.C. 1909. Range of *Lymnaea umbilicata*. The Nautilus 23: 80.

Baker, F.C. 1911. The Lymnaeidae of North and Middle America, recent and fossil. Chicago Academy of Sciences Special Publications 3: 1-539.

Baker, F.C. 1913. Mollusca from Wyoming Co., N.Y. The Nautilus 27: 54.

Baker, F.C. 1916a. The fresh-water Mollusca of Oneida Lake, New York. The Nautilus 30: 5-9.

Baker, F.C. 1916b. The relation of mollusks to fish in Oneida Lake. New York State College of Forestry at Syracuse University Technical Publication 4: 1-366.

Baker, F.C. 1918a. Further notes on the Mollusca of Oneida Lake, New York; The mollusks of Lower South Bay. The Nautilus 31: 81-93.

Baker, F.C. 1918b. The productivity of invertebrate fish food on the bottom of Oneida Lake, with special reference to the mollusks. New York State College of Forestry at Syracuse University Technical Publication 9: 1-264.

Baker, F.C. 1918c. The relation of shellfish to fish in Oneida Lake, New York. New York State College of Forestry at Syracuse University Circular 21: 1-34.

Baker, F.C. 1919a. Mollusks infested with parasitic worms. The Nautilus 32: 97-98.

Baker, F.C. 1919b. A new species of *Physa* from New York State. The Nautilus 33: 11-13.

Baker, F.C. 1927. Molluscan associations of White Lake, Michigan: A study of a small inland lake from an ecological and systematic viewpoint. Ecology 8: 353-370.

Baker, F.C. 1928a. The fresh water Mollusca of Wisconsin. Part I. Gastropoda. Wisconsin Geological and Natural History Survey Bulletin 70: 1-494.

Baker, F.C. 1928b. The Mollusca of Chautaugua Lake, New York, with descriptions of a new variety of *Ptychobranchus* and of *Helisoma*. The Nautilus 42: 48-60.

Baker, F.C. 1945. The molluscan family Planorbidae. University of Illinois Press, Urbana, Illinois. 530 pp.

Barnes, J.K. 1990. Biology and immature stages of *Sciomyza varia* (Diptera: Sciomyzidae), a specialized parasitoid of snails. Annals of the Entomological Society of America 83: 925-938.

Barnese, L.E. & R.L. Lowe. 1990. Comparative grazing efficiency of pulmonate and prosobranch snails. Journal of the North American Benthological Society 9: 35-44.

Basch, P.F. 1959. The anatomy of *Laevapex fuscus*, a freshwater limpet. Miscellaneous Publication of the Museum of Zoology, University of Michigan 108:1-56.

Basch, P.F. 1963. A review of the recent fresh-water limpet snails of North America. Bulletin of the Museum of Comparative Zoology, Harvard University 129(8): 401-461.

Beauchamp, W.M. 1886a. Erosion of freshwater shells. Conchologists' Exchange 1: 37.

Beauchamp, W.M. 1886b. Land and fresh-water shells of Onondaga County, with a supplemental list of New York species. Baldwinsville, N.Y. 12 pp.

Beauchamp, W.M. 1887. Notes on American shells. Conchologists' Exchange 2: 114-115

Beauchamp, W.M. 1891. Notes on familiar mollusks. The Nautilus 5: 52-53.

Beetle, D.E. 1960. Noteworthy records of Wyoming Mollusca. The Nautilus 73: 155-157.

Beetle, D.E. 1968. *Laevapex fuscus* on the Outer Banks of North Carolina. The Nautilus 81: 107.

Beetle, D.E. 1973. Freshwater mollusks from coastal Virginia. The Nautilus 87: 29.

Berg, C.O. 1963. Ch. 6, Middle Atlantic States. Pages 191-238 *in* D.G. Frey (ed.), Limnology in North America. University of Wisconsin Press, Madison, Wisconsin. 734 pp.

Berg, C.O. & L. Knutson. 1978. Biology and systematics of the Sciomyzidae. Annual Review of Entomology 23: 239-258.

Berry, E.G. 1943. The Amnicolidae of Michigan: Distribution, ecology, and taxonomy. Miscellaneous Publications of the Museum of Zoology (University of Michigan) 57: 1-68.

Binney, W.G. 1865. Land and fresh-water shells of North America. Part II. Pulmonata, Limnophila and Thalassophila. Smithsonian Miscellaneous Collections 143: 1-161.

Binney, W.G. 1867. Notes sur quelques espèces de mollusques fluviatiles de l'Amérique du Nord. Journal de Conchyliology 15: 427-432.

Blair, L. & J.B. Sickel. 1986. A survey of the freshwater gastropods in selected habitats of Land Between the Lakes, Kentucky and Tennessee. Transactions of the Kentucky Academy of Science 47: 6-12.

Blinn, D.W., R.E. Truitt, & A. Pickart. 1989. Feeding ecology and radular morphology of the freshwater limpet *Ferrissia fragilis*. Journal of the North American Benthological Society 8: 237-242.

Boag, D.A. & J.A. Bentz. 1980. The relationship between simulated seasonal temperatures and depth distributions in the freshwater pulmonate, *Lymnaea stagnalis*. Canadian Journal of Zoology 58: 198-201.

Boag, D.A. & P. S. M. Pearlstone. 1979. On the life cycle of *Lymnaea stagnalis* (Pulmonata: Gastropoda) in southwestern Alberta. Canadian Journal of Zoology 57: 353-362.

Boag, D.A., C. Thomson, & J. Van Es. 1984. Vertical distribution of young pond snails (Basommatophora: Pulmonata): implications for survival. Canadian Journal of Zoology 62: 1485-1490.

Boerger, H. 1975. A comparison of life cycles, reproductive ecologies, and size-weight relationships in *Helisoma anceps*, *H. campanulatum*, and *H. trivolvis*. Canadian Journal of Zoology 53: 1812-1824.

Bondeson, P. 1950. A comparative morphological-biological analysis of the egg capsules of freshwater pulmonate gastropods. Hygrophila, Basommatophora, Pulmonata. Naturhistorisk Museum, Aarhus, Denmark. 208 pp.

Boss, N.C., T.G. Laman, & H.D. Blankespoor. 1984. Dispersal movements of four species of pulmonate and operculate snails in Douglas Lake, Michigan. The Nautilus 98: 80-83.

Branson, B.A. 1963. Notes on snail distribution and leech feeding habits in Oklahoma. The Nautilus 76: 148-149.

Branson, B.A. 1987. Keys to the aquatic Gastropoda known from Kentucky. Transactions of the Kentucky Academy of Science 48: 11-19.

Branson, B.A. & D.L. Batch. 1969. Notes on exotic mollusks in Kentucky. Nautilus 82: 102-106.

Branson, B.A. & D.L. Batch. 1983. Gastropod and sphaeriacean clam records for streams west of the Kentucky River drainage, Kentucky. Transactions of the Kentucky Academy of Science 44: 8-12.

Branson, B.A., D. Batch, & S. Call. 1987. Distribution of aquatic snails (Mollusca: Gastropoda) in Kentucky with notes on fingernail clams (Mollusca: Sphaeriidae: Corbiculidae). Transactions of the Kentucky Academy of Science 48: 62-70.

Bretet, R. & E.J. Carswell. 1952. A rich locality in the New York City area. The Nautilus 65: 100-102.

Bright, R.C. 1981. A new record of *Valvata sincera ontariensis* F.C. Baker from Minnesota. The Nautilus 95: 20.

Bronmark, C. 1988. Effects of vertebrate predation on freshwater gastropods - an exclosure experiment. Hydrobiologia 169: 363-370.

Broughton, J.G., D.W. Fisher, Y.W. Isachsen, & L.V. Rickard. 1966. Geology of New York: A short account. New York State Museum and Science Service Educational Leaflet 20: 1-50.

Brown, D.S. 1980. Freshwater snails of Africa and their medical importance. Taylor & Francis Ltd., London. 487 pp.

Brown, K.M. 1979. The adaptive demography of four freshwater pulmonate snails. Evolution 33: 417-432.

Brown, K.M. 1982. Resource overlap and competition in pond snails: An experimental analysis. Ecology 63: 412-422.

Brown, K.M. 1991. Mollusca: Gastropoda. Pages 285-314 *in* J.H. Thorp & A.P. Covich (eds.), Ecology and classification of North American freshwater invertebrates. Academic Press, San Diego. 911 pp.

Brown, K.M., D. Varza, & T.D. Richardson. 1989. Life histories and population dynamics of two subtropical snails (Prosobranchia: Viviparidae). Journal of the North American Benthological Society 8: 229-242.

Browne, R.A. 1978. Growth, mortality, fecundity, biomass and productivity of four lake populations of the prosobranch snail, *Viviparus georgianus*. Ecology 59: 742-750.

Browne, R.A. 1982. Freshwater snails (Mollusca: Gastropoda) of North America (north of Mexico). Malacological Review 12: 97-100.

Buckley, D.A. 1977. The distribution and ecology of the aquatic molluscan fauna of the Black River drainage basin in northern New York. State University of New York College at Oneonta Biological Field Station (Cooperstown) Occasional Paper 6: 1-276.

Burch, J.B. 1959. Chromosomes of aquatic pulmonate snails (Basommatophora). Annual Report of the American Malacological Union 25: 9-10.

Burch, J.B. 1960. Chromosome studies of aquatic pulmonate snails. The Nucleus 3: 177-208.

Burch, J.B. 1982. Freshwater snails (Mollusca: Gastropoda) of North America. Environmental Monitoring and Support Laboratory, Office of Research and Development, United States Environmental Protection Agency (Cincinnati, Ohio), EPA-600/3-82-026: 1-294.

Burch, J.B. 1989. North American freshwater snails. Malacological Publications, Hamburg, Michigan. 365 pp.

Burdick, G.E. 1939. VI. Studies on the invertebrate fish food in certain lakes, bays, streams and ponds of the Lake Ontario watershed (inclusive of ecological data on Mollusca). Pages 147-166 *in* A biological survey of the Lake Ontario watershed. No. XVI. State of New York Conservation Department, Annual Report 29 (Supplement).

Burky, A.J. 1971. Biomass turnover, respiration and interpopulation variation in the stream limpet *Ferrissia rivularis* (Say). Ecological Monographs 41: 235-251.

Call, R.E. 1902. The European pond snail. Science 16: 65.

Carriker, M.R. 1946. Morphology of the alimentary system of the snail *Lymnaea stagnalis appressa* Say. Transactions of the Wisconsin Academy of Science, Arts, and Letters 38: 1-88.

Chamberlain, N.A. 1958. Life history studies of *Campeloma decisum*. The Nautilus 72: 22-29.

Clampitt, P.T. 1970. Comparative ecology of the snails *Physa gyrina* and *Physa integra* (Basommatophora: Physidae). Malacologia 10: 113-151.

Clampitt, P.T. 1973. Substratum as a factor in the distribution of pulmonate snails in Douglas Lake, Michigan. Malacologia 12: 379-399.

Clampitt, P.T. 1974. Seasonal migratory cycle and related movements of the fresh-water pulmonate snail, *Physa integra*. American Midland Naturalist 92: 275-300.

Clarke, A.H. 1973. The freshwater mollusca of the Canadian Interior Basin. Malacologia 13: 1-500.

Clarke, A.H. 1978. The Asian apple snail, *Cipangopaludina chinensis* (Viviparidae) in Oneida Lake, New York. The Nautilus 92: 134.

Clarke, A.H. 1979. Gastropods as indicators of trophic lake changes. The Nautilus 93: 138-142.

Clarke, A.H. 1981. The freshwater molluscs of Canada. National Museum of Natural Sciences, National Museum of Canada, Ottawa. 446 pp.

Clarke, A.H. & C.O. Berg. 1959. The freshwater mussels of central New York with an illustrated key to the species of northeastern North America. Cornell University Agricultural Experiment Station (Ithaca, New York) Memoir 367: 1-79.

Cleland, D.M. 1954. A study of the habits of Valvata piscinalis (Müller), and the structure and function of the alimentary canal and reproductive system. Proceedings of the Malacological Society of London 30: 167-203.

Clench, W.J. 1962. A catalogue of the Viviparidae of North America with notes on the distribution of Viviparus georgianus Lea. Occasional Papers on Mollusks (Museum of Comparative Zoology, Harvard University) 2: 261-288.

Clench, W.J. & S.L.H. Fuller. 1965. The genus Viviparus (Viviparidae) in North America. Occasional Papers on Mollusks (Museum of Comparative Zoology, Harvard University) 2: 385-412.

Clench, W.J. & R.D. Turner. 1955. The North American genus Lioplax in the family Viviparidae. Occasional Papers on Mollusks (Museum of Comparative Zoology, Harvard University) 2: 1-20.

Covich, A.P. 1981. Chemical refugia from predation for thin-shelled gastropods in a sulfide-enriched stream. Verhandlungen. Internationale Vereinigung für Theoretische und Angewandte Limnologie 21: 1632-1636

Currier, A.O. 1868. List of the shell-bearing Mollusca of Michigan, especially of Kent and adjoining counties. Miscellaneous Publication (Kent Science Institute) 1: 1-12.

Cvancara, A.M. 1983. Aquatic mollusks of North Dakota. Report of Investigation No. 78. North Dakota Geological Survey, Fargo. 141 pp.

Davis, D.S. 1983. The freshwater snail, Menetus dilatatus, (Planorbidae) in Nova Scotia. The Nautilus 97: 74-76.

Davis, G.M. 1967. The systematic relationship of Pomatiopsis lapidaria and Oncomelania hupensis formosana (Prosobranchia: Hydrobiidae). Malacologia 6: 1-143.

Dawley, C. 1947. Distribution of aquatic mollusks in Minnesota. American Midland Naturalist 38: 671-697.

Dazo, B.C. 1965. The morphology and natural history of Pleurocera acuta and Goniobasis livescens (Gastropoda: Cerithiacea: Pleuroceridae). Malacologia 3: 1-80.

De Kay, J.E. 1843 (1844). The New-York Fauna. Division II. Invertebrated animals. Class VI. Mollusca, part 5. Zoology of New York, or the New-York fauna. Natural History of New York. Albany. 271 pp.

DeWitt, R.M. & W.C. Sloan. 1958. The innate capacity for increase in numbers in the pulmonate snail, Lymnaea columella. Transactions of the American Microscopical Society 77: 290-294.

Dundee, D.S. 1957. Aspects of the biology of Pomatiopsis lapidaria (Say) (Mollusca: Gastropoda: Prosobranchia). Miscellaneous Publications of the Museum of Zoology (University of Michigan) 100: 1-37.

Dundee, D.S. 1974. Catalog of introduced molluscs of eastern North America (north of Mexico). Sterkiana 55: 1-37.

Dussart, G.B.J. 1979. Life cycles and distribution of the aquatic gastropod molluscs Bithynia tentaculata (L.), Gyraulus albus (Müller), Planorbis planorbis (L.) and Lymnaea peregra (Müller) in relation to water chemistry. Hydrobiologia 67: 223-239.

Eckblad, J.W. 1973. Population studies of three aquatic gastropods in an intermittent backwater. Hydrobiologia 41: 199-219.

Eisenberg, R.M. 1966. The regulation of density in a natural population of the pond snail, Lymnaea elodes. Ecology 47: 889-906.

Eisenberg, R.M. 1970. The role of food in the regulation of the pond snail, Lymnaea elodes. Ecology 51: 680-684.

Elliott, C.A. 1979. Biographical dictionary of American Science. The Seventeenth through the Nineteenth Centuries. Greenwood Press, Westport, Connecticut. 360 pp.

Evermann, B.W. & E.L. Goldsborough. 1901. Notes on the fishes and mollusks of Lake Chautauqua, New York. Report of the Forest, Fish and Game Commission of the State of New York 6: 357-366.

Evermann, B.W. & E.L. Goldsborough. 1902. Notes on the fishes and mollusks of Lake Chautauqua, New York. Report of the United States Commissioner of Fish and Fisheries 1901: 169-175.

Eversole, A.G. 1978. Life cycles, growth and population bioenergetics in the snail, Helisoma trivolvis (Say). Journal of Molluscan Studies 44: 209-222.

Finch, R.G. 1925. The story of the New York State canals, historical and commercial information. Albany, 23 pp.

Fluck, W.H. 1933. Valvata simplex Gould. The Nautilus 46: 19-22.

Franzen, D.S. & A.B. Leonard. 1942. A preliminary survey of the Mollusca of Kingman County, Kansas. Transactions of the Kansas Academy of Science 45: 334-343.

Freas, D.D. 1950a. Some snails in the city parks. The Nautilus 63: 140-141.

Freas, D.D. 1950b. *Viviparus chinensis.* The Nautilus 64: 35-36.

Freas, D.D. 1951. *Viviparus contectoides* in New York City. The Nautilus 64: 102.

Freed, S. 1957. Land and freshwater mollusks of Union County, New Jersey. The Nautilus 70: 135-136.

Fretter, V. & A. Graham. 1962. British prosobranch molluscs; their functional anatomy and ecology. The Ray Society, London. 755 pp.

Fretter, V. & J. Peake (eds.). 1975. Pulmonates. Volume 1. Functional anatomy and physiology. Academic Press, New York. 417 pp.

Garlinghouse, H.M. 1976. William Seward Teator (1860 - 1930). The Nautilus 90: 148-149.

Gerberich, A. 1981. The endangered and threatened freshwater mollusks of Maryland. Pages 245-266 *in* Maryland Natural Heritage Program, Threatened and endangered plants and animals of Maryland, Annapolis.

Gilbertson, D.E., O.O. Kassim, & J.L. Stumpf. 1978. Studies on the biology of *Bulimnea megasoma* (Say) (Gastropoda: Pulmonata). Journal of Molluscan Studies 44: 145-150.

Gomez, J.D., M. Vargas, & E.A. Malek. 1986. Freshwater molluscs of the Dominican Republic. The Nautilus 100: 130-134.

Goodrich, C. 1932. The Mollusca of Michigan. Michigan Handbook Series no. 3. University Museums, University of Michigan, Ann Arbor. 120 pp.

Goodrich, C. 1939a. Pleuroceridae of the Mississippi River basin exclusive of the Ohio River system. Occasional Papers of the Museum of Zoology, University of Michigan 406: 1-4.

Goodrich, C. 1939b. Pleuroceridae of the St. Lawrence River Basin. Occasional Papers of the Museum of Zoology, University of Michigan 404: 1-4.

Goodrich, C. 1942. The Pleuroceridae of the Atlantic Coastal Plain. Occasional Papers of the Museum of Zoology, University of Michigan 456: 1-6.

Goodrich, C. 1945. *Goniobasis livescens* of Michigan. Miscellaneous Publications of the Museum of Zoology, University of Michigan 64: 1-36.

Goodrich, C. & H. van der Schalie. 1939. Aquatic mollusks of the Upper Peninsula of Michigan. Miscellaneous Publications of the Museum of Zoology, University of Michigan 43: 1-45.

Gould, A.A. 1841. Report on the invertebrata of Massachusetts, comprising the Mollusca, Crustacea, Annelida, and Radiata. Folsom, Wells and Thurston, Cambridge, Massachusetts. 373 pp.

Haldeman, S.S. 1841. A monograph of the limniades or freshwater univalve shells of North America. J. Dobson, Philadelphia. 231 pp.

Harman, W.N. 1968a. Replacement of pleurocerids by *Bithynia* in polluted waters of central New York. The Nautilus 81: 77-83.

Harman, W.N. 1968b. *Valvata piscinalis* in Cayuga Lake, N.Y. The Nautilus 81: 143-144.

Harman, W.N. 1970. Alterations in the molluscan fauna of a meromictic marl lake. The Nautilus 84: 21-30.

Harman, W.N. 1971. Mollusks of Otsego Lake, New York. The Nautilus 85: 70-71.

Harman, W.N. 1972. Benthic substrates: their effect on freshwater mollusca. Ecology 53: 271-277.

Harman, W.N. 1973. The Mollusca of Canadarago Lake and a new record for *Lasmigona compressa* (Lea). The Nautilus 87: 114.

Harman, W.N. 1982. Pictorial keys to the aquatic mollusks of the upper Susquehanna. State University of New York College at Oneonta Biological Field Station (Cooperstown) Occasional Paper 9: 1-13.

Harman, W.N. & C.O. Berg. 1970. Fresh-water Mollusca of the Finger Lakes region. Ohio Journal of Science 70: 146-150.

Harman, W.N. & C. O. Berg. 1971. The freshwater snails of central New York. Search (Cornell University Agricultural Experiment Station, Ithaca, New York) 1(4): 1-68.

Harman, W.N. & J.L. Forney. 1970. Fifty years of change in the molluscan fauna of Oneida Lake, New York. Limnology and Oceanography 15: 454-460.

Harman, W.N. & D.F. Jackson. 1967. A late winter survey of the macroscopic invertebrates in Green Lake, Fayetteville, N.Y. Pages 188-214 *in* D. F. Jackson, Some aspects of meromixis. Department of Civil Engineering, Syracuse University, Syracuse, N.Y.

Harrison, R.E. & W.A.G. Charleston. 1976. The epidemiology of *Fasciola hepatica* infections in sheep on a *Lymnaea columella* habitat in the Manawatu. New Zealand Veterinary Journal 24: 11-17.

Harrison, R.E. & W.A.G. Charleston. 1977. An examination of the marsh microhabitats of *Lymnaea tomentosa* and *L. columella* (Mollusca: Gastropoda) by path analysis. New Zealand Journal of Zoology 4: 395-399.

Heard, W.H. 1963. Reproductive features of *Valvata.* The Nautilus 77: 64-68.

Henderson, J.B. 1907. Mollusks of Cazenovia, N. Y. The Nautilus 20: 97-98.

Henderson, J.B. 1918. Colorado mollusk notes. The Nautilus 32: 71.

Hendrix, S.S. 1986. Population biology of the pleurocerid snail, *Leptoxis carinata* (Brug.) in Marsh Creek, Adams County, PA (abstract). American Malacological Bulletin 4: 119.

Herrington, H.B. 1947. *Acella haldemani* in Ontario, Canada. The Nautilus 61: 20-25.

Herrmann, S.A. & W.N. Harman. 1975. Population studies on *Helisoma anceps* (Menke) (Gastropoda: Planorbidae). The Nautilus 89: 5-11.

Hoff, C.C. 1936. Studies on the lymnaeid snail, *Fossaria parva* (Lea). Part I. Winter habits. Transactions of the Illinois State Academy of Science 29: 259-262.

Hoff, C.C. 1937. Studies on the lymnaeid snail, *Fossaria parva* (Lea). Part II. Seasonal life history. Transactions of the Illinois State Academy of Science 30: 303-306.

Hoff, C.C. 1940. Anatomy of the ancylid snail, *Ferrissia tarda* (Say). Transactions of the American Microscopical Society 59: 224-242.

Horst, T.J. & R.R. Costa. 1975. Seasonal migration and density patterns of the freshwater snail, *Amnicola limosa*. The Nautilus 89: 56-59.

Hubbard, J.W. & S. Smith. 1865. Catalogue of the Mollusca of Staten Island, N.Y. Annals of the New York Academy of Sciences 8(4-5): 151-154.

Hubendick, B. 1951. Recent Lymnaeidae, their variation, morphology, taxonomy, nomenclature and distribution. Kungligu Svenska Vetenskaps-Akademiens Handlingar 3: 1-222.

Hubricht, L. 1960. *Pomatiopsis lapidaria* on the southern Atlantic coastal plain, with remarks on the status of *P. praelonga* and *P. hinkleyi*. The Nautilus 74: 33-34.

Humason, G.L. 1972. Animal tissue techniques. W.H. Freeman, San Francisco. 641 pp.

Humphreys, 1910. Recent fresh-water fossils from Bronx Borough, New York City. The Nautilus 23: 10-11.

Hunter, R.D. 1975a. Growth, fecundity, and bioenergetics in three populations of *Lymnaea palustris* in Upstate New York. Ecology 56: 50-63.

Hunter, R.D. 1975b. Variation in populations of *Lymnaea palustris* in upstate New York. American Midland Naturalist 94: 401-420.

Hunter, R.D. 1988. Effects of acid water on shells, embryos, and juvenile survival of *Planorbella trivolvis* (Gastropoda: Pulmonata): a laboratory study. Journal of Freshwater Ecology 4: 315-327.

Hunter, R.D. & W.W. Lull. 1977. Physiological and environmental factors influencing the calcium-to-tissue ratio in populations of freshwater pulmonate snails. Oecologia 29: 205-218.

Hyman, L.H. 1967. The invertebrates, Volume VI, Mollusca I. McGraw-Hill Book Company, New York. 792 pp.

Imlay, M.J., J.W. Arthur, B.J. Halligan, & J.H. Steinmetz. 1981. Life cycle of the freshwater snail *Campeloma decisum* (Viviparidae) in the laboratory. The Nautilus 95: 84-88.

Ingram, W.M. 1941. A winter thaw as a factor in reducing a freshwater mollusk population. The Nautilus 55: 32.

Ingram, W.M. & K.W. Kenyon. 1947. *Anodonta* and associated molluks from Stow Lake, Golden Gate Park, San Francisco, California. The Nautilus 61: 51-53.

Jacobson, M.K. 1945. A list of mollusks from Warren County, New York. The Nautilus 59: 26-29.

Jacobson, M.K. 1951. Two new molluscan records from the New York area. The Nautilus 64: 104.

Jacobson, M.K. 1965. New records for New York and New Jersey. The Nautilus 78: 83-85.

Jacobson, M.K. 1969. On *Lymnaea pseudopinguis* (F.C. Baker). The Nautilus 82: 110-112.

Jacobson, M.K. & W.K. Emerson. 1961. Shells from Cape Cod to Cape May, with special reference to the New York City Area. Dover Publishers, New York. 152 pp.

Johnson, C.W. 1915. Fauna of New England. 13. List of the Mollusca. Occasional Papers of the Boston Society of Natural History 7: 1-231.

Johnson, R. (ed.) 1904. The Twentieth Century biographical dictionary of notable Americans. The Biographical Society, Boston.

Johnson, R.I. 1945. *Radix auricularia* (L.) in Vermont. The Nautilus 58: 144-145.

Johnson, R.I. 1959. The types of Corbiculidae and Sphaeriidae (Mollusca: Pelecypoda) in the Museum of Comparative Zoology, and a bio-bibliographic sketch of Temple Prime, an early specialist in the group. Bulletin of the Museum of Comparative Zoology 120: 431-479.

Jokinen, E.H. 1978a. The aestivation pattern of a population of *Lymnaea elodes* (Say) (Gastropoda: Lymnaeidae). American Midland Naturalist 100: 43-53.

Jokinen, E.H. 1978b. Habitats of two species of freshwater limpet (*Ferrissia*: Ancylidae) from New England. The Nautilus 92: 156-160.

Jokinen, E.H. 1982. *Cipangopaludina chinensis* (Gastropoda: Viviparidae) in North America, review and update. The Nautilus 96: 89-95.

Jokinen, E.H. 1983. The freshwater snails of Connecticut. State Geological and Natural History Survey of Connecticut. Department of Environmental Protection Bulletin 109: 1-83.

Jokinen, E.H. 1984. Periostracal morphology of viviparid snail shells. Transactions of the American Microscopical Society 103: 312-316.

Jokinen, E.H. 1985. Comparative life history patterns within a littoral zone snail community. Verhandlungen. Internationale Vereinigung für Theoretische und Angewandte Limnologie 22: 3292-3299.

Jokinen, E.H. 1987. Structure of freshwater snail communities: species-area relationships and incidence categories. American Malacological Bulletin 5: 9-19.

Jokinen, E.H. 1991. The malacofauna of the acid and non-acid lakes and rivers of the Adirondack Mountains and surrounding lowlands, New York State, USA. Verhandlungen. Internationale Vereinigung für Theoretische und Angewandte Limnologie 24: 2940-2946.

Jokinen, E.H., J. Guerette, & R. Kortmann. 1982. The natural history of an ovoviviparous snail, *Viviparus georgianus* (Lea), in a soft-water eutrophic lake. Freshwater Invertebrate Biology 1(4): 2-17.

Katsigianis, T.S. & W.N. Harman. 1973. Variations in the radular teeth of *Helisoma anceps* (Menke). The Nautilus 87: 5-7.

Kershner, M.W. & D.M. Lodge. 1990. Effect of substrate architecture on aquatic gastropod-substrate associations. Journal of the North American Benthological Society 9: 319-326.

Kesler, D.K. 1980. Seasonal abundance of *Amnicola limosa* (Hydrobiidae) eggs and individuals in a Rhode Island pond. The Nautilus 94: 25-26.

Kesler, D.K. 1981. Periphyton grazing by *Amnicola limosa*: an enclosure-exclosure experiment. Journal of Freshwater Ecology 1: 51-59.

Kesler, D.K., E.H. Jokinen, & W.R. Munns, Jr. 1986. Trophic preferences and feeding morphology of two pulmonate species from a small New England pond, U.S.A. Canadian Journal of Zoology 64: 2570-2475.

Kesler, D.K. & W.R. Munns, Jr. 1989. Predation by *Belostoma flumineum* (Hemiptera) an important cause of mortality in freshwater snails. Journal of the North American Benthological Society 8: 342-350.

Krull, W.H. 1931. Importance of laboratory-raised snails in helminthology with life history notes on *Gyraulus parvus*. Occasional Papers of the Museum of Zoology, University of Michigan 226: 1-10.

Lanciani, C.A. & W.N. Harman. 1968. Snail shells as oviposition sites of water mites. The Nautilus 82: 34-35.

Lang, B.Z. & N.O. Dronen, Jr. 1970. Eggs and attachment sites for *Valvata lewisi*. The Nautilus 84: 9-12.

Lea, I. 1834. Observations on the naiades; and descriptions of new species of that and other families. Supplement. Transactions of the American Philosophical Society 5: 23-119.

Lea, I. 1838. Description of new freshwater and land shells. Transactions of the American Pholosophical Society 1-111.

Lea, I. 1841. Continuation of Mr. Lea's paper on fresh water and land shells. Proceedings of the American Philosophical Society 2: 30-34.

Leonard, A.B. 1959. Handbook of gastropods in Kansas. Miscellaneous Publication, University of Kansas Museum of Natural History 20: 1-224.

Letson, E.J. 1901. Post-Pliocene fossils of the Niagara River gravels. New York State Museum Bulletin 45: 238-252.

Letson, E.J. 1905. Check list of the Mollusca of New York. New York State Museum Bulletin 88: 1-112.

Letson, E.J. 1909. A partial list of shells found in Erie and Niagara Counties, and the Niagara Frontier. Bulletin of the Buffalo Society of Natural Sciences 9: 239-245.

Lewis, J. 1856a. Mollusca in Little Lakes, Otsego Co., N.Y. Proceedings of the Academy of Natural Science of Philadelphia 8: 259-260.

Lewis, J. 1856b. Shellbearing species of Mollusca observed in portions of Herkimer and Otsego Counties, New York. Proceedings of the Boston Society of Natural History 6: 2-4.

Lewis, J. 1860. Catalogue of the mollusks in the vicinity of Mohawk, New York. Proceedings of the Academy of Natural Science of Philadelphia 12: 17-19.

Lewis, J. 1868. Notes on certain fresh-water shells, observed in the vicinity of Mohawk, N.Y. American Journal of Conchology 4: 2-4.

Lewis, J. 1872. Shells of Herkimer and adjacent counties in the State of New York. Proceedings of the Academy of Natural Science of Philadelphia 24: 97-107.

Lewis, J. 1874. Land and freshwater shells of the State of New York. Bulletin of the Buffalo Society of Natural Sciences 2: 127-142.

Linnaeus, C. 1758. Systema naturae per regna tria naturae, edition 10, volume 1. Holmiae (= Stockholm). 824 pp.

Loker, E.S. 1979. Effects of *Schistosomatium douthitti* infection on the growth, survival, and reproduction of *Lymnaea catascopium*. Journal of Invertebrate Pathology 34: 138-144.

Ludlam, S.D., K.S. Hutchison, & G.E. Henderson. 1973. The limnology of Stockbridge Bowl, Stockbridge, Massachusetts. Water Resources Research Center (University of Massachusetts, Amherst) Completion Report FY-73-4, 59 pp.

MacNamara, M.C. & W.N. Harman. 1975. Further studies of the Mollusca of the Otsego Lake area. The Nautilus 89: 87-90.

Malek, E.A. & F.B. Cogswell. 1980. *Lymnaea (Pseudosuccinea) columella* in Columbia. The Nautilus 94: 112.

Malek, E.A. & P. Chrosciechowski. 1964. *Lymnaea (Pseudo-succinea) columella* from Venezuela, and notes on the distribution of *Pseudosuccinea*. The Nautilus 78: 54-56.

Marshall, W.B. 1892. Notes on the colonization of fresh-water shells. The Nautilus 5: 133-134.

Marshall, W.B. 1894. Land and fresh-water shells of New York exhibited at the World's Columbian Exposition, Chicago, Illinois, 1893. Annual Report of the New York State Museum 47 (1893): 49-75.

Marshall, W.B. 1895. List of shells inhabiting the vicinity of Albany and Troy, N.Y. Annual Report of the New York State Museum 48 (1894): 641-647.

Mattice, J.C. 1972. Production of a natural population of *Bithynia tentaculata* L. (Gastropoda, Mollusca). Ekologia Polska 20(39): 525-539.

Mattox, N.T. 1938. Morphology of *Campeloma rufum*, a parthenogenetic snail. Journal of Morphology 62: 243-261.

Maury, C.J. 1898. Chautauqua Lake shells, Elementary Natural History Series, No. 1., Harris Co., Ithaca, New York. 45 pp.

Maury, C.J. 1908. An interglacial fauna in Cayuga Valley and its relation to the Pleistocene of Toronto. Journal of Geology 16: 565-567.

Maury, C.J. 1916. Freshwater shells from central and western New York. The Nautilus 30: 29-33.

McCoy, Jr., C.J. 1964. On *Lymnaea auricularia* in Colorado. The Nautilus 78: 66.

McCraw, B.M. 1970. Aspects of the growth of the snail *Lymnaea palustris* (Müller). Malacologia 10: 399-413.

McDonald, S.L. 1969. The biology of *Lymnaea stagnalis* L. (Gastropoda: Pulmonata). Sterkiana 36: 1-17.

McKay, C.R. & D.J. Hartzband. 1970. Propylene phenoxytol: narcotic agent for unsorted benthic invertebrates. Transactions of the American Microscopical Society 89: 53-54.

McKillop, W.B. 1985. Distribution of aquatic gastropods across the Ordovician dolomite and Precambrian granite contact in southeastern Manitoba, Canada. Canadian Journal of Zoology 63: 278-288.

McKillop, W.B. & A.D. Harrison. 1972. Distribution of aquatic gastropods across an interface between the Canadian Shield and limestone formations. Canadian Journal of Zoology 50: 1433-1445.

McMahon, R.F. 1975. Growth, reproduction and bioenergetic variations in three populations of a freshwater limpet *Laevapex fuscus* (C. B. Adams). Proceedings of the Malacological Society of London 41: 331-351.

McMahon, R.F. 1976. Growth, reproduction and life cycle in six Texan populations of two species of freshwater limpets. American Midland Naturalist 95: 174-185.

McMahon, R.F. & D.W. Aldridge. 1976. New distribution records for three species of freshwater limpet (Pulmonata: Ancylidae) from north central Texas. Malacological Review 9: 124-125.

McMahon, R.F., R.D. Hunter, & W.D. Russell-Hunter. 1974. Variation in *Aufwuchs* at six freshwater habitats in terms of carbon biomass and of carbon:nitrogen ratio. Hydrobiologia 45: 391-404.

Mearns, E.A. 1898. A study of the vertebrate fauna of the Hudson Highlands, with observations on the Mollusca, Crustacea, Lepidoptera, and the flora of the region. Bulletin of the American Museum of Natural History 10: 303- 352.

Medcof, J.C. 1940. On the life cycle and other aspects of the snail, *Campeloma*, in the Speed River. Canadian Journal of Research 18(D): 165-172.

Meier-Brook, C. 1976a. An improved relaxing technique for mollusks using pentobarbital. Malacological Review 9: 115-117.

Meier-Brook, C. 1976b. The influence of varied relaxing and fixing conditions on anatomical characters in a *Planorbis* species. Basteria 40: 101-106.

Meier-Brook, C. & C.H. Kim. 1977. Notes on ciliary feeding in the Korean *Bithynia* species. Malacologia 16: 159-163.

Menke, C.T. 1830. Synopsis methodica molluscorum generum omnium et specierum earum, quae in Museo Menkeano adservantur; cum synonymia critica et novarum specierum diagnosibus. Georgi Uslar, Pyrmonti. 168 pp.

Metcalf, A.L. & R. Smart. 1972. Records of introduced mollusks: New Mexico and western Texas. The Nautilus 85: 144-145.

Mitchell, C.T. 1899. Notes of the Mollusca of Canandaigua Lake region, New York. The Nautilus 13: 87-90.

Morris, J.R. & D.A. Boag. 1982. On the dispersion, population structure, and life history of a basommatophoran snail, *Helisoma trivolvis*, in central Alberta. Canadian Journal of Zoology 60: 2931-2940.

Morrison, J.P.E. 1932. Studies on the life history of *Acella haldemani* ("Desh.," Binney). Transactions of the Wisconsin Academy of Science, Arts and Letters 27: 397-413.

Müller, O.F. 1774. Vermium terrestrium et fluviatilium, seu animalium infusiorum, helminthicorum et testaceorum, non marinorum, succincta historia, volume 2. Heineck et Faber, Havinae and Lipsiae. 214 pp.

Nylander, O.O. 1943. The Lymnaeidae of northern Maine and adjacent Canadian provinces and notes on Anson Allen and his collection. University of Maine Studies, Second Series, No. 58. Maine Bulletin 46: 1-43.

Oughton, J. 1938. *Valvata piscinalis* (Müller) in the Great Lakes. The Nautilus 52: 30-32, 60-62.

Pace, G.L., E.J. Szuch, & R.W. Dapson. 1979. Depth distribution of three gastropods in New Mission Bay, Lake Michigan. The Nautilus 93: 31-36.

Papp, J.P. 1977. Clinton's $7,000,000 ditch, the Erie Canal, Albany to Buffalo. Historical Publications, Schenectady, New York. 48 pp.

Payne, R. 1959. The Canal Builders. Macmillan Co., New York. 278 pp.

Pilsbry, H.A. 1890. Preliminary notices of new Anmicolidae. The Nautilus 4: 52-53.

Pilsbry, H.A. 1897. *Campeloma decisum* Say, reversed. The Nautilus 10: 118.

Pilsbry, H.A. 1898. Notes on new and little-known Amnicolidae. The Nautilus 12: 42-44.

Pilsbry, H.A. 1919. Elizabeth Letson Bryan, Sc.D. The Nautilus 32: 142-143.

Pilsbry, H.A. & J.H. Ferriss. 1907 (1906). Mollusca of the Ozarkian fauna. Proceedings of the Academy of Natural Sciences of Philadelphia 58: 529-567.

Pinel-Alloul, B. & E. Magnin. 1971. Cycle vital et croissance de *Bithynia tentaculata* L. (Mollusca, Gastropoda, Prosobranchia) du Lac St-Louis près de Montréal. Canadian Journal of Zoology 49: 759-766.

Pinel-Alloul, B. & E. Magnin. 1973. Observations sur le cycle vital et la croissance d'*Amnicola limosa* (Say) (Mollusca, Gastropoda, Prosobranchia) du lac Saint-Louis près de Montréal. Canadian Journal of Zoology 51: 311-313.

Pinel-Alloul, B. & E. Magnin. 1979. Étude de la nourriture de *Lymnaea catascopium catascopium* (Gastropoda, Lymnaeidae) dans le lac Saint-Louis, Fleuve Saint-Laurent, Québec. Le Naturaliste Canadien 106: 277-287.

Pinney, M.E. & R.E. Coker. 1934. Terrestrial and freshwater gastropods of the Allegany State Park in New York State. The Nautilus 48: 55-60.

Pip, E. 1987. Ecological differentiation within the genus *Helisoma* (Gastropoda: Planorbidae) in central Canada. The Nautilus 101: 33-44.

Pip, E. & W.F. Paulishyn. 1971. The ecology and distribution of *Promenetus exacuous* Say (Gastropoda: Planorbidae) in southern Manitoba. Canadian Journal of Zoology 49: 367-372.

Pratt, H.S. 1923. Preliminary report on the parasitic worms of Oneida Lake, New York. Roosevelt Wild Life Bulletin 23: 55-71.

Pratt, W.L. 1983. Living *Promenetus exacuous* (Pulmonata: Planorbidae) from North Central Texas. The Nautilus 97: 73-74.

Prime, T. 1880. The Mollusca of Riverdale, New York City. Forest and Stream 15: 245.

Pullan, N.B., F.M. Climo, & C.B. Mansfield. 1972. Studies on the distribution and ecology of the family Lymnaeidae (Mollusca: Gastropoda) in New Zealand. Journal of the Royal Society of New Zealand 2: 393-405.

Rafinesque, C.S. 1831. Enumeration and account of some remarkable, natural objects of the cabinet of Prof. Rafinesque in Philadelphia; being animals, shells, plants, and fossils, collected by him in North America, between 1816 and 1831. Philadelphia. 8 pp.

Rehder, H.A. 1949. Some land and freshwater mollusks from the coastal region of Virginia and North and South Carolina. The Nautilus 62: 121-126.

Richardot-Coulet, M. & L. Alfaro-Tijera. 1985. The life cycle and ecology of the freshwater Planorbidae *Armiger crista* L. Journal of Molluscan Studies 51: 31-51.

Richards, H.G. 1929. Freshwater snails in brackish water. The Nautilus 42: 129-130.

Richards, H.G. 1934. A list of mollusks of the District of Columbia and vicinity. American Midland Naturalist 15: 85-88.

Richardson, T.D. & K.M. Brown. 1989. Secondary production of two subtropical snails (Prosobranchia: Viviparidae). Journal of the North American Benthological Society 8: 229-236.

Robertson, I.C. 1933. *Viviparus contectoides* at Buffalo. The Nautilus 46: 106.

Robertson, I.C. 1945. *Valvata piscinalis* (Müller) in Lake Erie. The Nautilus 59: 36.

Robertson, I.C. & C.L. Blakeslee. 1948. The Mollusca of the Niagara Frontier region. Bulletin of the Buffalo Society of Natural Sciences 19 (3): 1-191.

Rollo, C.D. & M.D. Hawryluk. 1988. Compensatory scope and resource allocation in two species of aquatic snails. Ecology 69: 147-156.

Rowell, J. 1863. *Gundlachia* Pfeiffer. Proceedings of the California Academy of Sciences 3: 21-22.

Russell, R.H. 1971. The appearance of *Pseudosuccinea columella* (Say) in Arizona. The Nautilus 85: 71.

Russell-Hunter, W.D. (ed.). 1983. The Mollusca. Volume 6. Ecology. Academic Press, Orlando, Florida. 695 pp.

Russell-Hunter, W.D. & R.F. McMahon. 1976. Evidence for functional protandry in a freshwater basommatophoran limpet, *Laevapex fuscus*. Transactions of the American Microscopical Society 95: 174-182.

Schmeck, E.H. 1942. *Viviparus malleatus* in Niagara River. The Nautilus 55: 102-103.

Say, T. 1816. Conchology. 15 pages *in* W. Nicholson, 1816-1817, American edition of the British encyclopedia, or dictionary of arts and sciences comprising an accurate and popular view of the present improved state of human knowledge, first edition, volume 1. Samuel A. Mitchell and Horace Ames, Philadelphia (no pagination).

Say, T. 1817. Description of seven species of American freshwarter and land shells, not noticed in the systems. Journal of the Academy of Natural Sciences of Philadelphia 1(1): 13-16, 1(2): 17-18.

Say, T. 1821. Descriptions of univalve shells of the United States. Journal of the Academy of Natural Sciences of Philadelphia 2: 149-179..

Say, T. 1824. Appendix. Part I. - Natural History. 1. Zoology. Mollusca. Pages 256-265 *in* W.H. Keating, Narrative of an expedition to the source of St. Peter's River, Lake Winnepeek, Lake of the Woods, etc. etc., performed in the year 1823, by order of the Hon. J.C. Calhoun, Secretary of War, under the command of Stephen Long, Major, U.S.T.E., volume 2. Philadelphia.

Say, T. 1825. Descriptions of some new species of freshwater and land shells of the United States. Journal of the Academy of Natural Sciences of Philadelphia 5: 119-131.

Say, T. 1829. Descriptions of some new terrestrial and fluviatile shells of North America. New Harmony Disseminator of Useful Knowledge 2 (15): 229-245.

Schuchert, C. 1904. Charles Emerson Beecher. The American Journal of Science 17: 411-422.

Selander, R.K., E.D. Parker, & R.A. Browne. 1977. Clonal variation in the parthenogenetic snail *Campeloma decisa* (Viviparidae). Veliger 20: 349-351.

Sheldon, S.P. 1987. The effects of herbivorous snails on submerged macrophyte communities in Minnesota lakes. Ecology 68: 1920-1931.

Smith, B. 1926. William Martin Beauchamp, 1830-1925. The Nautilus 39: 138-140.

Smith, D.G. 1980. *Goniobasis virginica* (Gastropoda: Pleuroceridae) in the Connecticut River. The Nautilus 94: 50-54.

Smith, D.G. 1983. Notes on Mississippi River Basin Mollusca presently occurring in the Hudson River system. The Nautilus 97: 128-131.

Smith, D.G. 1986. The rediscovery of *Pomatiopsis lapidaria* (Say) in New England. Malacological Review 19: 115-166.

Smith, D.G. 1987. Keys to the freshwater macroinvertebrates of Massachusetts (No. 2): Mollusca Mesogastropoda (operculate snails). Massachusetts Department of Environmental Quality Engineering, Division of Water Pollution Control (Westborough). 34 pp.

Smith, M. 1906. Shells of Richfield Springs, New York and vicinity. The Nautilus 20: 89-91.

Smith, S. & T. Prime. 1870. Report on the Mollusca of Long Island, New York, and its dependencies. Annals of the Lyceum of Natural History of New York 9: 377-407.

Stańczykowska, A., E. Magnin, & A. Dumouchel. 1971. Étude de trois populations de *Viviparus malleatus* (Reeve) (Gastropoda, Prosobranchia) de la région de Montréal. I. Croissance, fécondité, biomasse et production annuelle. Canadian Journal of Zoology 49: 1431-1441.

Stańczykowska, A., M. Plinski, & E. Magnin. 1972. Étude de trois populations de *Viviparus malleatus* (Reeve) (Gastropoda, Prosobranchia) de la région de Montréal. II. Etude qualitative et quantitative de la nourriture. Canadian Journal of Zoology 50: 1617-1624.

Strayer, D. 1987. Ecology and zoogeography of the freshwater mollusks of the Hudson River basin. Malacological Review 20: 1-68.

Strayer, D. 1990. Freshwater Mollusca. Pages 335-372 *in* B.L. Peckarsky, P.R. Fraissinet, M.A. Penton, & D.J. Conklin, Jr., Freshwater macroinvertebrates of northeastern North America. Cornell University Press, Ithaca, New York. 442 pp.

Taki, A. 1981. The fecundity of a mud snail, *Cipangopaludina japonica*. Verhandlungen Internationale Vereinigung für Theoretische und Angewandte Limnologie 21: 1637-1639.

Taylor, D.W. 1960. Late Cenozoic molluscan faunas from the High Plains. United States Geological Survey Professional Paper 337: 1-94.

Taylor, D.W. 1981. Freshwater mollusks of California: A distributional checklist. California Fish and Game 67: 140-163.

Taylor, D.W. & R.C. Bright. 1987. Drainage history of the Bonneville Basin. Pages 239-256 *in* Cenozoic geology of western Utah - sites for precious metal and hydrocarbon accumulation. Utah Geological Association Publication 16.

Taylor, D.W. & E.H. Jokinen. 1984. A new species of freshwater snail (*Physa*) from seasonal habitats in Connecticut. Freshwater Invertebrate Biology 3: 189-202.

Taylor, D.W., H.J. Walter, & J.B. Burch. 1963. Freshwater snails of the subgenus *Hinkleyia* (Lymnaeidae: *Stagnicola*) from the western United States. Malacologia 1: 237-281.

Te, G. 1975. Michigan Physidae, with systematic notes on *Physella* amd *Physodon*. Malacological Review 8: 7-30.

Te, G. 1978. The systematics of the family Physidae (Basommatophora: Pulmonata). Ph.D. Dissertaion, University of Michigan, Ann Arbor. 325 pp.

Thompson, F.G. 1968. The aquatic snails of the family Hydrobiidae of peninsular Florida. University of Florida Press, Gainesville. 268 pp.

Thompson, F.G. 1983. The planorbid snail *Micromenetus dilatatus avus* (Pilsbry) in the West Indies and Central America. The Nautilus 97: 68-69.

Thompson, F.G. 1984a. The freshwater snails of Florida. A manual for identification. University of Florida Press, Gainesville. 94 pp.

Thompson, F.G. 1984b. North American freshwater snail genera of the hydrobiid subfamily Lithoglyphinae. Malacologia 25: 109-141.

Townes, Jr., H.K. 1936. Studies of the food organisms of fish. Pages 217-230 *in* A biological survey of the Lower Hudson watershed: State of New York Conservation Department Annual Report 26 (Supplement).

Townes, Jr., H.K. 1937. Studies on the food organisms of fish. Pages 162-175 *in* A biological survey of the Allegheny and Chemung watersheds. State of New York Conservation Department Annual Report 27 (Supplement).

Tryon, G.W., Jr. 1863. Descriptions of new species of fresh water Mollusca, belonging to the families Amnicolidae, Valvatidae, and Lymnaeidae; inhabiting California. Proceedings of the Academy of Natural Sciences of Philidelphia 1863: 147-150.

Tryon, G.W., Jr. 1866. Descriptions of new fluviatile Mollusca. American Journal of Conchology 2: 111-113.

Tudorancea, C., R.H. Green, & J. Huebner. 1979. Structure, dynamics and production of the benthic fauna in Lake Manitoba. Hydrobiologia 64: 59-95.

Turgeon, D.D., A.E. Bogan, E.V. Coan, W.K. Emerson, W.G. Lyons, W.L. Pratt, C.F.E. Roper, A. Scheltema, F.G. Thompson, & J.D. Williams. 1988. Common and scientific names of aquatic invertebrates from the United States and Canada: mollusks. American Fisheries Society Special Publication 16. 277 pp.

Vail, V.A. 1978. Seasonal reproductive patterns in three viviparid gastropods. Malacologia 17: 73-97.

Vanatta, E.G. 1902. *Limnaea auricularia* in America. The Nautilus 16: 58.

van Cleave, H.J. 1933. An amphibious habitat on vertical sandstone cliffs. Ecology 14: 149-151.

van Cleave, H.J. 1935. The seasonal life history of an amphibious snail, *Fossaria modicella*, living on sandstone cliffs: Ecology 16: 101-108.

van Cleave, H.J. 1943. Frank Collins Baker (December 14, 1867 to May 7, 1942). The Nautilus 56: 97-99.

van Cleave, H.J. & R. Chambers. 1935. Studies on the life history of a snail of the genus *Lioplax*. American Midland Naturalist 16: 913-920.

van der Leeden, F., F.L. Troise, & D.K. Todd. 1990. The water encyclopedia, second edition. Lewis Publishers, Chelsea, Michigan. 808 pp.

van der Schalie, H. 1953. Nembutol as a relaxing agent for mollusks. American Midland Naturalist 50: 511-512.

van der Schalie, H. 1965. Observations on the sex of *Campeloma* (Gastropoda: Viviparidae). Occasional Papers of the Museum of Zoology (University of Michigan) 641: 1-15 pp.

Van Diver, B.B. 1985. Roadside geology of New York. Mountain Press Publishing Co., Missoula, Montana. 411 pp.

Vincent, B. 1979. Étude du benthos d'eau douce dans le haut-estuaire du Saint-Laurent (Québec). Canadian Journal of Zoology 57: 2171-2182.

Vincent, B. 1981. Profondeur, vase et courant, facteurs de micro-répartition transversale du benthos dans l'estuaire d'eau douce du Saint-Laurent (Québec). Canadian Journal of Zoology 59: 2297-2305.

Vincent, B. & M. Gaucher. 1983. Variations de la fécondité et de la structure des populations chez *Bithynia tentaculata* L. (Gastropoda: Prosobranchia). Canadian Journal of Zoology 61: 2417-2423.

Vincent, B. & G. Vaillancourt. 1981. Méthode de détermination de l'âge, longévité et croissance annuelle de *Bithynia tentaculata* L. (Gastropoda: Prosobranchia) dans le Saint-Laurent (Québec). Canadian Journal of Zoology 59: 982-985.

Vincent, B., G. Vaillancourt, & M. Harvey. 1981. Cycle de développement, croissance, effectifs, biomasse et production de *Bithynia tentaculata* L. (Gastropoda: Prosobranchia) dans le Saint-Laurent (Québec). Canadian Journal of Zoology 59: 1237-1250.

Wade, J.Q. 1980. The Gastropoda of Conesus Lake, Livingston County, New York. Contribution of the Environmental Resource Center No. 85. State University of New York, Geneseo, New York.

Wade, J.Q. 1987. Studies in the gastropods of Conesus Lake, Livingston County, New York. II. Identification, occurrence and ecology of species. Proceedings of the Rochester Academy of Science, Inc. 15: 206-212.

Wade, J.Q. & C.E. Vasey. 1976. A study of the gastropods of Conesus Lake, Livingston County, New York. Proceedings of the Rochester Academy of Science 13: 17-21.

Walker, B. 1901. A new Amnicola. The Nautilus 14: 113-114.

Walter, H.J. 1969. Illustrated biomorphology of the "angulata" lake form of the basommatophoran snail Lymnaea catascopium Say. Malacological Review 2: 1-102.

Walton, J. 1891. The Mollusca of Monroe County, New York. Proceedings of the Rochester Academy of Science 2: 3-18.

Walton, J. 1898. The Mollusca of Monroe County, N.Y. The Museum 4: 132-134.

Wheat, S.C. 1907a. List of Long Island shells. Bulletin of the Brooklyn Conchological Club 1: 7-10.

Wheat, S.C. 1907b. Shells in city gardens and ponds. Bulletin of the Brooklyn Conchological Club 1: 6.

Whitford, N.E. 1906. History of the canal system of the State of New York together with brief histories of the canals of the United States and Canada, volume 1. Supplement to the Annual Report of the State Engineer and Surveyor of the State of New York. Albany. 1025 pp.

Whittemore, T.J. 1859. Notes on Mohawk shells. Proceedings of the Boston Society of Natural History 7: 151.

Winsor, C.P. 1933. The eggs of Goniobasis virginica and Anculosa carinata. Journal of the Washington Academy of Science 23: 34-36.

Winsor, C.P. & A.A. Winsor. 1935. Longevity and fertility in the pond snail, Lymnaea columella. Journal of the Washington Academy of Sciences 25: 302-307.

Wood, D.H. 1978. Temperature adaptation in the freshwater snail, Helisoma trivolvis (Say), in an artificially heated reservoir in the southeastern United States. Journal of Thermal Biology 3: 187-194.

Wurtz, C.B. 1956. Fresh-water mollusks and stream pollution. The Nautilus 69: 96-100.

APPENDIX A. COLLECTION SITES

The numbers of the following sites are the original numbers assigned by the author and surveyor. Omitted numbers are assigned to collections made outside New York State. The following abbreviations are used: Bk. - Brook; Co. - County; Cr. - Creek; E - East(ern); km - kilometer(s); L. - Lake; m - meter(s); N - North(ern); Pd. - Pond; R. - River; Rd. - Road; Rte. - Route; S - South(ern); St. - Street; T.M. - Topographic map; Twp. - Township; W - West(ern).

96A. Hudson R., river mile 82, West Park, Esopus Twp., Ulster Co., Hyde Park T.M. 7.5' (1963), Hudson R. watershed.

96B. Hudson R., river mile 90, Sturgeon Point, Rhinecliff Twp., Dutchess Co., Kingston East T.M. 7.5' (1980), Hudson R. watershed.

96C. Hudson R., river mile 98, Turkey Point, S of Glasco, Saugerties Twp., Ulster Co., Saugerties T.M. 7.5' (1963), Hudson R. watershed.

96D. Hudson R., river mile 139, S of Van Wies Point, across river from Staats Point, Bethlehem Twp., Albany Co., Delmar T.M. 7.5' (1980), Hudson R. watershed.

96E. Hudson R., river mile 140, across river from Van Wies Point, East Greenbush Twp., Rensselaer Co., Delmar T.M. 7.5' (1980), Hudson R. watershed.

96F. Hudson R., river mile 140, Van Wies Point, Bethlehem Twp., Albany Co., Delmar T.M. 7.5' (1980), Hudson R. watershed.

96G. Hudson R., river mile 145, S of Lower Patroon Island., Rensselaer, East Greenbush Twp., Rensselaer Co., Troy South T.M. 7.5' (1980), Hudson R. watershed.

96H. Hudson R., river mile 149, S of Rte. 2, across from Breaker Island, Troy Twp., Rensselaer Co., Troy South T.M. 7.5' (1980), Hudson R. watershed.

96I. Hudson R., river mile 148, across from S end of Breaker Island, North Greenbush Twp., Rensselaer Co., Troy South T.M. 7.5' (1980), Hudson R. watershed.

141A. L. Champlain, Kelly Bay Access, Alburg Twp., Grand Isle Co., Vermont, Rouses Point T.M. 7.5' (1966), St. Lawrence R. watershed.

141B. L. Champlain, Dillenbeck Bay Access, Alburg Twp., Grand Isle Co., Vermont, Rouses Point T.M. 7.5' (1966), St. Lawrence R. watershed.

141C. L. Champlain, base of bridge at South Alburg Twp., Grand Isle Co., Vermont, Rouses Point T.M. 7.5' (1966), St. Lawrence R. watershed.

141D. L. Champlain, N of bridge near Knight Point, North Hero Twp., Grand Isle Co., Vermont, North Hero T.M. 7.5' (1966), St. Lawrence R. watershed.

212. Gleneida L., Carmel Twp., Putnam Co., Lake Carmel T.M. 7.5' (1981), Hudson R. watershed.

250. Pond, unnamed, SE of Hay Harbor, Fishers Island, Southold Twp., Suffolk Co., Mystic T.M. 7.5' (1958), Atlantic Coastal drainage.

251. Middle Farms Pd., Fishers Island, Southold Twp., Suffolk Co., Mystic T.M. 7.5' (1958), Atlantic Coastal drainage.

252. Pond, unnamed, East Harbor Golf Course, W of road, 0.1 km WSW of clubhouse, Fishers Island, Southold Twp., Suffolk Co., Mystic T.M. 7.5' (1958), Atlantic Coastal drainage.

253. Pond, unnamed, East Harbor Golf Course, W of road, 0.15 km SW of clubhouse, Fishers Island, Southold Twp., Suffolk Co., Mystic T.M. 7.5' (1958), Atlantic Coastal drainage.

254. Money Pd., near East Point, S of road, Fishers Island, Southold Twp., Suffolk Co., Mystic T.M. 7.5' (1958), Atlantic Coastal drainage.

259A. Dead Cr., W of Rte. 9, Plattsburgh Twp., Clinton Co., Plattsburgh T.M. 7.5' (1966), St. Lawrence R. watershed.

259B. Dead Cr., W of Rte. 9, Plattsburgh Twp., Clinton Co., Plattsburgh T.M. 7.5' (1966), St. Lawrence R. watershed.

260. L. Champlain, Ausable Marsh State Game Reserve Area, N of Dead Cr. inlet, Peru Twp., Clinton Co., Keeseville T.M. 7.5' (1966), St. Lawrence R. watershed.

261. L. Champlain, Municipal Beach, 0.7 km SE of intersection of Rtes. 9 & 314, Plattsburg Twp., Clinton Co., Plattsburgh T.M. 7.5' (1966), St. Lawrence R. watershed.

262. Dead Cr. Marsh, Ausable Marsh State Game Reserve Area, Peru Twp., Clinton Co., Keeseville T.M. 7.5' (1966), St. Lawrence R. watershed.

263. Dead Cr., at L. Champlain, Plattsburgh Twp., Clinton Co., Plattsburgh T.M. 7.5' (1966), St. Lawrence R. watershed.

264. L. Champlain, Grand Isle Ferry Dock, Cumberland Head, Plattsburgh Twp, Clinton Co., Plattsburgh T.M. 7.5' (1966), St. Lawrence R. watershed.

265. Saratoga L., Saratoga Lake Village, E foot of Rte. 9P, State Boat Launch, Saratoga Twp., Saratoga Co., Quaker Springs T.M. 7.5' (1967), Hudson R. watershed.

266. Polaris Spring, *Typha* ditch, Saratoga Spa State Park, Saratoga Springs Twp., Saratoga Co., Saratoga Springs T.M. 7.5' (1967), Hudson R. watershed.

267. Geyser Bk., Hayes Spring in Saratoga Spa State Park, at geyser, Saratoga Springs Twp., Saratoga Co., Saratoga Springs T.M. 7.5' (1967), Hudson R. watershed.

268. Kayaderosseras Cr., unnamed tributary, E entrance road, Saratoga Spa State Park, 100 m E of toll gate, Saratoga Springs Twp., Saratoga Co., Saratoga Springs T.M. 7.5' (1967), Hudson R. watershed.

269. Geyser Bk., *Typha* marsh, NW of Geyser Rd. (Adams Rd.) & Rte. 50, Saratoga Springs Twp., Saratoga Co., Saratoga Springs T.M. 7.5' (1967), Hudson R. watershed.

270. Crook Brook Pd., E of cemetery, SE of East Galway Village, Galway Twp., Saratoga Co., Middle Grove T.M. 7.5' (1967), Hudson R. watershed.

271. Ludlow Swamp, impoundment of Glowegee Cr., Rte. 147, N of Alexander Rd., Galway Twp., Saratoga Co., Galway T.M. 7.5' (1970), Hudson R. watershed.

272. Galway L. (Amsterdam Reservoir), N shore on Lake Rd., Galway Twp., Saratoga Co., Galway T.M. 7.5' (1970), Hudson R. watershed.

273. Thirteenth L., E shore, Garnet Hill Lodge beach access, Johnsburg Twp., Warren Co., Thirteenth Lake T.M. 15.0' (1954), Hudson R. watershed.

274. Raquette Bk., unnamed beaver pond, Rte. 28, 4 km W of Hudson R., Indian Lake Twp., Hamilton Co., Newcomb T.M. 15.0' (1954), Hudson R. watershed.

275. Beaver Meadow Bk., unnamed tributary, Rte. 28, 6 km E of L. Abanakee, Indian Lake Twp., Hamilton Co., Newcomb T.M. 15.0' (1954) Hudson R. watershed.

276. L. Abanakee, NW shore, Rte. 28 at Indian Lake Water Dept. inlet stream, Chain Lakes Rd., Indian Lake Twp., Hamilton Co., Newcomb T.M. 15.0' (1954), Hudson R. watershed.

277. L. Durant, N shore, Rtes. 28 & 30, 4 km E of Blue Mountain Lake Village, Indian Lake Twp., Hamilton Co., Blue Mountain T.M. 15.0' (1954), Hudson R. watershed.

278. Mirror L., W shore, Lake Placid Village, North Elba Twp., Essex Co., Lake Placid T.M. 15.0' (1953), St. Lawrence R. watershed.

279. Barber Pd., impoundment of Phelps Cr., Rte. 9, 5 km N of Rte. 9N, Elizabethtown Twp., Essex Co., Elizabethtown T.M. 15.0' (1955), St. Lawrence R. watershed.

280. Pumping Station Pd., Rte. 9, 1 km S of Rte. 9N, across road from cemetery, Elizabethtown Twp., Essex Co., Elizabethtown T.M. 15.0' (1955), St. Lawrence R. watershed.

281. L. Champlain, North West Bay, Westport Twp., Essex Co., Port Henry T.M. 15.0' (1945), St. Lawrence R. watershed.

282. Paradox Cr. backwater, 1 km W of Flemings Pd., Hamlet of Paradox, Schroon Twp., Essex Co., Paradox Lake T.M. 7.5' (1973), Hudson R. watershed.

283. Flemings Pd., 1.5 km NE of Hamlet of Paradox, Letsonville Rd., Schroon Twp., Essex Co., Paradox Lake T.M. 7.5' (1973), Hudson R. watershed.

284. Paradox L., Dark Bay, Rte. 74, 5 km E of Severance, State Boat Launch, Schroon Twp., Essex Co., Paradox Lake T.M. 7.5' (1973), Hudson R. watershed.

285. Cemetery Pd., Rte. 74, 2 km W of Severance, Schroon Twp., Essex Co., Pharaoh Mountain T.M. 7.5' (1973), Hudson R. watershed.

286. Hudson R., North Bay, Tivoli Marshes, Red Hook Twp., Dutchess Co., Saugerties T.M. 7.5' (1963), Hudson R. watershed.

287. Saw Kill, stream and mill pond, Bard College Ecology Field Station, Annandale-on-Hudson, Red Hook Twp., Dutchess Co., Saugerties T.M. 7.5' (1963), Hudson R. watershed.

288. Saw Kill, unnamed tributary impoundment, Rte. 199, 0.5 km E of Echo Valley Rd., Red Hook Twp., Dutchess Co., Rock City T.M. 7.5' (1963), Hudson R. watershed.

289. Wilbur Pd., W shore, Rte. 199, 2 km NE of Lafayetteville, Lafayette Multiple Use Area, Milan Twp., Dutchess Co., Pine Plains T.M. 7.5' (1960), Hudson R. watershed.

290. Thompson Pd., N shore, Lake Rd., Pine Plains Twp., Dutchess Co., Pine Plains T.M. 7.5' (1960), Hudson R. watershed.

291. Stissing Pd., SE shore, Lake Rd., Pine Plains Twp., Dutchess Co., Pine Plains T.M. 7.5' (1960), Hudson R. watershed.

292. L. Taghkanic, Lake Taghkanic State Park, Gallatin Twp., Colombia Co., Ancram T.M. 7.5' (1960), Hudson R. watershed.

293. Queechy L., NW shore, Lake Drive, Canaan Twp., Columbia Co., Canaan T.M. 7.5' (1973), Hudson R. watershed.

294. Beebe Pd., Canaan Twp., Columbia Co., Canaan T.M. 7.5' (1973), Housatonic R. watershed.

295. Barrett Pd., Beebe Hill State Forest, Austerlitz Twp., Columbia Co., State Line T.M. 7.5' (1973), Hudson R. watershed.

297. Moreau L., Moreau Lake State Park, Moreau Twp., Saratoga Co., Gansevoort T.M. 7.5' (1968), Hudson R. watershed.

298. Crandall Park Pd., Crandall Park, Glens Falls, Queensbury Twp., Warren Co., Glens Falls T.M. 7.5' (1966), St. Lawrence R. watershed.

299. Glens Falls Feeder Canal, Rte. 9, Glens Falls, Queensbury Twp., Warren Co., Glens Falls T.M. 7.5' (1966), Hudson R. watershed.

300. Pumping Station Pd., pumping station, Bluebird Rd., Fernwood Village, Moreau Twp., Saratoga Co., Glens Falls T.M. 7.5' (1966), Hudson R. watershed.

301. Hudson R., at pumping station, Bluebird Rd., Fernwood Village, Moreau Twp., Saratoga Co., Glens Falls T.M. 7.5' (1966), Hudson R. watershed.

302. Pond, unnamed, East River Dr., 1 km SE of Rte. 9N, Lake Luzerne Village, Lake Luzerne Twp., Warren Co., Lake Luzerne T.M. 7.5' (1968), Hudson R. watershed.

303. L. Luzerne, W shore, Rte. 9N, boat launch site, Lake Luzerne Twp., Warren Co., Lake Luzerne T.M. 7.5' (1968), Hudson R. watershed.

304. Stewart Bk., Lake Tour Rd. bridge, Lake Luzerne Village, Lake Luzerne Twp., Warren Co., Lake Luzerne T.M. 7.5' (1968), Hudson R. watershed.

305. Fourth L., Fourth Lake State Park, Lake Luzerne Twp., Warren Co., Lake Luzerne T.M. 7.5' (1968), Hudson R. watershed.

306. Pond, unnamed, Lake George Beach State Park, across road from S shore of L. George, Lake George Twp., Warren Co., Lake George T.M. 7.5' (1966), St. Lawrence R. watershed.

307. Little Chazy R., Stetson Rd., 2.5 km NW of Chazy Village, Chazy Twp., Clinton Co., Champlain T.M. 7.5' (1966), St. Lawrence R. watershed.

308. Great Chazy R., railroad bridge on Lake Shore Rd., 1 km SE of Coopersville, Champlain Twp., Clinton Co., Champlain T.M. 7.5' (1966), St. Lawrence R. watershed.

309. L. Alice, Lake Alice State Game Management Area, Chazy Twp., Clinton Co., Beekmantown T.M. 7.5' (1966), St. Lawrence R. watershed.

310. Great Chazy R., Feinberg Park, Altona Twp., Clinton Co., Altona T.M. 7.5' (1966), St. Lawrence R. watershed.

311. Chazy L., W shore, Seine Bay, Dannemora Twp., Clinton Co., Ellenberg Mountain T.M. 7.5' (1964), St. Lawrence R. watershed.

312. Hudson-Champlain Canal, Rte. 4, 2 km S of Comstock, Fort Ann Twp., Washington Co., Fort Ann T.M. 7.5' (1944), St. Lawrence R. watershed.

313. Bog, unnamed, W of Hudson-Champlain Canal, W side of Rte. 4, 2 km S of Comstock, Fort Ann Twp., Washington Co., Fort Ann T.M. 7.5' (1944), St. Lawrence R. watershed.

314. Pond, unnamed, W side of Rte. 4, E of railroad tracks, 1.2 km S of Comstock, Fort Ann Twp., Washington Co., Fort Ann T.M. 7.5' (1944), St. Lawrence R. watershed.

315. Mettawee R., bridge at North Granville, Granville Twp., Washington Co., Granville T.M. 7.5' (1944), St. Lawrence R. watershed.

316. Rathbun Pd., Pine Hill Rd., 1.5 km N of Granville Village, Granville Twp., Washington Co., Granville T.M. 7.5' (1944), St. Lawrence R. watershed.

317. Chamberlain Mills Pd., impoundment of Black Cr., 1.5 km W of East Hebron, Hebron Twp., Washington Co., West Pawlet T.M. 7.5' (1944), Hudson R. watershed.

318. L. Cossayuna Outlet Pd., at Veterans Memorial, Cossayuna Village, Greenwich Twp., Washington Co., Cossayuna T.M. 7.5' (1944), Hudson R. watershed.

319. Cossayuna L., Argyle Twp., Washington Co., Cossayuna T.M. 7.5' (1944), Hudson R. watershed.

320. Carter Pd., 2 km S of Cossayuna Village, Rte. 338, Carter Pond Conservation Area, Greenwich Twp., Washington Co., Cossayuna T.M. 7.5' (1944), Hudson R. watershed.

321. Mill Pd., Grafton Lakes State Park, Grafton Twp., Rensselaer Co., Grafton T.M. 7.5' (1954), Hudson R. watershed.

322. Swamp, unnamed, S of Silver L., North Rd., Greenport, Long Island, Southold Twp., Suffolk Co., Greenport T.M. 7.5' (1956), Atlantic Coastal drainage.

331. Rutland L., N shore, Rte. 126, Rutland Twp., Jefferson Co., Rutland Center T.M. 7.5' (1959), St. Lawrence R. watershed.

332. Rutland Gorge Stream, Ridge Rd., Huntingtonville Village, Rutland Twp., Jefferson Co., Rutland Center T.M. 7.5' (1959), St. Lawrence R. watershed.

333. Black R., Ridge Rd., 3 km E of Weaver Rd., Huntingtonville Village, Rutland Twp., Jefferson Co., Rutland Center T.M. 7.5' (1959), St. Lawrence R. watershed.

334. Black R., 0.3 km E of Rte. 3, across from Delano Island, Huntingtonville Village, Rutland Twp., Jefferson Co., Rutland Center T.M. 7.5' (1959), St. Lawrence R. watershed.

335. Black R., unnamed tributary, 0.3 km E of Rte. 3, Huntingtonville Village, Rutland Twp., Jefferson Co., Rutland Center T.M. 7.5' (1959), St. Lawrence R. watershed.

336. Perch L., W end of spillway, Perch River Wildlife Management Area, Brownville Twp., Jefferson Co., Brownville T.M. 7.5' (1982), St. Lawrence R. watershed.

337. Chaumont R. Impoundment, Rte. 180, La Fargeville Twp., Jefferson Co., La Fargeville T.M. 7.5' (1958), St. Lawrence R. watershed.

338. Butterfield L., S shore, State Boat Launch, Redwood Village, Alexandria Twp., Jefferson Co., Redwood T.M. 7.5' (1982), St. Lawrence R. watershed.

339. Black L., W shore, public boat launch, Black Lake Rd., 1.6 km S of Rte. 58, Edwardsville Twp., St. Lawrence Co., Edwardsville T.M. 7.5' (1963), St. Lawrence R. watershed.

340. St. Lawrence R., 0.2 km S of Nevins Point, Oswegatchie Twp., St. Lawrence Co., Ogdensburg West T.M. 7.5' (1963), St. Lawrence R. watershed.

341. Oswegatchie R., Eelwier State Park, Oswegatchie Twp., St. Lawrence Co., Ogdensburg East T.M. 7.5' (1963), St. Lawrence R. watershed.

342. Brown Church Road Pd., Brown Church Rd., Waddington Twp., St. Lawrence Co., Sparrowhawk Point T.M. 7.5' (1963), St. Lawrence R. watershed.

343. St. Lawrence R., embayment 1.3 km SE of Iroquois Dam, 0.5 km E of Browns Church Rd., Waddington Twp., St. Lawrence Co., Sparrowhawk Point T.M. 7.5' (1963), St. Lawrence R. watershed.

344. Grass R., E of bridge on Louisville Rd., Louisville Village, Louisville Twp., St. Lawrence Co., Louisville T.M. 7.5' (1964), St. Lawrence R. watershed.

345. Raquette R., N. Raquette River Rd., 0.6 km E of Haverstock, Massena Twp., St. Lawrence Co., Raquette River T.M. 7.5' (1964), St. Lawrence R. watershed.

346. St. Regis R., McIntyre Rd., 2 km NE of Helena Village, Brasher Twp., St. Lawrence Co., Hogansburg T.M. 7.5' (1964), St. Lawrence R. watershed.

347. Malone Memorial Recreation Park Pd., Malone Memorial Recreation Park, Malone Twp., Franklin Co., Malone T.M. 7.5' (1964), St. Lawrence R. watershed.

348. Lamica L., impoundment of Salmon R., at Cady Rd. bridge, Malone Twp., Franklin Co., Constable T.M. 7.5' (1964), St. Lawrence R. watershed.

349. Lower Chateaugay L., at dam, The Forge, Chateaugay Twp., Franklin Co., Brainardsville T.M. 7.5' (1964), St. Lawrence R. watershed.

350. Chateaugay Narrows, Rte. 374 at Shutts Rd., Upper Chateaugay Department of Environmental Conservation State Boat Launch, Ellenburg Twp., Clinton Co., Ellenburg Center T.M. 7.5' (1964), St. Lawrence R. watershed.

351. Lyon Mountain Pd., Rte. 374, Lyon Mountain Village, Dannemora Twp., Clinton Co., Lyon Mountain T.M. 7.5' (1968), St. Lawrence R. watershed.

352. Silver L., Hawkeye Village, Black Brook Twp., Clinton Co., Redford T.M. 7.5' (1968), St. Lawrence R. watershed.

353. Union Falls Pd., Union Falls Village, Black Brook Twp., Clinton Co., Alder Brook T.M. 7.5' (1968), St. Lawrence R. watershed.

354. Cranberry L., Cranberry Lake Village, Clifton Twp., St. Lawrence Co., Cranberry Lake T.M. 7.5' (1968), St. Lawrence R. watershed.

355. Dillon Pd., 3 km W of Cranberry Lake Village on Tooley Pond Rd., State Fishing Access Site, Clifton Twp., St. Lawrence Co., Cranberry Lake T.M. 7.5' (1968), St. Lawrence R. watershed.

356. Childwold Pd., Rte. 3, 1.5 km E of junction with Rte. 56, Colton Twp., St. Lawrence Co., Childwold T.M. 7.5' (1968), St. Lawrence R. watershed.

357. Catamount Pd., N shore, Piercefield Twp., St. Lawrence Co., Childwold T.M. 7.5' (1968), St. Lawrence R. watershed.

358. Tupper L., Simon Pd. marshes, Rte. 30, Moody Village, Altamount Twp., Franklin Co., Long Lake T.M. 15.0' (1955), St. Lawrence R. watershed.

359. Limekiln L., NE shore, Inlet Twp., Hamilton Co., Old Forge T.M. 15.0' (1954), St. Lawrence R. watershed.

360. Fourth L., Fulton Chain, E shore, Inlet Twp., Hamilton Co., Big Moose T.M. 15.0' (1954), St. Lawrence R. watershed.

361. Eagle Cr., Big Moose Rd., Eagle Bay Village, Webb Twp., Herkimer Co., Big Moose T.M. 15.0' (1954), St. Lawrence R. watershed.

362. Big Moose L., SE shore, public boat launch, Webb Twp., Herkimer Co., Big Moose T.M. 15.0' (1954), St. Lawrence R. watershed.

363. Moss L., NW shore, Webb Twp., Herkimer Co., Big Moose T.M. 15.0' (1954), St. Lawrence R. watershed.

364. Bald Mountain Pd., Rte. 28, 5 km E of Old Forge Village, Webb Twp., Herkimer Co., Old Forge T.M. 15.0' (1954), St. Lawrence R. watershed.

365. Nicks L., 3 km S of Old Forge Village, Webb Twp., Herkimer Co., Old Forge T.M. 15.0' (1954), St. Lawrence R. watershed.

366. Black R., Rte. 28, above spillway, Hawkinsville Village, Boonville Twp., Oneida Co., Boonville T.M. 7.5' (1955), St. Lawrence R. watershed.

367. Black R. Canal, Rte. 46, 1.5 km S of Jackson Hill Rd., Boonville Twp., Oneida Co., Boonville T.M. 7.5' (1955), Hudson R. watershed.

368. Lansing Kill, above Pixley Falls, Boonville Gorge State Park, Hurlbutville Village, Boonville Twp., Oneida Co., Boonville T.M. 7.5' (1955), Hudson R. watershed.

369. Lansing Kill, gaging station, Hillside Village, Western Twp., Oneida Co., Westernville T.M. 7.5' (1955), Hudson R. watershed.

370. Mohawk R., Webster Hill Rd., Hillside Village, Western Twp., Oneida Co., Westernville T.M. 7.5' (1955), Hudson R. watershed.

371. Hennesey Road Pd., S side of Hennesey Rd., 0.4 km W of Potato Hill Rd., Boonville Twp., Oneida Co., Boonville T.M. 7.5' (1955), St. Lawrence R. watershed.

372. Sugar R., Denley Rd., 1.3 km E of Talcottville Village, Leyden Twp., Oneida Co., Port Leyden T.M. 7.5' (1966), St. Lawrence R. watershed.

373. Cold Bk., Marmon Rd., 0.1 km N of East Main St., Lyonsdale Twp., Lewis Co., Port Leyden T.M. 7.5' (1966), St. Lawrence R. watershed.

374. Black R., Community Memorial Park, W of Lyons Falls Village, Lyonsdale Twp., Lewis Co., Port Leyden T.M. 7.5' (1966), St. Lawrence R. watershed.

375. Whetstone Cr., Whetstone Gulf State Park, Martinsburg, Lewis Co., Glenfield T.M. 7.5' (1966), St. Lawrence R. watershed.

376. Ditch, E side of East Rd., 0.2 km from Rte. 12D, Turin Twp., Lewis Co., Glenfield T.M. 7.5' (1966), St. Lawrence R. watershed.

377. Kayuta L., Dustin Rd. Causeway, Forestport Twp., Oneida Co., Forestport T.M. 7.5' (1945), St. Lawrence R. watershed.

378. Cincinnati Cr., 0.3 km S of Rte. B28, Remsen Village, Trenton Twp., Oneida Co., Remsen T.M. 7.5' (1955), Hudson R. watershed.

379. West Canada Cr., strand pools, below bridge E of Trenton Falls Village, Russia Twp., Herkimer Co., Remsen T.M. 7.5' (1955), Hudson R. watershed.

380. Feeder Canal from West Canada Cr., Trenton Falls Village, Trenton Twp., Oneida Co., Remsen T.M. 7.5' (1955), Hudson R. watershed.

381. Hinckley Reservoir, impoundment of West Canada Cr., SE shore N of West Canada Cr. inlet, Hinckley Reservoir State Park, Russia Twp., Herkimer Co., Hinckley T.M. 7.5' (1946), Hudson R. watershed.

382. *Typha* marsh, entrance gate of Hinckley Reservoir State Park, Russia Twp., Herkimer Co., Hinckley T.M. 7.5' (1946), Hudson R. watershed.

383. Pond, unnamed, 0.6 km N of Grant Village, Russia Twp., Herkimer Co., Hinckley T.M. 7.5' (1946), Hudson R. watershed.

384. Piseco L., Irondequoit Bay, Arietta Twp., Hamilton Co., Piseco Lake T.M. 15.0' (1954), Hudson R. watershed.

385. L. Alma, impoundment of Kennels Pd. outlet, Rte. 10, 1.0 km NW of Averys Place, Arietta Twp., Hamilton Co., Piseco Lake T.M. 15.0' (1954), Hudson R. watershed.

386. West L. Inlet, Rte. 10, 0.6 km NW of Mud L., West Lake State Boat Launch, Caroga Lake Twp., Fulton Co., Canada Lake T.M. 7.5' (1945), Hudson R. watershed.

387. Great Sacandaga L., SW shore, Rte. 30, W of Paradise Point, marshy area next to inlet stream, Mayfield Twp., Fulton Co., Northville T.M. 7.5' (1970), Hudson R. watershed.

388. Susquehanna R., S bank, Rte. 17 rest stop, 0.7 km SW of Squaw Island, Nichols Twp., Tioga Co., Owego T.M. 7.5' (1969), Susquehanna R. watershed.

389. Wappasening Cr., Kirby Park, Nichols Village, Nichols Twp., Tioga Co., Owego T.M. 7.5' (1969), Susquehanna R. watershed.

390. Catharine Cr., Rte. 14 & road to Chemung College, 1 km S of Hoffsomer Rd., 1.4 km S of Pine Valley Village, Veteran Twp., Chemung Co., Horseheads T.M. 7.5' (1969), St. Lawrence R. watershed.

391. Newton Cr., bridge at Bowman Hill Rd., 0.2 km S of Rte. 223, Horseheads Twp., Chemung Co., Horseheads T.M. 7.5' (1969), Susquehanna R. watershed.

392. Johnson Hollow Stream, unnamed pond, 3 km NW of Rte. 14, Catlin Twp., Chemung Co., Montour Falls T.M. 7.5' (1978), St. Lawrence R. watershed.

393. Sleeper Cr., Rte. 14 bridge, Veteran Twp., Chemung Co., Montour Falls T.M. 7.5' (1978), St. Lawrence R. watershed.

394. Diversion Channel, from Catharine Cr. to Barge Canal, 0.1 km S of Rte. 224, Montour Falls Twp., Schuyler Co., Montour Falls T.M. 7.5' (1978), St. Lawrence R. watershed.

395. Barge Canal, Marina Rd., 1.2 km NE of Rte. 14, Montour Falls Twp., Schuyler Co., Montour Falls T.M. 7.5' (1978), St. Lawrence R. watershed.

396. Bad Indian Swamp, across Rte. 14 from Aunt Sarah's Falls, Montour Falls Twp.. Schuyler Co., Montour Falls T.M. 7.5' (1978), St. Lawrence R. watershed.

397. Aunt Sarah's Falls & Pool, Rte. 14, Montour Falls Twp., Schuyler Co., Montour Falls T.M. 7.5' (1978), St. Lawrence R. watershed.

398. Seneca L., S shore, Lakeside Park, Watkins Glen Village, Dix Twp., Schuyler Co., Burdett T.M. 7.5' (1950), St. Lawrence R. watershed.

399. Tobehanna Cr., unnamed tributary, Altay Rd., 0.1 km E of Rte. 226, Altay Village, Tyrone Twp., Schuyler Co., Wayne T.M. 7.5' (1953), Susquehanna R. watershed.

400. Lamoka & Waneta Lakes, unnamed connecting stream, 1.3 km W of Weston Village, Department of Environmental Conservation Waneta-Lamoka Fishing Access Site, Tyrone Twp., Schuyler Co., Wayne T.M. 7.5' (1953), Susquehanna R. watershed.

401. Keuka L., inlet, Rte. 54, Chaplin Beach, 1 km E of Rte. 54A, Hammondsport Village, Urbana Twp., Steuben Co., Hammondsport T.M. 7.5' (1953), St. Lawrence R. watershed.

402. Keuka L., SW shore, Liberty St., Hammondsport Village, Urbana Twp., Steuben Co., Hammondsport T.M. 7.5' (1953), St. Lawrence R. watershed.

403. Pond, unnamed, Gaging Station Rd. & Rte. 63, 3 km S of Geneseo Village, Geneseo Twp., Livingston Co., Geneseo T.M. 7.5' (1978), St. Lawrence R. watershed.

404. Genesee R., Jones Bridge Rd., Leicester Twp., Livingston Co., Geneseo T.M. 7.5' (1978), St. Lawrence R. watershed.

405. Beards Cr., Rte. 39, Boyd-Parker State Park, Leicester Twp., Livingston Co., Geneseo T.M. 7.5' (1978), St. Lawrence R. watershed.

406. Beards Cr., unnamed tributary, River Rd., 0.2 km S of Jones Bridge Rd., 1.5 km S of Cuylerville Village, Leicester Twp., Livingston Co., Geneseo T.M. 7.5' (1978), St. Lawrence R. watershed.

407. Silver L. Outlet, old railroad bridge, 0.5 km W of Rte. 39, Perry Village, Perry Twp., Wyoming Co., Castile T.M. 7.5' (1972), St. Lawrence R. watershed.

408. Silver L. Outlet, Silver Lake Rd. boat launch, Perry Twp., Wyoming Co., Castile T.M. 7.5' (1972), St. Lawrence R. watershed.

409. Silver Lake, unnamed tributary impoundment, East Lake Rd., Silver Lake State Park, Castile Twp., Wyoming Co., Castile T.M. 7.5' (1972), St. Lawrence R. watershed.

410. Ditch, unnamed, East Lake Rd., Silver Lake State Park, Castile Twp., Wyoming Co., Castile T.M. 7.5' (1972), St. Lawrence R. watershed.

411. Pond, unnamed seepage, Letchworth State Park, 1.5 km S of Castile entrance, Genesee Falls Twp., Wyoming Co., Portageville T.M. 7.5' (1972), St. Lawrence R. watershed.

412. Trout Pd., Letchworth State Park, falls section, Genesee Falls Twp., Wyoming Co., Portageville T.M. 7.5' (1972), St. Lawrence R. watershed.

413. Moss L., Sand Hill Rd., Caneadea Twp., Allegany Co., Houghton T.M. 7.5' (1964), St. Lawrence R. watershed.

414. Rushford L., W shore, picnic area W of Caneadea Dam, Caneadea Twp., Allegany Co., Houghton T.M. 7.5' (1964), St. Lawrence R. watershed.

415. Genesee Valley Canal, South Rd., 1 km S of Rte. 305, Cuba Twp., Allegany Co., Black Creek T.M. 7.5' (1964), Mississippi R. watershed.

416. Allegheny R., N shore, bridge 0.6 km SE of North Ninemile Rd., Vandalia Village, Allegany Twp., Cattaraugus Co., Knapp Creek T.M. 7.5' (1979), Mississippi R. watershed.

417. Tonungwant Cr., Irvine Mills Rd. bridge, Allegany State Park, Irvine Mills Village, Carrollton Twp., Cattaraugus Co., Limestone T.M. 7.5' (1961), Mississippi R. watershed.

418. Limestone Bk., Limestone Run Rd., 2 km W of South Carrollton Rd., Allegany State Park, Carrollton Twp., Cattaraugus Co., Limestone T.M. 7.5' (1961), Mississippi R. watershed.

419. Red House Bk., France Brook Rd., Allegany State Park, Red House Twp., Cattaraugus Co., Limestone T.M. 7.5' (1961), Mississippi R. watershed.

420. Red House L., NE shore, Allegany State Park, Red House Twp., Cattaraugus Co., Limestone T.M. 7.5' (1961), Mississippi R. watershed.

421. Quaker Run & S shore of Quaker L., at Cain Hollow, Allegany State Park, Elko Twp., Cattaraugus Co., Red House T.M. 7.5' (1980), Mississippi R. watershed.

422. Stillson Pd. Inlet, Rte. 394, 1.2 km SE of East Randolph Village, Cold Spring Twp., Cattaraugus Co., Randolph T.M. 7.5' (1979), Mississippi R. watershed.

423. Randolph High School Pd. No. 1, Rte. 394, Randolph High School, 0.5 km E of Rte. 241, Randolph Twp., Cattaraugus Co., Randolph T.M. 7.5' (1979), Mississippi R. watershed.

424. Randolph High School Pd. No. 2, Rte. 394, Randolph High School, 0.3 km E of Rte. 241, Randolph Twp., Cattaruagus Co., Randolph T.M. 7.5' (1979), Mississipi R. watershed.

425. Little Conewango Cr., Rte. 394, Randolph Village, Randolph Twp., Cattaraugus Co., Randolph T.M. 7.5' (1979), Mississippi R. watershed.

426. Ditch, roadside, Jones-Gifford Ave. & Walden Ave., NW corner of Jamestown City, Ellicott Twp., Chautauqua Co., Lakewood T.M. 7.5' (1954), Mississippi R. watershed.

427A. Chautauqua L., Sherman's Bay, Rte. 17J, 0.4 km NW of Rte. 74, Busti Twp., Chautauqua Co., Lakewood T.M. 7.5' (1954), Mississippi R. watershed.

427B. Chautauqua L., Long Point, boat launch, Chautauqua Lake State Park, Ellery Twp., Chautauqua Co., Chautauqua T.M. 7.5' (1954), Mississippi R. watershed.

428. Goose Cr., Rte. 394 (17J), 0.7 km S of Loomises Village, Busti Twp., Chautauqua Co., Lakewood T.M. 7.5' (1954), Mississippi R. watershed.

429. French Cr. unnamed tributary, S of East Main St. (Rte. 430) & Warden, Sherman Village, Sherman Twp., Chautauqua Co., Sherman T.M. 7.5' (1954), Mississippi R. watershed.

430A. Findley L., N shore, State Boat Launch, Rte. 430 & 426, Mina Twp., Chautauqua Co., Clymer T.M. 7.5' (1954), Mississippi R. watershed.

430B. Findley L., S shore at Shady Rd., Mina Twp., Chautauqua Co., Clymer T.M. 7.5' (1954), Mississippi R. watershed.

431. French Cr., Rte. 430, below Findley Lake Dam, Mina Twp., Chautauqua Co., Clymer T.M. 7.5' (1954), Mississippi R. watershed.

432. Findley L. Inlet, unnamed pond, S of Shady Side Rd., 0.5 km W of Rte. 426, Mina Twp., Chautauqua Co., Clymer T.M. 7.5' (1954), Mississippi R. watershed.

433. Chautauqua Cr., Rte. 5 bridge, Barcelona Village, Westfield Twp., Chautauqua Co., Westfield T.M. 7.5' (1954), St. Lawrence R. watershed.

436. Fishing Pd., Joseph Davis State Park, Rte. 18F, Lewiston Twp., Niagara Co., Lewiston T.M. 7.5' (1980), St. Lawrence R. watershed.

437. Niagara R., Joseph Davis State Park fishing dock, Rte. 18F, Lewiston, Niagara Co., Lewiston T.M. 7.5' (1980), St. Lawrence R. watershed.

438. Niagara R., Fort Niagara State Park boat launch, Porter Twp., Niagara Co., Fort Niagara T.M. 7.5' (1980), St. Lawrence R. watershed.

439. Sixmile Cr. Marsh, Rte. 18, Porter Twp., Niagara Co., Sixmile Creek T.M. 7.5' (1965), St. Lawrence R. watershed.

440. Twelvemile Cr., east branch, Rte. 18, Wilson Twp., Niagara Co., Wilson T.M. 7.5' (1965), St. Lawrence R. watershed.

441. Eighteenmile Cr., Olcott Village, Town of Newfane Boat Launch, Newfane Twp., Niagara Co., Newfane T.M. 7.5' (1978), St. Lawrence R. watershed.

442. Johnson Cr., Rte. 63, below dam, Lyndonville Village, Yates Twp., Orleans Co., Lyndonville T.M. 7.5' (1979), St. Lawrence R. watershed.

443. Erie Canal, boat launch at N side of Bates Rd. bridge, Medina Village, Ridgeway Twp., Orleans Co., Knowlesville T.M. 7.5' (1950), St. Lawrence R. watershed.

444. Pond, unnamed, S of Otter Cr. at Erie Canal, Presbyterian Rd., 2 km E of Knowlesville Village, Albion Twp., Orleans Co., Knowlesville T.M. 7.5' (1950), St. Lawrence R. watershed.

445A. L. Ontario, Irondequoit Bay, Empire Boulevard (Rte. 404), 1.2 km E of Rte. 590 (Rte. 47), Irondequoit Twp., Monroe Co., Rochester East T.M. 7.5' (1971), St. Lawrence R. watershed.

445B. L. Ontario, Irondequoit Bay, Empire Boulevard (Rte. 404), boat launch 1.9 km E of Rte. 590 (Rte. 47), Penfield Twp., Monroe Co., Rochester East T.M. 7.5' (1971), St. Lawrence R. watershed.

445C. L. Ontario, Irondequoit Bay, boat launch at Bay Front St. & Orchard Park Boulevard, Irondequoit Bay Park, Irondequoit Twp., Monroe Co., Rochester East T.M. 7.5' (1971), St. Lawrence R. watershed.

448A. Oneida L., Muskrat Bay, Oneida Shores County Park, Cicero Twp., Onondaga Co., Cicero T.M. 7.5' (1973), St. Lawrence R. watershed.

448B. Oneida L., S shore, Eagle Bay, Shackleton Point State Boat Launch, Sullivan Twp., Madison Co., Cleveland T.M. 7.5' (1957), St. Lawrence R. watershed.

449. Chittenango Cr., Anchorage Marina, Hitchcock Rd., 3.5 km NW of Bridgeport Village, Sullivan Twp., Madison Co., Cleveland T.M. 7.5' (1957), St. Lawrence R. watershed.

450. Ditch, Oneida Shores County Park, Cicero Twp., Onondaga Co., Cicero T.M. 7.5' (1973), St. Lawrence R. watershed.

451. Stream, unnamed, & vernal pond, Orange Camp Rd., 0.9 km SE of Scotchtown Rd., Highland Lakes State Park, Wallkill Twp., Orange Co., Goshen T.M. 7.5' (1957), Hudson R. watershed.

452. Pond, unnamed, S side of Pufftown Rd., 0.7 km E of Scotchtown Rd., Highland Lakes State Park, Wallkill Twp., Orange Co., Goshen T.M. 7.5' (1957), Hudson R. watershed.

453. Masonic Cr., Bert Crawford Rd., Middletown, Wallkill Twp., Orange Co., Middletown T.M. 7.5' (1969), Hudson R. watershed.

454. Neversink R., Rte. 209, Meyers Road Village, Deerpark Twp., Orange Co., Otisville T.M. 7.5' (1976), Delaware R. watershed.

455. Delaware-Hudson Canal, Delaware-Hudson Canal Park, Hoag Rd., S of Cuddebackville, Deerpark Twp., Orange Co., Otisville T.M. 7.5' (1976), Delaware R. watershed.

456. Neversink R., at Delaware-Hudson Canal, S of Cuddeville, Deerpark Twp., Orange Co., Otisville T.M. 7.5' (1976), Delaware R. watershed.

457. Martin L. & Gold Cr. (outlet), Cejwin Camp, Rte. 209, 3 km S of Huguenot, Deerpark Twp., Orange Co., Port Jervis North T.M. 7.5' (1942), Delaware R. watershed.

458. Delaware R., West Main St., 1.5 km NW of Germantown, Deerpark Twp., Orange Co., Port Jervis North T.M. 7.5' (1942), Delaware R. watershed.

459. Pond, unnamed, N side of Thornton Rd, 0.2 km E of Rte. 209, Phillipsport, Mamakating Twp., Sullivan Co., Ellenville T.M. 7.5' (1969), Hudson R. watershed.

460. Delaware-Hudson Canal, Thornton Rd., 1.6 km SW of Phillipsport, Mamakating Twp., Sullivan Co., Ellenville T.M. 7.5' (1969), Hudson R. watershed.

461. Homowack Kill, 0.5 km SW of Phillipsport Village, Rte. 209, Mamakating Twp., Sullivan Co., Ellenville T.M. 7.5' (1969), Hudson R. watershed.

462. Delaware-Hudson Canal, Rte. 209, Summitville, Mamakating Twp., Sullivan Co., Wurtsboro T.M. 7.5' (1969), Delaware R. watershed.

463. Delaware-Hudson Canal, McDonald Rd., 3 km N of Wurtsboro Village, Mamakating Twp., Sullivan Co., Wurtsboro T.M. 7.5' (1969), Delaware R. watershed.

464. Pond, unnamed, road paralleling N to Rte. 17, 1 km S of Wanaksink L., Thompson Twp., Sullivan Co., Yankee Lake T.M. 7.5' (1966), Delaware R. watershed.

465. White L., W shore, State Boat Launch, Rte. 55 & Lake Drive, Kauneoga Lake Village, Bethel Twp., Sullivan Co., White Lake T.M. 7.5' (1967), Delaware R. watershed.

466. L. Superior, at outlet, Duggan Rd., Lake Superior State Park, Bethel Twp., Sullivan Co., White Lake T.M. 7.5' (1967), Delaware R. watershed.

467. Black Lake Cr., Moscoe Rd., at Toronto Reservoir, 1.3 km SE of Black Lake Village, Bethel Twp., Sullivan Co., White Lake T.M. 7.5' (1967), Delaware R. watershed.

468. Swan L., S shore, causeway, 2 km NW of Swan Lake Village, Liberty Twp., Sullivan Co., Liberty West T.M. 7.5' (1965), Delaware R. watershed.

469. Beaver Kill, unnamed tributary ditch, Old Rte. 17 at Tweedie Rd., E of Ben Gray Hollow, Hancock Twp., Delaware Co., Horton T.M. 7.5' (1982), Delaware R. watershed.

470. Delaware R., East Branch backwater, Earlys Flat, Roadside Park, 2.5 km W of East Branch Village, Hancock Twp., Delaware Co., Fishs Eddy T.M. 7.5' (1965), Delaware R. watershed.

471. Delaware R., East Branch, Fishs Eddy Village, at bridge, Hancock Twp., Delaware Co., Fishs Eddy T.M. 7.5' (1965), Delaware R. watershed.

472. Outlet of unnamed pond, West Main St. & Front St., Hancock Village, Hancock Twp., Delaware Co., Hancock T.M. 7.5' (1965), Delaware R. watershed.

473. Whitaker Brook Pd., McCabe Hollow Rd., Deposit Twp., Delaware Co., Deposit T.M. 7.5' (1965), Delaware R. watershed.

474. Pond, unnamed, Columbia Lake Rd., NE of Laurel Hill Cemetery, Deposit Twp., Delaware Co., Deposit T.M. 7.5' (1965), Delaware R. watershed.

475. Deer L. at Fly Cr. (outlet), Old Rte. 17, Sanford-Windsor Township line, Broome Co., Gulf Summit T.M. 7.5' (1952), Delaware R. watershed.

476. Tuscarora Cr., Old Rte. 17, Windsor-Sanford Township line, Broome Co., Gulf Summit T.M. 7.5' (1952), Susquehanna R. watershed.

477. Belden Bk., unnamed tributary, Rte 79 & Hickox Rd., Colesville Twp., Broome Co., Belden T.M. 7.5' (1957), Susquehanna R. watershed.

478. Marsh, unnamed, Rte. 79, 1.6 km SE of North Colesville Village, Colesville Twp., Broome Co., Belden T.M. 7.5' (1957), Susquehanna R. watershed.

493. Onondaga L., NE shore, 0.2 km SE of Salt Museum, Liverpool Twp., Onondaga Co., Syracuse West T.M. 7.5' (1978), St. Lawrence R. watershed.

494. Pond, unnamed, Onondaga Lake Park, 2 km SE of lake outlet, Liverpool Twp., Onondaga Co., Syracuse West T.M. 7.5' (1978), St. Lawrence R. watershed.

495. Oswego R., S of Battle Island, Battle Island State Park, Granby Twp., Oswego Co., Fulton T.M. 7.5' (1978), St. Lawrence R. watershed.

496. Pond, unnamed, 1.3 km S of Minetto Village, Rte. 48, Minetto Twp., Oswego Co., Oswego East T.M. 7.5' (1978), St. Lawrence R. watershed.

497. Sterling Valley Cr., 0.7 km WNW of McKnight Corners, McIntyre Rd., Sterling Twp., Cayuga Co., Fair Haven T.M. 7.5' (1976), St. Lawrence R. watershed.

498. The Pond, W shore, Fair Haven State Park, Sterling Twp., Cayuga Co., Fair Haven T.M. 7.5' (1976), St. Lawrence R. watershed.

499. L. Ontario, Little Sodus Bay, SW shore public boat launch, West Bay Rd., Sterling Twp., Cayuga Co., Fair Haven T.M. 7.5' (1976), St. Lawrence R. watershed.

500. Red Cr., Broadway Rd. bridge, Wolcott Twp., Wayne Co., North Wolcott T.M. 7.5' (1953), St. Lawrence R. watershed.

501. Wolcott Cr., Rte. 104, Wolcott Falls Park, below falls, Wolcott Twp., Wayne Co., Wolcott T.M. 7.5' (1953), St. Lawrence R. watershed.

502A. L. Ontario, Sodus Bay, Ridge Rd., Resort Village, Huron Twp., Wayne Co., Rose T.M. 7.5' (1978), St. Lawrence R. watershed.

502B. L. Ontario, Sodus Bay, Sawmill Cove, Red Mill Rd., Huron Twp., Wayne Co., Rose T.M. 7.5' (1978), St. Lawrence R. watershed.

503. Canandaigua Outlet, Rte. 31 bridge, Lyons Village, Lyons Twp., Wayne Co., Lyons T.M. 7.5' (1953), St. Lawrence R. watershed.

504. The Wide Waters, Erie Canal, Rte. 31, Wide Waters Park, Arcadia Twp., Wayne Co., Palmyra T.M. 7.5' (1952), St. Lawrence R. watershed.

505. Conesus L., East Lake Rd., State boat launch, 0.5 km S of Hartson Pt., Livonia Twp., Livingston Co., Livonia T.M. 7.5' (1951), St. Lawrence R. watershed.

506. North McMillan Cr., East Lake Rd. bridge, Conesus Twp., Livingston Co., Conesus T.M. 7.5' (1942), St. Lawrence River watershed.

507. Conesus Lake Inlet, Sliker Hill Rd., Conesus Twp., Livingston Co., Conesus T.M. 7.5' (1942), St. Lawrence R. watershed.

508. *Typha* ditch, N side of Sliker Hill Rd., E of Conesus Inlet, Conesus Twp., Livingston Co., Conesus T.M. 7.5' (1942), St. Lawrence R. watershed.

509. Ditch, unnamed, Rte. 15, 1.2 km N of Liberty Rd., Springwater Twp., Livingston Co., Springwater T.M. 7.5' (1942), St. Lawrence R. watershed.

510. Pond, unnamed, E of Rte. 15, 1.1 km N of Liberty Rd., Springwater Twp., Livingston Co., Springwater T.M. 7.5' (1942), St. Lawrence R. watershed.

511. Hemlock L., N shore, Hemlock Lake Park, Glenville Village, Livonia Twp., Livingston Co., Honeoye T.M. 7.5' (1951), St. Lawrence R. watershed.

512. Hemlock L. Outlet, Rix Hill Rd., Hemlock Lake Park, Glenville Village, Livonia Twp., Livingston Co., Honeoye T.M. 7.5' (1951), St. Lawrence R. watershed.

513. Canadice L. Outlet, N end of Canadice L., Canadice, Ontario Co., Springwater T.M. 7.5' (1942), St. Lawrence R. watershed.

514. Keuka L., E shore, Rte. 54, 9 km S of Penn Yan, Sunset Point, Milo Twp., Steuben Co., Keuka Park T.M. 7.5' (1942), St. Lawrence R. watershed.

515. Keuka L., N shore, Seneca Point, Red Jacket Park, Milo Twp., Steuben Co., Penn Yan T.M. 7.5' (1942), St. Lawrence R. watershed.

516. Nettle Valley Cr., Rte. 364, Potter Twp., Yates Co., Potter T.M. 7.5' (1942), St. Lawrence R. watershed.

517. Flint Cr., Rte. 364, Potter Park, Potter Village, Potter Twp., Yates Co., Potter T.M. 7.5' (1942), St. Lawrence R. watershed.

518A. Canandaigua L., E shore, Rte. 364, 0.1 km N of County Rd. 1, Deep Run Park, Cottage City Village, Gorham Twp., Ontario Co., Canandaigua Lake T.M. 7.5' (1951), St. Lawrence R. watershed.

518B. Canandaigua L., N shore, Rte. 20, Kershaw Park, Canandaigua Twp., Ontario Co., Canandaigua Lake T.M. 7.5' (1951), St. Lawrence R. watershed.

519. Deep Run, Rte. 364, Cottage City Village, Gorham Twp., Ontario Co., Canandaigua T.M. 7.5' (1951), St. Lawrence R. watershed.

520. Canandaigua Outlet backwater pond, 0.4 km N of Rte. 20, 0.7 km E of Feeder Canal, City of Canandaigua, Canandaigua Twp., Ontario Co., Canandaigua T.M. 7.5' (1951), St. Lawrence R. watershed.

521. Canandaigua Outlet Control Pd., N of Rte. 5 & 20 at dam, 0.3 km NW of Rte. 364, Canandaigua Twp., Ontario Co., Canandaigua Lake T.M. 7.5' (1951), St. Lawrence R. watershed.

522. Ditch, unnamed, E side of Kearney Rd. at Rte. 5 & 20, Aloquin Village, Hopewell Twp., Ontario Co., Rushville T.M. 7.5' (1978), St. Lawrence R. watershed.

523. Pond, unnamed, S side of Rte. 5 & 20, between County Rd. 17 & Spangle Rd., Hopewell Twp., Ontario Co., Rushville T.M. 7.5' (1978), St. Lawrence R. watershed.

524A. Seneca L., N shore, Geneva Twp., Seneca Co., Geneva South T.M. 7.5' (1978), St. Lawrence R. watershed.

524B. Seneca L., N shore at Point, Geneva Twp., Seneca Co., Geneva South T.M. 7.5' (1978), St. Lawrence R. watershed.

525. Ditch, west, into Seneca L., Seneca Lake State Park, Waterloo Twp., Ontario Co., Geneva South T.M. 7.5' (1978), St. Lawrence R. watershed.

526. Ditch, east, into Seneca L., Seneca Lake State Park, Waterloo Twp., Ontario Co., Geneva South T.M. 7.5' (1978), St. Lawrence R. watershed.

527. Cayuga & Seneca Canal, Seneca Lake State Park piers, Waterloo Twp., Seneca Co., Geneva South T.M. 7.5' (1978), St. Lawrence R. watershed.

528. Hoopes Park Pd., East Genesee St. (Rte. 20), City of Auburn, Sennett Twp., Cayuga Co., Auburn T.M. 7.5' (1954), St. Lawrence R. watershed.

529. Owasco L. Outlet, Rte. 38A, Emerson Park, Owasco Twp., Cayuga Co., Auburn T.M. 7.5' (1954), St. Lawrence R. watershed.

530. Owasco L., N shore, Rte. 38A, Emerson Park, Owasco Twp., Cayuga Co., Auburn T.M. 7.5' (1954), St. Lawrence R. watershed.

531. Cayuga & Seneca Canal, Mud Lock Rd., Mud Lock State Boat Launch, Aurelius Twp., Cayuga Co., Cayuga T.M. 7.5' (1954), St. Lawrence R. watershed.

532. Canal, abandoned, Mud Lock Rd., 0.1 km S of Mudlock Canal, Aurelius Twp., Cayuga Co., Cayuga T.M. 7.5' (1954), St. Lawrence R. watershed.

533. Montezuma Marsh main pool, E shore, Montezuma National Wildlife Refuge, Tyre Twp., Seneca Co., Cayuga T.M. 7.5' (1954), St. Lawrence R. watershed.

534. Cayuga & Seneca Canal, State Boat Launch, 0.1 km S of Rte. 5 & 20, Montezuma National Wildlife Refuge, Tyre Twp., Seneca Co., Cayuga T.M. 7.5' (1954), St. Lawrence R. watershed.

535. Cayuga L., W shore, Rte. 89, Cayuga Lake State Park, Seneca Falls Twp., Seneca Co., Seneca Falls T.M. 7.5' (1953), St. Lawrence R. watershed.

536. Ditch, unnamed, S of and paralleling Cohocton R., 0.2 km E of Rte. 15, Erwin Twp., Steuben Co., Corning T.M. 7.5' (1969), Susquehanna R. watershed.

537. Tioga R., unnamed tributary, Rte. 17 culvert, Erwin Twp., Steuben Co., Corning T.M. 7.5' (1969), Susquehanna R. watershed.

538. Cohocton R., 0.3 km E of Canada Rd., 1.1 km NW of Rte. 17/15, Erwin, Steuben Co., Corning T.M. 7.5' (1969), Susquehanna R. watershed.

539. Meads Cr., Meads Creek Rd. bridge, 0.6 km N of Rte. 17, Campbell Twp., Steuben Co., Campbell T.M. 7.5' (1978), Susquehanna R. watershed.

540. Van Keuren L., E shore, Round Lake Rd., Bath Twp., Steuben Co., Savona T.M. 7.5' (1953), Susquehanna R. watershed.

541. Van Keuren L. Inlet, Round Lake Rd., Bath Twp., Steuben Co., Savona T.M. 7.5' (1953), Susquehanna R. watershed.

542. Sanford L., SW shore, Sanford Lake State Recreation Area, Bath Twp., Steuben Co., Savona T.M. 7.5' (1953), Susquehanna R. watershed.

543. Salubria L., S shore, Rte. 415, Bath Twp., Steuben Co., Bath T.M. 7.5' (1978), Susquehanna R. watershed.

544. Fivemile Cr., gaging station, Hemlock Rd., Wheeler Twp., Steuben Co., Rheims T.M. 7.5' (1978), Susquehanna R. watershed.

545. Mud L., E shore, 0.9 km E of Rte. 53, Beans Station, Prattsburg Twp., Steuben Co., Rheims T.M. 7.5' (1978), Susquehanna R. watershed.

546. Goff Cr., 2 km E of Palmer Rd., 0.8 km S of Starr Rd., Howard Twp., Steuben Co., Canisteo T.M. 7.5' (1978), Susquehanna R. watershed.

547. Canacadea Cr., Main St. (Rte. 21), 2 km W of Rte. 36, at gaging station, Hornellsville Twp., Steuben Co., Hornell T.M. 7.5' (1978), Susquehanna R. watershed.

548. Ditch, Rte. 36, E side, 0.9 km S of Gravel Run, Canisteo Twp., Steuben Co., South Canisteo T.M. 7.5' (1954), Susquehanna R. watershed.

549. Fuller Hollow Cr., Murray Hill Rd. & Rte. 434, Vestal Twp., Broome Co., Binghamton West T.M. 7.5' (1968), Susquehanna R. watershed.

550. Glen Castle Cr., Rte. 12 bridge, Chenango Twp., Broome Co., Castle Creek T.M. 7.5' (1976), Susquehanna R. watershed.

551. Thomas Cr., Rte. 12A bridge, Chenango Bridge Village, Chenango Twp., Broome Co., Castle Creek T.M. 7.5' (1976), Susquehanna R. watershed.

552. Chenango L. Outlet, Chenango Valley State Park, Fenton Twp., Broome Co., Chenango Forks T.M. 7.5' (1968), Susquehanna R. watershed.

553. Chenango L., S shore, Chenango Valley State Park, Fenton Twp., Broome Co., Chenango Forks T.M. 7.5' (1968), Susquehanna R. watershed.

554. Chenango Canal, S end of Chenango Valley State Park, Fenton Twp., Broome Co., Chenango Forks T.M. 7.5' (1968), Susquehanna R. watershed.

555. Otselic Cr., unnamed marshy tributary, Landers Corner Rd., 0.3 km W of Rte. 26, Willet Twp., Cortland Co., Willet T.M. 7.5' (1949), Susquehanna R. watershed.

556. Otselic R., Landers Corners Rd., Landers Corners fishing access site, Willet Twp., Cortland Co., Willet T.M. 7.5' (1949), Susquehanna R. watershed.

557. Tioughnioga R., Rte. 11, fishing access site, 2.2 km NNW of Marathon Village, Marathon Twp., Cortland Co., Marathon T.M. 7.5' (1950), Susquehanna R. watershed.

558. Casterline Pd., Rte. 11, public fishing access site, 1.5 km N of Homer Village, Homer Twp., Cortland Co., Homer T.M. 7.5' (1955), Susquehanna R. watershed.

559. Grout Bk. (Skaneateles L. Inlet), East Lake Rd., 0.2 km S of Glen Haven Rd., Scott Twp., Cortland Co., Spafford T.M. 7.5' (1955), St. Lawrence R. watershed.

560. Grout Bk., Glen Haven Rd., Scott Twp., Cortland Co., Spafford T.M. 7.5' (1955), St. Lawrence R. watershed.

561. Grout Bk., dry strand pool, near mouth of Skaneateles L., Scott Twp., Cortland Co., Spafford T.M. 7.5' (1955), St. Lawrence R. watershed.

562. Cazenovia L., S shore, Lakeside Park, Cazenovia Village, Cazenovia Twp., Madison Co., Cazenovia T.M. 7.5' (1943), St. Lawrence R. watershed.

563. Cazenovia L. marsh, Rte. 20, S shore of Cazenovia L., Cazenovia Twp., Madison Co., Cazenovia T.M. 7.5' (1943), St. Lawrence R. watershed.

564. Chittenango Cr., Rte. 13, fishing access site, 1 km S of Chittenango Falls State Park, Cazenovia Twp., Madison Co., Cazenovia T.M. 7.5' (1943), St. Lawrence R. watershed.

565. Old Erie Canal, Lakeport Rd. bridge, Old Erie Canal State Park, N edge of Chittenango Village, Sullivan Twp., Madison Co., Canastota T.M. 7.5' (1957), St. Lawrence R. watershed.

566. Marsh, unnamed, E of Beebe Bridge Rd., S of Old Erie Canal, Old Erie Canal State Park, Lenox Twp., Madison Co., Canastota T.M. 7.5' (1957), St. Lawrence R. watershed.

567. Tioughnioga R., West Branch, Clinton Avenue bridge, Cortland City, Cortland Twp., Cortland Co., Cortland T.M. 7.5' (1955), Susquehanna R. watershed.

568. Callico Pd., Callico Pond State Park, Rte. 41, Cincinnatus Twp., Cortland Co., Cincinnatus T.M. 7.5' (1943), Susquehanna R. watershed.

569. Solon Pd., W shore, Taylor Center, Taylor Twp., Cortland Co., Cincinnatus T.M. 7.5' (1943), Susquehanna R. watershed.

570. Melody L. (Ellis L.), Melody Lake Rd., Willet Twp., Cortland Co., Willet T.M. 7.5' (1949), Susquehanna R. watershed.

571. Cincinnatus L., S shore, Willet Twp., Cortland Co., Smithville Flats T.M. 7.5' (1948), Susquehanna R. watershed.

572. Cincinnatus L., spillway stream, Lakeville Village, Smithville Twp., Chenango Co., Smithville Flats T.M. 7.5' (1948), Susquehanna R. watershed.

573. Long Pd., NW shore, Rte. 141, State Fishing Access Site, Smithville Twp., Chenango Co., Smithville Flats T.M. 7.5' (1948), Susquehanna R. watershed.

574. Bowman L., N shore, Bowman Lake State Park, McDonough Twp., Chenango Co., East Pharsalia T.M. 7.5' (1943), Susquehanna R. watershed.

575. Mead Pd., Rte. 12, North Norwich Twp., Chenango Co., Norwich T.M. 7.5' (1943), Susquehanna R. watershed.

576. Charlotte Cr., Rte. 23, 1 km W of Prosser Hollow, Davenport Twp., Delaware Co., West Davenport T.M. 7.5' (1943), Susquehanna R. watershed.

577. Neahwa Park Pd., Neahwa Park, City of Oneonta, Oneonta Twp., Otsego Co., Oneonta T.M. 7.5' (1943), Susquehanna R. watershed.

578. Susquehanna R., flood plain, Catella Park, City of Oneonta, Oneonta Twp., Otsego Co., Oneonta T.M. 7.5' (1943), Susquehanna R. watershed.

579. Gilbert L., N shore, Gilbert Lake State Park, New Lisbon Twp., Otsego Co., Morris T.M. 7.5' (1943), Susquehanna R. watershed.

580. Butternut Cr., impoundment, fairgrounds, Morris Village, Morris Twp., Otsego Co., Morris T.M. 7.5' (1943), Susquehanna R. watershed.

581. Pond, unnamed, S side of County Rd. 13, 0.5 km S of Deming School, Pittsfield Twp., Otsego Co., New Berlin South T.M. 7.5' (1943), Susquehanna R. watershed.

582. Silver L., W shore, Silver Lake Village, Pittsfield Twp., Otsego Co., New Berlin South T.M. 7.5' (1943), Susquehanna R. watershed.

583. Wharton Cr., County Rd. 18 bridge, 1.2 km W of New Berlin Village, Pittsfield Twp., Otsego Co., New Berlin South T.M. 7.5' (1943), Susquehanna R. watershed.

584. Unadilla R., Adams Rd. bridge, Columbus Twp., Chenango Co., New Berlin North T.M. 7.5' (1943), Susquehanna R. watershed.

585. Stream, unnamed, Rte. 20, 2.4 km E of Otsego-Herkimer County line, Richfield Twp., Otsego Co., Millers Mills T.M. 7.5' (1943), Susquehanna R. watershed.

586. Canadarago L., W shore, Rte. 28, public boat launch, Richfield Twp., Otsego Co., Schuyler Lake T.M. 7.5' (1943), Susquehanna R. watershed.

587. *Typha* ditch, SW side of Rte. 5-S, 2 km NW of Mucky Run Rd., Frankfort Twp., Herkimer Co., Ilion T.M. 7.5' (1943), Hudson R. watershed.

588. Mohawk R., backwater, 0.3 km NW of Railroad St., Frankfort Village, Frankfort Twp., Herkimer Co., Ilion T.M. 7.5' (1943), Hudson R. watershed.

589. Fulmer Cr., State Fishing Access Site, Rte. 5-S, Mohawk Village, German Flats Twp., Herkimer Co., Ilion T.M. 7.5' (1943), Hudson R. watershed.

590. Pond, unnamed, SE corner of Rte. 28 & Allens Lake Rd. intersection, Richfield, Otsego Co., Richfield Springs T.M. 7.5' (1943), Susquehanna R. watershed.

591. Allen L. Outlet, County Rd. 26, Springfield Twp., Otsego Co., Richfield Springs T.M. 7.5' (1943), Susquehanna R. watershed.

592. Clarke Pd., E shore, Rte. 80, golf course, Springfield Twp., Otsego Co., Richfield Springs T.M. 7.5' (1943), Susquehanna R. watershed.

593. Shipman Pd., NW shore, Rte. 80, Springfield Center Village, Springfield Twp., Otsego Co., East Springfield T.M. 7.5' (1943), Susquehanna R. watershed.

594. Beaver pond, unnamed, County Rd. 31, Glimmerglass State Park, Springfield Twp., Otsego Co., East Springfield T.M. 7.5' (1943), Susquehanna R. watershed.

595. Shadow Br., Glimmerglass State Park, Springfield Twp., Otsego Co., East Springfield T.M. 7.5' (1943), Susquehanna R. watershed.

596. Canajoharie Cr., County Rd. & White Rd. bridge, 1.8 km E of Rte. 163, Canajoharie Twp., Montgomery Co., Sprout Brook T.M. 7.5' (1943), Hudson R. watershed.

599. Pond, unnamed, W side of Stringham Rd., 1 km S of Rte. 55, La Grange Twp., Dutchess Co., Pleasant Valley T.M. 7.5' (1957), Hudson R. watershed.

600. Sprout Cr., unnamed tributary, Stringham Rd., Stringham bridge, La Grange Twp., Dutchess Co., Pleasant Valley T.M. 7.5' (1957), Hudson R. watershed.

601. Sprout Cr., Noxon Rd. bridge, La Grange Twp., Dutchess Co., Pleasant Valley T.M. 7.5' (1957), Hudson R. watershed.

602. L. Walton, at NW bay, East Fishkill Twp., Dutchess Co., Hopewell Junction T.M. 7.5' (1981), Hudson R. watershed.

603. Hudson R., E shore, Breakneck Point, Hudson Highlands State Park, Fishkill Twp., Dutchess Co., West Point T.M. 7.5' (1981), Hudson R. watershed.

604. Mohansic L., N shore, Roosevelt (Mohansic) State Park, Yorktown Twp., Westchester Co., Mohegan Lake T.M. 7.5' (1981), Hudson R. watershed.

605. Rockland L., NW shore, Rockland Lake State Park, Clarkstown Twp., Rockland Co., Haverstraw T.M. 7.5' (1979), Hackensack R. watershed.

606. East Bk., North Entrance Rd., Rockland Lake State Park, Clarkstown Twp., Rockland Co., Haverstraw T.M. 7.5' (1979), Hackensack R. watershed.

607. L. Tiorati, E shore, Tiorati Lake Rd., Palisades Interstate Park, Tuxedo Twp., Orange Co., Popolopen Lake T.M. 7.5' (1957), Hudson R. watershed.

608. Pond, unnamed, S side of Rte. 43, 1 km E of West Sand Lake Village, Sand Lake Twp., Rensselaer Co., Averill Park T.M. 7.5' (1980), Hudson R. watershed.

609. Pond, unnamed, S side of Rte. 43, 0.7 km W of Averill Park Village, at Mary Rd., Sand Lake Twp., Rensselaer Co., Averill Park T.M. 7.5' (1980), Hudson R. watershed.

610. Crystal L., NW shore, Lake Rd., Averill Park Village, Sand Lake Twp., Rensselaer Co., Averill Park T.M. 7.5' (1980), Hudson R. watershed.

611. Pond, unnamed, across road from NE shore of Crystal L., 1 km N of Averill Park Village, Sand Lake, Rensselaer Co., Averill Park T.M. 7.5' (1980), Hudson R. watershed.

612. Glass L., Glass Lake Rd., Glass Lake Village, Sand Lake Twp., Rensselaer Co., Averill Park T.M. 7.5' (1980), Hudson R. watershed.

613. Glass L. Outlet, Glass Lake Rd., Sand Lake Twp., Rensselaer Co., Averill Park T.M. 7.5' (1980), Hudson R. watershed.

614. Kinderhook Cr., E shore, 0.2 km W of Nassau-Stephentown Township line, fishing access site, East Nassau Village, Nassau Twp., Rensselaer Co., Nassau T.M. 7.5' (1953), Hudson R. watershed.

615. Kinderhook Cr., Rte. 20-66, 2 km W of Brainard Village, Nassau Twp., Rensselaer Co., East Chatham T.M. 7.5' (1953), Hudson R. watershed.

616. Greens L., SW shore, Athens Twp., Greene Co., Leeds T.M. 7.5' (1953), Hudson R. watershed.

APPENDIX B. WATER CHEMISTRY AT COLLECTION SITES

The following entries are arranged alphabetically by site name (see Appendix A for site locations). Abbreviations: Cond.: conductivity in μmhos/cm; Ca^{++}: calcium ion concentration in ppm; Mg^{++}: magnesium ion concentration in ppm; Na^+: sodium ion concentration in ppm; K^+: potassium ion concentration in ppm; n.d.: no data.

Site Name (Site No.)	pH	Cond.	Ca^{++}	Mg^{++}	Na^+	K^+
Allegheny R. (416)	7.0	130	5	3	2	2
Allen L. Outlet (591)	6.9	284	6	2	12	4
Aunt Sarahs Falls & Pool (397)	7.7	398	15	34	18	3
Bad Indian Swamp (396)	7.7	495	20	14	63	4
Bald Mountain Pd. (364)	6.7	230	8	1	35	1
Barber Pd. (279)	6.5	1755	74	12	193	8
Barge Canal (395)	8.0	488	41	19	25	3
Barrett Pd. (295)	6.5	63	7	1	2	1
Beards Creek (405)	7.8	747	54	22	63	6
Beards Creek tributary (406)	8.0	1121	65	24	115	7
Beaver Kill tributary ditch (469)	7.4	75	7	1	1	1
Beaver Meadow Brook (275)	7.1	84	9	1	7	1
Beebe Pd. (294)	8.3	330	33	12	13	1
Belden Brook tributary (477)	7.6	334	12	5	56	4
Big Moose L. (362)	5.2	27	1	1	1	1
Black L. (339)	7.3	226	20	6	6	2
Black L. Creek (467)	7.1	54	1	1	1	1
Black R. (333)	7.2	96	7	1	8	1
Black R. (334)	7.2	96	7	1	8	1
Black R. (366)	6.6	45	5	1	2	1
Black R. (374)	6.9	85	9	1	3	1
Black R. Canal (367)	7.2	105	12	1	4	1
Black R. tributary (335)	7.6	530	50	10	19	2
Bog, unnamed (313)	7.6	212	17	6	7	1
Bowman L. (574)	6.0	83	1	1	2	1
Brown Church Road Pd. (342)	7.7	325	24	24	5	5
Butterfield L. (338)	7.3	139	12	3	40	2

Site Name (Site No.)	pH	Cond.	Ca^{++}	Mg^{++}	Na^+	K^+
Butternut Creek impoundment (580)	6.6	95	3	1	2	1
Callico Pd. (568)	6.1	83	3	1	1	1
Canacadea Creek (547)	6.5	316	4	10	25	8
Canadarago L. (586)	6.6	313	5	5	9	5
Canadice L. Outlet (513)	8.5	150	9	1	8	2
Canajoharie Creek (596)	7.1	879	10	8	15	12
Canal, abandoned (532)	7.5	2050	94	29	21	5
Canandaigua L. (518A-B)	7.7	301	27	16	13	3
Canandaigua L. Outlet (503)	7.4	670	51	21	36	5
Canandaigua Outlet control pd. (521)	7.5	278	24	16	13	3
Canandaigua Outlet backwater pd. (520)	7.5	278	24	16	13	3
Carter Pd. (320)	7.9	212	33	6	5	1
Casterline Pd. (558)	6.6	452	7	9	60	10
Catamount Pd. (357)	6.0	48	3	1	5	1
Catharine Creek (390)	7.7	419	33	21	19	1
Cayuga & Seneca Canal (527)	n.d.					
Cayuga & Seneca Canal (531)	8.4	600	26	15	92	5
Cayuga & Seneca Canal (534)	8.0	602	26	16	88	4
Cayuga L. (535)	7.9	398	16	15	52	2
Cazenovia L. (562)	6.9	288	7	10	20	6
Cazenovia L. marsh (563)	6.7	288	7	10	20	6
Cemetary Pd. (285)	6.7	118	11	2	7	1
Chamberlain Mills Pd. (317)	7.6	214	35	5	7	1
Charlotte Creek (576)	6.7	232	4	3	2	2
Chateaugay Narrows (350)	6.7	92	8	3	5	1
Chaumont R. impoundment (337)	7.3	520	31	12	10	10
Chautauqua Creek (433)	7.6	398	35	12	18	7
Chautauqua L. (427A-B)	7.3	229	20	7	4	2
Chazy L. (311)	7.8	67	5	2	4	1
Chenango Canal (554)	6.6	283	5	7	22	7
Chenango L. (553)	6.8	229	4	8	8	4
Chenango L. Outlet (552)	6.8	229	4	8	8	4
Childwold Pd. (356)	6.0	150	3	1	24	1

Site Name (Site No.)	pH	Cond.	Ca^{++}	Mg^{++}	Na^+	K^+
Chittenango Creek (449)	7.5	n.d.				
Chittenango Creek (564)	6.7	422	6	21	26	7
Cincinnati Creek (378)	7.5	230	25	2	7	1
Cincinnatus L. (571)	6.7	90	2	1	1	1
Cincinnatus L. spillway stream (572)	6.4	91	3	1	1	1
Clarke Pd. (592)	7.6	345	6	7	6	4
Cohocton R. (538)	6.1	345	7	12	32	9
Cold Brook (373)	7.1	88	8	2	4	1
Conesus L. (505)	7.4	368	30	15	28	3
Conesus L. Inlet (507)	7.8	359	28	13	24	2
Cranberry L. (354)	5.8	28	2	1	2	1
Crandall Park Pd. (298)	7.1	271	16	4	15	1
Crook Brook Pd. (270)	7.3	188	13	6	7	1
Crystal L. (610)	6.6	198	3	2	39	4
Dead Creek (259)	7.2	371	44	14	10	2
Dead Creek (262)	6.6	87	9	2	4	1
Dead Creek (263)	7.2	371	44	13	10	2
Deep Run (519)	7.6	570	66	22	31	4
Deer L. (475)	9.5	144	3	2	15	1
Delaware R. (458)	8.6	77	2	1	1	1
Delaware R., East Branch (471)	6.9	84	4	1	1	1
Delaware R., East Branch backwater (470)	7.1	242	7	2	45	2
Delaware-Hudson Canal (455)	8.5	86	1	1	1	2
Delaware-Hudson Canal (460)	7.9	240	27	11	1	1
Delaware-Hudson Canal (462)	8.4	156	23	4	1	1
Delaware-Hudson Canal (463)	7.5	70	4	1	1	1
Dillon Pd. (355)	5.6	23	2	1	1	1
Ditch (376)	7.1	284	32	4	10	1
Ditch (410)	7.6	275	26	14	3	1
Ditch (426)	7.9	763	70	23	25	5
Ditch (450)	n.d.					
Ditch (509)	n.d.					
Ditch (522)	7.8	660	44	24	57	4

Site Name (Site No.)	pH	Cond.	Ca^{++}	Mg^{++}	Na^+	K^+
Ditch (536)	n.d.					
Ditch (548)	6.6	316	6	12	14	6
Ditch into Seneca L. (525)	7.6	1240	58	33	134	7
Ditch into Seneca L. (526)	7.8	760	60	24	88	6
Diversion Channel (394)	8.3	444	19	44	19	2
Eagle Creek (361)	6.2	46	3	1	3	1
East Brook (606)	6.6	245	4	5	21	6
Eighteenmile Creek (441)	7.6	775	50	16	64	8
Erie Canal (443)	7.7	526	41	16	32	4
Feeder Canal - West Canada Creek (380)	7.4	56	6	1	3	1
Findley L. (430A-B)	7.7	234	21	9	1	2
Findley L. Inlet pond (432)	n.d.					
Fishing Pd. (436)	7.8	349	17	16	28	3
Fivemile Creek (544)	6.3	288	6	10	22	7
Flemings Pd. (283)	6.7	42	6	1	1	1
Flint Creek (517)	8.0	368	37	17	17	3
Fourth L. (305)	6.8	68	5	2	4	1
Fourth L. (360)	6.9	52	5	1	3	1
French Creek (431)	n.d.					
French Creek tributary (429)	7.8	706	60	19	41	8
Fuller Hollow Creek (549)	6.5	522	7	8	77	12
Fulmer Creek (589)	6.9	442	7	8	18	9
Galway L. (272)	7.1	223	27	9	7	1
Genesee R. (404)	7.8	401	32	14	20	3
Genesee Valley Canal (415)	7.2	191	25	7	1	1
Geyser Brook (269)	7.4	376	36	9	17	1
Geyser Brook (267)	7.5	345	35	9	13	1
Gilbert L. (579)	6.4	69	2	1	2	1
Glass L. (612)	6.7	110	3	1	35	1
Glass L. Outlet (613)	6.3	128	3	2	8	1
Glen Castle Creek (550)	6.5	327	6	5	45	8
Gleneida L. (212)	7.1	505	14	4	10	2
Glens Falls Feeder Canal (299)	7.3	80	6	2	5	1

Site Name (Site No.)	pH	Cond.	Ca^{++}	Mg^{++}	Na^+	K^+
Goff Creek (546)	6.4	380	7	14	17	7
Goose Creek (428)	7.8	280	31	10	3	2
Grass R. (344)	7.4	130	9	5	6	2
Great Chazy R. (308)	7.5	173	14	5	7	1
Great Chazy R. (310)	7.0	93	8	3	3	1
Great Sacandaga L. (387)	6.1	48	5	1	1	1
Greens L. (616)	7.2	368	6	5	23	9
Grout Brook (559)	6.7	422	6	15	20	6
Grout Brook (560)	6.8	340	6	15	9	5
Grout Brook (561)	n.d.					
Hemlock L. (511)	7.5	225	20	2	12	2
Hemlock L. Outlet (512)	7.5	225	20	2	12	2
Hennesey Road Pd. (371)	6.8	164	18	2	3	1
Hinckley Reservoir (381)	7.0	58	6	1	3	1
Homowack Kill (461)	7.5	161	17	4	1	1
Hoopes Park Pd. (528)	8.8	260	19	15	18	3
Hudson R. (96A-I)	n.d.					
Hudson R. (286)	7.9	208	29	5	7	1
Hudson R. (301)	7.4	220	14	4	12	2
Hudson R. (603)	7.0	n.d.	5	8	62	21
Hudson-Champlain Canal (312)	7.9	293	41	10	10	2
Johnson Creek (442)	7.9	687	48	19	49	5
Johnson Hollow Stream pond (392)	7.6	261	17	9	25	2
Kayaderosseras Creek (268)	7.8	461	55	9	13	1
Kayuta L. (377)	6.7	43	5	1	2	1
Keuka L. (402)	7.6	312	27	14	11	3
Keuka L. (514)	8.0	236	21	5	8	3
Keuka L. (515)	8.0	236	21	5	8	3
Keuka L. inlet (401)	7.7	308	12	28	16	2
Kinderhook Creek (614)	6.9	179	4	4	8	3
Kinderhook Creek (615)	6.9	173	3	4	10	2
L. Abanakee (276)	6.6	188	10	1	16	1
L. Alice (309)	8.3	158	14	6	4	1

Site Name (Site No.)	pH	Cond.	Ca^{++}	Mg^{++}	Na^+	K^+
L. Alma (385)	6.4	33	5	1	2	1
L. Champlain (141A-D, 260, 281)	6.9	162	13	5	7	1
L. Champlain (261)	n.d.	142	13	n.d.		
L. Champlain (264)	n.d.	142	n.d.			
L. Cossayuna (319)	7.5	193	16	5	6	1
L. Cossayuna Outlet Pd. (318)	7.5	193	16	5	6	1
L. Durant (277)	6.8	282	13	1	20	1
L. Luzerne (303)	6.6	62	5	1	3	1
L. Ontario, Irondequoit Bay (445A-C)	7.9	1030	58	27	85	5
L. Ontario, Little Sodus Bay (499)	7.3	305	26	11	18	2
L. Ontario, Sodus Bay (502A-B)	7.5	430	36	21	27	3
L. Superior (466)	7.2	60	1	1	1	2
L. Taghkanic (292)	7.0	93	11	2	4	1
L. Tiorati (607)	6.3	62	2	1	16	1
L. Walton (602)	6.6	345	5	7	25	6
Lamica L. (348)	6.7	94	6	3	4	1
Lamoka-Waneta Lakes connecting stream (400)	8.0	498	9	11	2	2
Lansing Kill (368)	7.3	149	17	2	5	1
Lansing Kill (369)	7.3	185	19	2	5	1
Limekiln L. (359)	6.0	27	2	1	1	1
Limestone Brook (418)	6.9	91	2	2	1	1
Little Chazy R. (307)	7.5	254	19	9	8	2
Little Conewango Creek (425)	7.6	286	29	10	2	1
Long Pd. (573)	6.6	91	n.d.			
Lower Chateaugay L. (349)	6.7	92	8	3	5	1
Ludlow Swamp (271)	7.2	297	33	6	12	1
Lyon Mountain Pd. (351)	6.9	400	15	4	49	2
Malone Memorial Recreation Park Pd. (347)	7.0	75	5	2	4	1
Marsh, unnamed (478)	7.7	239	4	2	49	1
Marsh, unnamed (566)	6.6	896	4	28	19	7
Martin L. & Gold Creek (457)	9.2	71	1	1	1	1
Masonic Creek (453)	7.8	332	30	10	28	2
Mead Pd. (575)	7.8	65	3	7	9	12

Site Name (Site No.)	pH	Cond.	Ca^{++}	Mg^{++}	Na^{+}	K^{+}
Meads Creek (539)	6.2	153	6	2	9	4
Melody L. (570)	6.9	90	2	1	1	1
Mettawee R. (315)	8.5	229	36	5	7	1
Middle Farms Pd. (251)	8.6	95	2	1	13	1
Mill Pd. (321)	7.5	42	5	1	1	1
Mirror L. (278)	6.4	124	9	2	12	1
Mohansic L. (604)	6.9	300	4	7	26	8
Mohawk R. (370)	7.8	174	19	4	6	1
Mohawk R. backwater (588)	6.6	413	5	8	22	9
Money Pd. (254)	n.d.					
Montezuma Marsh main pool (533)	8.2	680	40	16	70	4
Moreau L. (297)	7.2	102	12	2	3	1
Moss L. (363)	6.4	33	2	1	2	1
Moss L. (413)	5.5	38	1	1	1	1
Mud L. (545)	6.0	372	6	13	29	9
Neahwa Park Pd. (577)	6.7	188	4	3	6	3
Nettle Valley Creek (516)	7.9	350	43	6	3	2
Neversink R. (454)	7.5	78	2	1	1	1
Neversink R. (456)	7.5	78	2	1	1	1
Newton Creek (391)	7.8	308	28	12	12	2
Niagara R. (437)	7.9	300	27	12	10	2
Niagara R. (438)	7.7	296	27	12	8	2
Nicks L. (365)	5.9	28	1	1	2	1
North McMillan Creek (506)	7.5	570	44	19	53	4
Old Erie Canal (565)	6.4	863	6	26	43	7
Oneida L. (448A-B)	7.5	n.d.	6	9	18	6
Onondaga L. (493)	7.0	2320	89	24	291	8
Oswegatchie R. (341)	7.2	124	9	3	8	1
Oswego R. (495)	7.2	905	44	19	117	8
Otselic R. (556)	6.4	165	4	1	10	4
Otselic R. tributary marsh (555)	6.5	110	4	1	20	4
Outlet of unnamed pond (472)	9.6	260	11	6	26	2
Owasco L. (530)	7.7	282	17	13	8	2

Site Name (Site No.)	pH	Cond.	Ca^{++}	Mg^{++}	Na^+	K^+
Owasco Lake Outlet (529)	7.7	282	17	13	8	2
Paradox Creek backwater (282)	6.9	160	28	1	4	1
Paradox L. (284)	6.5	68	9	1	4	1
Perch L. (336)	7.7	267	23	71	1	1
Piseco L. (384)	6.7	85	10	2	3	1
Polaris Spring (266)	6.9	201	54	36	181	54
Pond, unnamed (250)	n.d.					
Pond, unnamed (252)	n.d.					
Pond, unnamed (253)	n.d.					
Pond, unnamed (302)	n.d.	90	6	3	5	1
Pond, unnamed (306)	6.9	274	16	6	15	1
Pond, unnamed (314)	7.7	226	18	6	7	1
Pond, unnamed (383)	6.5	68	8	1	2	0
Pond, unnamed (403)	7.7	859	64	34	41	5
Pond, unnamed (411)	7.8	464	54	21	1	1
Pond, unnamed (444)	7.8	531	41	16	32	4
Pond, unnamed (452)	7.5	408	50	12	14	2
Pond, unnamed (459)	8.2	189	19	8	1	1
Pond, unnamed (464)	7.3	302	7	2	54	2
Pond, unnamed (474)	8.0	48	1	1	1	1
Pond, unnamed (494)	7.3	820	35	20	125	7
Pond, unnamed (496)	7.3	680	34	17	83	4
Pond, unnamed (510)	7.7	281	25	5	20	2
Pond, unnamed (523)	8.2	349	36	20	58	2
Pond, unnamed (581)	6.1	80	3	1	2	1
Pond, unnamed (590)	6.5	422	6	4	38	12
Pond, unnamed (594)	7.0	127	4	2	1	1
Pond, unnamed (599)	6.8	365	6	6	22	8
Pond, unnamed (608)	6.7	250	4	6	20	7
Pond, unnamed (609)	6.4	413	4	6	3	13
Pond, unnamed (611)	6.6	367	3	6	20	10
Pumping Station Pd. (280)	7.1	80	8	2	4	1
Pumping Station Pd. (300)	7.3	335	37	6	16	3

Site Name (Site No.)	pH	Cond.	Ca^{++}	Mg^{++}	Na$^+$	K$^+$
Quaker Run, Quaker L. (421)	7.2	80	1	2	1	1
Queechy L. (293)	7.3	297	36	13	9	1
Randolph High School Pd. 1 (423)	7.3	859	33	17	124	5
Randolph High School Pd. 2 (424)	7.6	621	56	18	38	5
Raquette Brook Pd. (274)	7.2	765	61	4	75	2
Raquette R. (345)	6.6	64	4	2	3	1
Rathbun Pd. (316)	7.7	179	17	3	7	1
Red Creek (500)	7.8	498	41	19	34	6
Red House Brook (419)	7.0	85	1	3	1	1
Red House L. (420)	7.1	69	1	1	1	1
Rockland L. (605)	6.3	279	4	6	21	6
Rushford L. (414)	7.3	164	14	5	1	2
Rutland Gorge Stream (332)	7.3	400	44	5	8	2
Rutland L. (331)	7.0	347	39	3	7	1
Salubria L. (543)	6.5	169	6	2	11	5
Sanford L. (542)	6.6	245	4	12	16	5
Saratoga L. (265)	7.3	249	32	6	12	1
Saw Kill (287)	7.6	335	49	5	10	1
Saw Kill tributary impoundment (288)	7.6	315	52	4	6	1
Seneca L. (398)	7.7	805	31	14	107	5
Seneca L. (524A-B)	7.4	760	29	14	122	6
Shadow Brook (595)	7.2	365	7	6	9	6
Shipman Pd. (593)	7.5	367	7	7	8	5
Silver L. (352)	6.7	47	4	1	2	1
Silver L. (582)	6.6	172	4	4	3	1
Silver L. Outlet (407)	7.3	452	35	14	23	3
Silver L. Outlet (408)	7.3	452	35	14	23	3
Silver L. tributary impoundment (409)	7.5	271	25	14	2	1
Sixmile Creek Marsh (439)	7.6	606	34	22	59	4
Sleeper Creek (393)	8.0	412	47	20	6	3
Solon Pd. (569)	5.8	148	3	2	4	4
Sprout Creek (601)	7.1	297	5	6	19	5
Sprout Creek tributary (600)	7.1	257	4	6	15	4

Site Name (Site No.)	pH	Cond.	Ca^{++}	Mg^{++}	Na^+	K^+
St. Lawrence R. (340)	7.9	359	26	9	22	3
St. Lawrence R. (343)	7.6	520	36	22	20	4
St. Regis R. (346)	7.2	113	7	4	5	1
Sterling Valley Creek (497)	7.7	381	33	18	23	3
Stewart Brook (304)	6.4	69	5	2	3	1
Stillson Pd. Inlet (422)	7.4	248	27	10	1	1
Stissing Pd. (291)	7.1	278	33	9	10	1
Stream, unnamed (585)	6.7	432	10	5	9	7
Stream, unnamed & vernal pd. (451)	8.0	212	13	6	18	2
Sugar R. (372)	8.2	274	31	4	7	2
Susquehanna R. (388)	7.7	251	21	6	7	2
Susquehanna R. (578)	6.0	201	3	3	14	5
Swamp, unnamed (322)	7.1	484	40	7	21	9
Swan L. (468)	6.9	39	1	1	1	1
The Pond (498)	7.4	301	26	11	18	2
Thirteenth L. (273)	7.2	41	5	1	1	1
Thomas Creek (551)	6.6	293	6	8	23	6
Thompson Pd. (290)	7.0	248	34	5	7	1
Tioga R. tributary (537)	6.0	301	4	8	47	7
Tioughnioga R. (557)	6.4	397	7	11	41	9
Tioughnioga R., West Branch (567)	7.3	397	7	8	12	9
Tobehanna Creek tributary (399)	7.8	393	18	10	26	2
Tonungwant Creek (417)	7.0	523	21	10	75	4
Trout Pd. (412)	7.4	369	35	21	1	1
Tupper L.-Simon Pd. marshes (358)	6.3	42	3	1	3	1
Tuscarora Creek (476)	7.9	300	10	6	50	3
Twelvemile Creek, East (440)	7.6	818	46	23	74	8
Typha ditch (508)	7.6	1020	33	5	195	6
Typha ditch (587)	6.6	487	7	8	29	10
Typha marsh (382)	6.5	58	6	1	2	1
Unadilla R. (584)	6.4	368	8	7	8	5
Union Falls Pd. (353)	6.7	67	4	2	5	1
Van Keuren L. (540)	6.3	252	6	11	16	5

Site Name (Site No.)	pH	Cond.	Ca^{++}	Mg^{++}	Na^+	K^+
Van Keuren L. Inlet (541)	6.5	353	7	14	22	6
Wappasening Creek (389)	7.4	128	7	4	1	2
West Canada Creek (379)	7.4	56	6	1	3	1
West L. Inlet (386)	6.0	54	4	1	4	1
Wharton Creek (583)	6.6	207	5	3	6	1
Whetstone Creek (375)	7.1	77	8	3	2	1
Whitaker Brook Pd. (473)	8.0	46	1	1	1	1
White L. (465)	7.3	77	2	1	3	1
Wide Waters (504)	7.4	640	40	17	67	5
Wilbur Pd. (289)	7.2	149	13	3	10	1
Wolcott Creek (501)	7.7	540	49	20	26	5